ESSENTIALS OF NUTRITION

THE MACMILLAN COMPANY
NEW YORK · BOSTON · CHICAGO
DALLAS · ATLANTA · SAN FRANCISCO

MACMILLAN AND CO., LIMITED
LONDON · BOMBAY · CALCUTTA
MADRAS · MELBOURNE

THE MACMILLAN COMPANY
OF CANADA, LIMITED
TORONTO

ESSENTIALS
OF
NUTRITION

HENRY C. SHERMAN
AND
CAROLINE SHERMAN LANFORD
COLUMBIA UNIVERSITY

Third Edition

THE MACMILLAN COMPANY: NEW YORK

Third Edition Copyright, 1951, by The Macmillan Company

ALL RIGHTS RESERVED—NO PART OF THIS BOOK MAY BE REPRODUCED IN ANY FORM WITHOUT PERMISSION IN WRITING FROM THE PUBLISHER, EXCEPT BY A REVIEWER WHO WISHES TO QUOTE BRIEF PASSAGES IN CONNECTION WITH A REVIEW WRITTEN FOR INCLUSION IN MAGAZINE OR NEWSPAPER.

Printed in the United States of America

First printing

First and second editions copyright 1940 and 1943 by The Macmillan Company

PREFACE

The purpose of this book is to offer its readers a thoroughly adequate and up-to-date view of the essentials of nutrition.

We hope that it will be found useful both to those who do and those who do not expect to proceed later to a more detailed, professional study of nutrition and dietetics. It assumes no prerequisite training in science. Special care has therefore been given to the mode of dealing with such terms as nutrition uses in common with other sciences, and such as are just now in course of becoming everyday words. Recognizing that the effectiveness of the text depends largely upon freedom from interruption by formal definitions, we have sought rather to introduce each scientific term only as its employment becomes clearly useful, and then functionally. For cases in which more dictionary-like definitions may also be useful, a glossary is provided in the Appendix.

It is realized that at present the teaching of nutrition, like the scientific subject matter itself, is in a rapidly developing stage. It is hoped that this text will contribute to this development, and that its use will enable the teacher more readily to meet the demands of the growth of fundamental scientific knowledge of nutrition within the time-limits of the non-technical course.

The present approach to the facts and principles of the science of nutrition is mainly through the relations of food to health and efficiency. Chief prominence is given to the case of the normal young person such as the majority of the readers of this book will presumably be; though the concluding chapters take up also the problems of food for family groups, and of making nutritional knowledge more widely effective. Most of the Exercises at the ends of the chapters are, like the text itself, put in terms of the student's own experience and objectives. The Exercises and Suggested Readings are to be regarded as entirely optional. In many courses, no doubt, actual laboratory work will be provided instead of, or in addition to, such Exercises. One of our main objects is to provide a textbook which leaves the teacher entirely free to design the accompanying laboratory work, or collateral reading, or both, in accordance with the circumstances and purposes of the particular course. The sequence of topics is also readily adjustable.

The subject matter of the text begins with an introductory chapter which is intended to indicate both the position of the present-day science of nutrition and its constructive aims. For many, such an advance indication of the far-reaching significance of our newest knowledge of nutrition increases the interest and effectiveness of the study. Those, however, who prefer to omit or postpone such evaluation will find it entirely feasible to make a logical beginning with the second or even with the third or fourth chapter.

Then follows the central body of the topical subject matter, treated in the order which most teachers prefer: (1) the energy aspects of nutrition, (2) the proteins and their amino acids, (3) the mineral elements, and (4) the vitamins. This is generally found the most readily teachable sequence from the viewpoint of the interrelationships of the topics. It has also another important advantage. To a noteworthy extent it corresponds with the chronological sequence in which the main aspects of the present-day science of nutrition have developed. Thus we study first the parts of our subject which have had the longest time in which to take definite shape and which can therefore be presented most simply and concisely. After this we are better prepared for the somewhat more detailed treatment which the newer subject matter of the vitamins requires if its study is to be of equal scientific soundness. Some of the most recent advances of knowledge in the vitamin field are so important, in the light which they throw upon everyday nutritional problems, that the somewhat fuller mode of exposition here finds a practical reward as well as a teaching reason.

The chapters on vitamins are so written that they may be studied in any sequence desired. The order followed in this text is the one which to us seems, in the present state of knowledge, best adapted to effective teaching.

As a further and important aid to interest, and therefore to effectiveness, the arrangement within each chapter is determined by the merits of its own subject matter, in preference to the rigid following of a fixed form.

The last four chapters deal with applications or extensions of nutrition study. Any of them may be omitted, without impairing the scientific coherence of the body of the book, when adaptation to a shorter course is desired or the teacher prefers to develop some other line of application.

The tables in the body of the text are kept short for comfortable reading. Data of food values thus used to illustrate any particular chapter, are taken as typical from among the much more numerous data tabulated in the Appendix.

For the privilege of using unpublished data in drawing our deductions, for the use of illustrative materials, and for aid in other ways, we are indebted to many scientific friends among whom acknowledgment is gratefully made to Drs. E. L. Batchelder, F. G. Benedict, L. E. Booher, C. A. Browne, H. L. Campbell, T. M. Carpenter, E. F. DuBois, Martha Eliot, C. J. Farmer, E. C. Kendall, C. G. King, H. E. Munsell, John B. Nichols, and M. S. Rose.

Additional Preface to Third Edition

In offering this new edition, the authors desire to express their high appreciation both to the users of the book for the gratifying reception accorded to it, and to the publishers for making possible so early an opportunity to incorporate the most recent advances in the science of nutrition, and in the movement to make this science ever more effective in the service of health and efficiency.

While the general character and scope are much the same as in the previous editions, each chapter has been carefully revised with the double objective of bringing it thoroughly up to date and of improving the clarity and conciseness of the text wherever possible. Fortunately several fundamental advances have reached points permitting clearer interpretations almost at the moment that this is written. Calorie values of foods and needs in nutrition (Chapters IV and V), the quantitative requirements of individual amino acids and the light thus thrown upon the supplementary relations between proteins (Chapters VI and XIX), the values of newly discovered vitamins in the maintenance of the health of the blood (Chapter IX), the firm establishment of the fact that at least one mineral element (Chapter VIII) and three vitamins (Chapters XI, XIII, and XV) continue to bring increasing long-term benefits from increasingly liberal intakes up to levels at least twice those of minimal adequacy ("actual" need), are illustrations of the fact that the newest chemistry of nutrition has in these most recent days "revealed much more than had been foreseen." Thus today's essentials of nutrition deal with potentialities beyond those that the science of yesterday thought possible.

All food composition data have been revised in the light of the governmental publication of June 1950.

In addition to the acknowledgments in the original preface, the writers desire to make grateful record of the generous collaboration of M. E. Bal, Alice Beister, Grace MacLeod, C. S. Pearson, and J. M. Schwank in the preparation of the present edition.

CONTENTS

CHAPTER		PAGE
I.	The Nutritional Improvement of Life	1
II.	The More Abundant Nutrients in Foods	13
III.	What Happens to Food in the Body: Digestion and Metabolism	28
IV.	Energy Aspects of Nutrition	47
V.	How to Meet the Energy Need and Have the Body Weight You Want	67
VI.	How to Meet the Need for Protein	85
VII.	Mineral Elements and Regulatory Processes in Nutrition	107
VIII.	Phosphorus and Calcium	121
IX.	Iron and the Nutrition of the Blood	141
X.	Iodine	161
XI.	Ascorbic Acid (Vitamin C)	172
XII.	Thiamine (Vitamin B_1)	198
XIII.	Riboflavin, Niacin (Nicotinic Acid), and the Problem of Pellagra with its Related Ills	217
XIV.	Other Water-Soluble Vitamins	240
XV.	Vitamin A and Its Precursors	251
XVI.	Rickets and the Vitamins D	275
XVII.	Other Fat-Soluble Vitamins	294
XVIII.	Some Relations of Food to the Teeth	301
XIX.	Nutritional Characteristics of Food Commodities	317
XX.	Food Costs and Values: Nutritional Guidance in Food Economics	346
XXI.	How to Make Nutritional Knowledge More Effective	369

APPENDIX		
A	Fatty Acids	389
B	Digestive Enzymes	391
C	Composition and Nutritive Values of Foods	393
D	Recommended Dietary Allowances	415
E	Glossary	420
	Subject Index	429

I

THE NUTRITIONAL IMPROVEMENT OF LIFE

Students now enter American colleges taller and yet younger than were their parents and other predecessors when they entered the same colleges thirty to forty years ago. This is shown consistently by all the available records, and is true of both boys and girls. There has not been any known change in proportions of racial stocks which could account for the differences. The explanation is to be found not in inheritance in the biological sense but in a social inheritance,—the increase of scientific knowledge and its use in the betterment of conditions of living.

Prominent among the advances in knowledge of life and health, and resulting improvement of ways of living, has been the development of the science of nutrition and its influence upon the daily choice and use of food. The twentieth-century science of nutrition enjoys, even more than other sciences, the impetus of both the two great motive powers of modern progress: the spirit of wonder, and the spirit of service.

A generation or two ago, all the more abundant constituents of food were sufficiently known to chemists so that one might analyze a food with a satisfactory approximation to 100 per cent; yet one could not successfully nourish himself or an experimental animal with a mixture of the food constituents which analysis revealed.

Professor (later Sir) Frederick Gowland Hopkins of Cambridge University reported briefly in 1906 and fully in 1912 his experiments which made clear to students of normal nutrition that there must exist in certain foods some substance or substances not previously known, but essential to the nutritional process. He showed that laboratory animals soon ceased to thrive on mixtures of purified proteins, fats, carbohydrates, and salts even when these were selected and proportioned in the light of all available knowledge; but that the addition of a small amount of milk, fresh or dried, or of the alcohol-extract of dried milk or of certain vegetables (but not the ashes of such foods or extracts) made the diet adequate. Figures 1 and 2 show graphically the results of typical experiments with young animals. Those experiments showed that some then unidentified alcohol-soluble organic substance or substances must function in normal nutrition. We now know that there are several

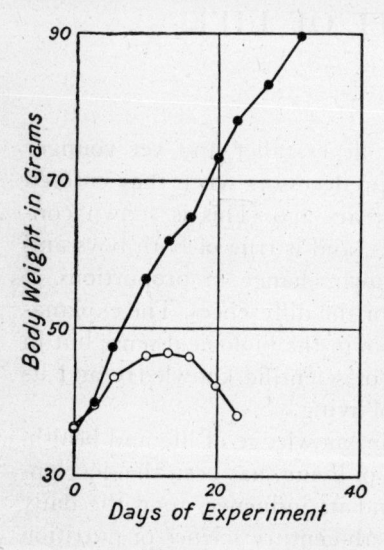

Fig. 1. Growth curves of rats in early experiments of Sir Frederick Gowland Hopkins. The lower curve represents the average body weight of a group of rats after varying intervals on an artificial diet of highly purified foodstuffs. The upper curve shows the growth of an initially similar group of rats receiving 2 or 3 cc. of milk each per day in addition to the artificial diet. (Courtesy of Sir F. Gowland Hopkins.)

such substances, some soluble in water and others in fat. Individually, they will be studied in Chapters XI-XVII. In the present discussion we are concerned with the general relation of this discovery and its sequel to the significance of nutrition as a factor in our understanding of nature and in the scientific management of our own lives.

For the discovery of these substances,—tentatively called vitamins and beginning to be known by more distinctive individual names,—has proven to be only the first step in a very far-reaching scientific development of great importance to the improvement of life.

Modern science constantly strives to make itself more and more exact. So as soon as the existence of "vitamins" was discovered, even without waiting for their complete chemical identification, studies were begun upon such quantitative questions as: (1) the relative abundance of a given vitamin in different kinds of food; (2) the amounts needed in nutrition; and (3) the more ambitious question, how much of each gives the *best* results, *i.e.*, what is the level of *optimal* as distinguished from merely adequate *nutritional intake*.

Our present-day realization of the importance of this latter problem is a development of much greater significance than is yet generally understood.

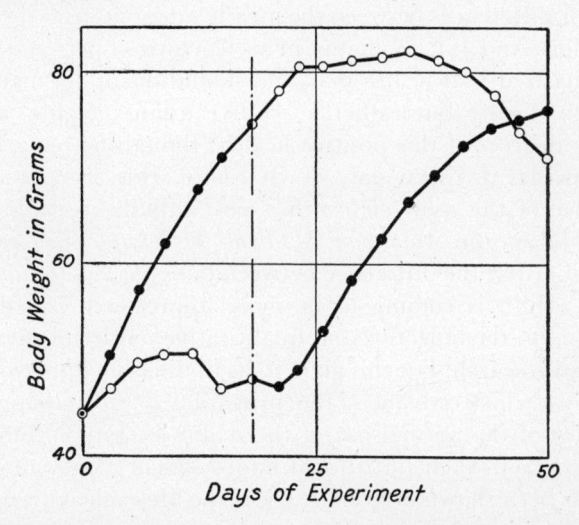

Fig. 2. Growth curves of rats in early experiments of Sir Frederick Gowland Hopkins. The lower curve represents the growth of rats receiving (up to the 18th day of the experiment) only the purified diet; the upper curve, similar rats having (up to the 18th day) 3 cc. of milk each per day in addition to this food. From the 18th day of the experiment, marked by the vertical dotted line, the milk was transferred from the latter set of animals to the former. (Courtesy of Sir F. Gowland Hopkins.)

While this fact was revealed largely through experiments which grew out of the investigation of the newly-discovered vitamins, it is equally true of one of the mineral elements which have long been recognized as essential to nutrition but whose far-reaching potentialities have but recently been brought fully to light. (For example, the work with different levels of calcium intake, noted in Chapter VIII.)

The rapid sequence of such discoveries has been in great measure due to the increasing use of laboratory animals as instruments and reagents of nutritional research. By use of a species whose nutritional chemistry is closely similar to ours (with respect to the substance under investigation) and which runs much more rapidly than we do through its growth and development and the subsequent events of its life history, science can now study the relations between food intake, nutritional responses, and resulting health, much more comprehensively than had previously been possible.

For about thirty years McCollum has taught that there may be important differences between the merely adequate and the optimal in nutrition. And J. F. Williams, in his teaching of personal hygiene, has emphasized that health may and should mean not merely freedom from disease but rather a positive quality of life, and that there are degrees of this positive health; though he remarked that for some years this view only slowly found wide acceptance. That acceptance of this view of health is now rapidly spreading, or, as the *Journal of the American Medical Association* has editorially phrased it, "that the difference between buoyant health and merely passable health is coming to be more appreciated," is doubtless largely due to the objective and quantitative nature of present-day nutritional research. For this gives to its findings an impersonal convincingness which advances the principle of the nutritional improvability of the normal out of the realm of opinion into that of established fact. Such nutritional improvement of already-normal health has been shown at every stage of the life cycle with statistical convincingness and conclusiveness of a very much higher order than science considers necessary to establish a physiological fact as "undoubted."

Thus notwithstanding individual (physiological) variability, the well-controlled colony of experimental animals, from which large numbers of strictly comparable individuals of known hereditary and nutritional antecedents can be drawn, becomes an instrument of research such as had not existed before. By the use of this instrument, higher precision and deeper insight both become possible, and these in turn are revealing an essentially new concept of the influence of nutrition.

To make this clear and definite, let us glance at some recent and current work at Columbia University where there is maintained for research of this kind a colony of laboratory-bred experimental rats in which the hereditary and nutritional background of each individual is known for so many generations as to correspond with a human population whose food supply had been known and whose blood had been unmixed for over 2000 years. With such a colony to draw upon, strictly parallel test groups can be placed simultaneously upon the different dietaries which it is desired to compare.

In all such controlled research, we plan to introduce only one variable at a time. In nutritional problems of the sort which we are considering, the experimental variables are of two kinds: (1) individual chemical factors, elements or compounds as the case may be; and (2) the actual articles of food which nature and agriculture produce and which people obtain and consume.

In a case of the latter type, a certain basal *Diet A* showed itself adequate under the severe test of maintaining normal health with successful reproduction and rearing of young, generation after generation; yet when the proportion of milk in this food supply was doubled the resulting *Diet B* was better in that it induced a more buoyant health, or built the already-normal health to a higher level.

Whether or not the actual optimum* has been reached in any case, the measured differences in well-being, between the adequately nourished families on Diet A and their cousins who received the more scientifically balanced Diet B, show clearly and conclusively that our knowledge of nutrition has now entered a new era in which it can (and doubtless will) play a larger part in the attainment of a higher general level of health and efficiency than had previously been thought possible.

In the investigation just mentioned, the only experimental variable was the proportion in which the natural foods entered into the diet; but the increased proportion of milk when translated into chemical terms meant major enrichments of the diet in the three chemical factors calcium, vitamin A, and riboflavin-plus-protein which we shall study individually in Chapters VIII, XIII, and XV. New series of experiments were therefore begun in which these nutrients were studied independently and at successively increased levels of intake.

Here it was found that calcium and vitamin A each is capable of conferring successively increased benefit at successively higher levels of intake through an unexpectedly wide range.† Hitherto, it

* The words optimal and optimum are explained in the Glossary at the back of this book.

† Gains were also indicated as resulting from the joint effect of extra riboflavin and extra protein fed together.

had been the accepted view (sometimes even expounded as a fundamental economic principle) that one cannot advantageously consume much more food than one actually needs; in other words that, in the case of food, the level of minimal adequacy is very nearly the optimal level of consumption. This now proves to have been an oversimplified view. A more discriminating statement is needed. Of total food as measured in calories a very small surplus above actual need *does* suffice to bring us to the optimal level of intake of *this* nutritional factor. And probably of many other factors the optimal level is only moderately higher than that of minimal adequacy, perhaps around fifty per cent higher as is commonly assumed for protein and for phosphorus in the teaching of dietetics. But for *some* factors we now find that the beneficial margins are much higher or wider.

This finding, with its consequences which we shall later study more fully, has such far-reaching significance that some have inclined to call it "a new principle of liberality in dietetics"; but it should not be confused with a merely open-handed attitude. The *principle* is one of *scientific discrimination.* What is true of calcium is *not* to be assumed to be true of other mineral elements; and what is true of vitamins A and C, and riboflavin is not to be assumed to be true for other vitamins (though it may be for some of them). The factors here discussed were not taken at random for the investigation above mentioned. They were investigated because the results of previous study pointed directly and specifically to them as probable keys to the fuller understanding of a newly discovered nutritional improvability of an already-normal condition or level of health.

Undoubtedly, hitherto, if we have appreciated the reality of degrees of positive health, we have been too fatalistic in our attitude toward it, attributing the superior vitality which some people enjoy too largely to their luck in being born with good constitutions and too little to their intelligent habits of life.

Lately, it is becoming increasingly clear that, however important the inherited constitution, there is yet a very great opportunity open to each of us to provide through sane daily living, and notably through intelligent food habits, for such a favorable internal environment* as shall permit our native endowments to develop and function to the best advantage.

* See Glossary (Appendix E).

Hopkins, speaking in the most conservative terms as President of the Royal Society, said that "nurture can assist nature to a larger extent" than the passing generation had thought.

That differences which are really nutritional have doubtless sometimes been attributed to racial factors was emphasized by Hopkins in the leading article of the then newly established *Nutrition Abstracts and Reviews* in 1931. A community, he explained, may be found in equilibrium with an environment which includes its food supply, and the fact of such equilibrium has hitherto been taken as evidence that the environment supplies everything needed. Hence any inferiority was taken to be racial, whereas actually a racial potentiality of higher development may become manifest with an improvement in the food.

This is illustrated in the fact, repeatedly emphasized by Boas, that in immigrant families supposedly representing physically inferior racial stocks the children and grandchildren approach the typical American physique with surprising rapidity when living under American conditions.

And the fact that physique is only the most obvious and not necessarily the most important of the gains to be expected is illustrated by Dr. McLester's statement in an official address as President of the American Medical Association: that science now offers, to those who will use the newer knowledge of nutrition, greater vigor "and a higher level of cultural attainment."

Thus we are now in a new era of nutritional knowledge, in which this knowledge serves the improvement of life in two ways: (1) correctively, in the cure and prevention of deficiency diseases and of the less well recognized states of nutritional shortage or subnormality; and (2) constructively, in the improvement of already-normal health.

We can now see that the teaching of science has until recently assumed the normal internal chemistry of each species to be somewhat more rigidly specific than it really is. The newer knowledge of nutrition shows us, among other things, how our daily choice of food influences that internal environment of the body which directly environs and conditions the life process. And the new knowledge has brought a really new view.

For hitherto, while we included nutrition among environmental factors by definition, yet when we actually thought about environment it was chiefly to think about our surroundings. As we come to realize how significantly our daily choice and use of food influences that more important environment which we carry within our own bodies, we see that we ourselves have a much larger measure of ability to improve the life process than science has hitherto supposed to be possible.

The chapters which follow will seek to make clear the essentials both of the facts of our present-day nutritional knowledge and of the functioning of this knowledge in the guidance of daily food habits and the attainment of higher health.

Some recent developments may well be mentioned at this point.

By cooperation of the Federal Department of Agriculture, a number of the State Agricultural Experiment Stations, and Cornell University, there has been established at Ithaca a laboratory for research into the nutritional interrelationships of soils, plants, farm animals, and man. Ultimately, such research may point the way to important improvement in the nutritive values of foods; and in any case should clarify the question as to how far the conditions of production do influence such nutritive values. Meanwhile the very existence of this laboratory will serve as a continuing reminder that not only genetic (hereditary) but also environmental (nutritional) influences do measurably and significantly modify the internal bodily states and thus the life processes of both plant and animal species, including our own.

At about the same time, the National Research Council reestablished its Committee on Food and Nutrition which within a year developed so greatly in response to the present-day recognition of the importance of this field that it has now been reconstituted as a Food and Nutrition Board with a number of separate but coordinated committees.

In May, 1941, there was held in Washington a large National Nutrition Conference through which wide publicity was given to the importance of food supply and of nutritional research, and to the "New Yardstick of Good Nutrition," more scientifically known as the Table of *Recommended Daily Allowances of Specific Nutrients,* or *Recommended Dietary Allowances,* issued by the National Research Council. This Table as revised in 1948 with its official explanatory footnotes is given in full in the Appendix at the back of this book. At several points in the intervening text we shall refer to these Recommended Allowances in our discussions of specific nutrients. Carefully to be distinguished from these *Rec-*

ommended Allowances are the lower figures set up as *minimum requirements* for the special purposes of the Federal Food and Drug Administration, particularly in its regulation of the labels of foods for which "special dietary properties" are claimed. To avoid confusion we should be careful always to use the appropriate one of the conventional names italicized in the preceding sentence, rather than to speak of a "standard" or "standards" in either case.

The present book will make use of the *Recommended Allowances,* because, while attempts to ascertain minimum requirements have certain technical uses, it is *good* nutrition to which our attention is here directed, with the double goal that all our people shall be well nourished, and that wherever possible we may also build from good to better.

The goal of improvement upon hitherto accepted norms, and the fact that an element of judgment necessarily enters into the recommendations which aim at such a goal, are recognized in the following paragraph with which the Bureau of Human Nutrition and Home Economics introduced its discussion of the planning of diets by the "new yardstick":

"The Nutrition of the Nation depends in large part on the tables set by the Nation's homemakers. A new high aim for meal planning was announced during the National Nutrition Conference for Defense in May 1941. The food and nutrition committee of the National Research Council recommended dietary allowances for persons differing in age and activity. The figures rest on experimental evidence of human nutritional needs and on the careful judgment of recognized authorities in nutrition."

The United Nations has established a Food and Agriculture Organization (FAO).

EXERCISES

N. B.—While the wording of these Exercises, and those appended to other chapters, is addressed to the individual student, some involve work for instructors, or instructors and students jointly, according to circumstances.

1. Record your present height, weight, and age (dating and signing the record). Note also the age, and (if you know them correctly) the height and weight at which you entered college. How do your height and weight compare with the normal average or standard for your age? Is your build average, or slender (linear), or stocky (lateral)?

2. Make an accurate record of the kinds of food and beverage and

the amount of each which you consume (*a*) in a 24-hour day; (*b*) in each of 7 consecutive days.

3. Check the foregoing record against the accompanying U. S. Department of Agriculture Card, or such other guide as may be selected. The writers have here chosen, for reasons more fully explained beyond, a card designed primarily for young people.

Checking Card of

UNITED STATES DEPARTMENT OF AGRICULTURE
EXTENSION SERVICE
DIVISION OF COOPERATIVE EXTENSION
(Adapted)

Check Your Meals Daily for These Foods

Milk... 1½ pints to 1 quart
Butter or fortified margarine .... 1 to 3 servings
Fruits and vegetables.............................. 4 to 5 servings
   (interchangeable to some extent)
   A good balance is:
      1 serving potato
      1 serving citrus fruit, tomatoes, or raw cabbage
      1 serving green or yellow vegetable
      2 additional servings—fruits or vegetables
        (chosen according to preference and season)
Enriched or whole-grain bread or cereals............. 1 to 2 servings
Eggs, meat, fish, cheese, dried beans or peas, nuts, or
   peanut butter.................................. 2 servings
   (select two different kinds)
Total liquids (water, milk, soup, fruit juices and other
   beverages).................................... 2 quarts or more

---

Cod-liver oil...................................... 1 teaspoon
   (a fine supplement in winter or when you cannot afford plenty of whole milk, butter, eggs, and green-colored vegetables)

With the above, use additional bread and cereals and moderate amounts of sweets and fats to make up sufficient food energy (total calories).

(Remember that the somewhat conventional use of any such score card would lose much of its convenience if it were subject to frequent change; and that, therefore, it can not be expected to reflect precisely the most up-to-date knowledge, and its implied judgments need not be regarded as final.

Perhaps you may find reason to modify some of them as a result of your study of nutrition. Nevertheless its use may be helpful to thinking and discussion.)

SUGGESTED READINGS

AYKROYD, W. R. 1948 Food and nutrition: Certain international aspects and developments. *J. Am. Dietet. Assoc.* **24**, 1–4.

BEESON, K. C. 1949 The soil factor in human nutritional problems. *Nutr. Rev.* **7**, 353–355.

BOUDREAU, F. G. 1947 Nutrition in war and peace. *Milbank Mem. Fund Quart.* **25**, 231–245.

CHENOWITH, L. B. 1937 Increase in height and weight and decrease in age of college freshmen. *J. Am. Med. Assoc.* **108**, 354–356.

GREGORY, R. 1937 Nutritional science and its social aspects. *Nutr. Abs. Rev.* **7**, 1–5.

HAMBIDGE, G. 1939 Nutrition as a national problem. *J. Home Econ.* **31**, 361–364.

HESELTINE, M. M. 1948 The health and welfare of the world's children. *J. Am. Dietet. Assoc.* **24**, 91–93.

HOPKINS, F. G. 1931 Nutrition and human welfare. *Nutr. Abs. Rev.* **1**, 3–6.

KING, C. G. 1949 New advances in the science of nutrition. *J. Am. Dietet. Assoc.* **25**, 109–111.

KING, C. G. 1949b Progress in nutrition research. *Trans. Am. Assoc. Cereal Chem.* **7**, 49–55.

MACLEOD, F. L. 1939 Home economics research in progress in the South. *J. Home Econ.* **31**, 374–377.

MACLEOD, G., and C. M. TAYLOR 1944 *Rose's Foundations of Nutrition*, 4th Ed. (Macmillan.)

MCCOLLUM, E. V., E. ORENT-KEILES, and H. DAY 1939 *The Newer Knowledge of Nutrition*, 5th Ed. (Macmillan.)

MCLESTER, J. S. 1935 Nutrition and the future of man. *J. Am. Med. Assoc.* **104**, 2144–2147.

MENDEL, L. B. 1923 *Nutrition: The Chemistry of Life.* (Yale University Press.)

MEREDITH, H. V. 1941 Stature and weight of children of the United States. *Am. J. Diseases Children* **62**, 909–932.

MINOT, G. R. 1947 Nutrition and health. *Nutr. Rev.* **5**, 321–322.

NATIONAL NUTRITION CONFERENCE 1942 Proceedings of the Conference held in Washington, May 1941. (Government Printing Office.)

ORR, J. B. 1941 Nutrition and human welfare. *Nutr. Abs. Rev.* **11**, 3–11.

Rose, M. S. 1940 *Feeding the Family,* 4th Ed. (Macmillan.)

Shank, R. E. 1949 Nutrition in preventive medicine. *Nutr. Rev.* 7, 1–3.

Stare, F. J. 1943 Nutrition and resistance. *Ann. Internal Med.* 19, 735–740.

Stiebeling, H. K. 1947 The world nutrition situation. *J. Home Econ.* 39, 7–11.

Stuart, H. C. 1949 Children's nutritional needs during growth and development. *J. Am. Dietet. Assoc.* 25, 934–936.

Turner, D. F. 1947 Nutrition and dietetics. *Nutr. Rev.* 5, 289–290.

Wiehl, D. G., and H. D. Kruse 1941 Medical evaluation of nutritional status. V. Prevalence of deficiency diseases in their subclinical stage. *Milbank Mem. Fund Quart.* 19, 241–251.

Wilder, R. M. 1950 The profession of dietetics. *J. Am. Dietet. Assoc.* 26, 497–502.

II

THE MORE ABUNDANT NUTRIENTS IN FOODS

The food as a whole *nourishes* the body in three ways:

(1) it furnishes the body-fuels, the substances whose burning (oxidation) in the body supplies the *energy* for its activities;

(2) it provides the materials for the *building* and *upkeep* of the body tissues; and

(3) it supplies the substances by means of which the conditions and processes in the body are *regulated*, or the *precursors* from which the body makes its regulatory substances.

A *nutrient* is a substance which takes part in a nutritive function of any of these three kinds. Some nutrients function in more than one of these ways. Strictly speaking, air and water are nutrients[*]; but more commonly the body's supplies of air and water are treated rather as parts of the study of physiology and hygiene, while the study of nutrition takes them for granted and concentrates its attention upon the food supply and the fate and functions of the foodstuffs (nutrients) in the body.

An individual food may serve one, or two, or all, of the three types of function above mentioned according to the nutrient or nutrients which it contains.

This brief indication of functions will probably serve better to introduce the study of the nutrients, than would a set of formal definitions. It may, perhaps, be worth while to note at this point that the literature of nutrition uses the term "foodstuffs" in two senses. Some writers follow popular usage in making no distinction between "foodstuffs" and "foods," meaning in both cases articles

---

[*] Some of the early observations upon the essential function of air and the significance of respiration as related to nutrition are interestingly described in *Rose's Foundations of Nutrition,* revised (1944) by MacLeod and Taylor (Macmillan).

of food, or food commodities. Others use the term foodstuffs rather as a scientific term to mean the "stuffs" in the sense of the constituent or component substances of which foods are composed. When used in this latter sense, the word foodstuff becomes practically interchangeable with the word nutrient.

Because of their many important interrelations, the nutrients cannot be rigidly classified according to which of the three main types of nutritive function they serve. This will become clearer as subsequent chapters are studied. The present chapter relates chiefly to the nutrients which bulk largest in the food as a whole.

As we saw in the preceding chapter, the vitamins which play such a prominent part in recent discussions of food and nutrition are concerned in such very small amounts as for a long time to have been missed in the accounting for the composition of foods. The longer-known constituents of foods are proteins, fats, carbohydrates, organic acids, inorganic salts or mineral elements, and water.

Typical examples of these constituents of foods may be illustrated in observations readily made upon milk, the one thing whose sole function in nature is to serve as food. As one receives a bottle of milk from the dealer, a partial separation of its constituents is usually already visible in the presence of a cream layer, due to the fact that the globules of *fat* which the milk contains, being lighter than the watery medium in which they float, are rising to the top. The fat of the milk may be removed by skimming-off the cream, or more quickly by means of a centrifugal separator, leaving the skimmed milk. Either whole or skimmed milk when treated with rennet or when simply allowed to sour *curdles,* the curd being due essentially to casein, the characteristic *protein* of milk. (This and other proteins will be studied briefly later in this chapter, and more fully in Chapters VI and XIX.)

When the fat and the curd have been removed from milk the remaining whey, if concentrated and allowed to stand, yields crystals of *milk sugar,* which belongs, like the other sugars and the starches, to the group of substances called *carbohydrates.*

If whey residue, or if the original milk, be dried and burned there remains a mixture of *mineral* matters,—the *ash.* In addition to water and (other*) mineral matters, protein, fat, and carbohydrate, milk contains citric acid, typical of the *organic acids* and

* The science of mineralogy claims water as a mineral.

most readily recognized in the citrus fruits; and soured milk contains lactic acid, the most familiar of those organic acids whose presence in foods is chiefly due to fermentation of one kind or another.

The *vitamins*, while of great importance to the nutritive value of the diet, constitute as we have seen such an elusively small fraction of the weight of any food that they are usually treated separately from the general discussions of the foodstuffs. Often, too, the minor organic constituents are either ignored or counted with the proteins, fats, or carbohydrates, whichever they most resemble. And there is another reason for postponing further consideration of the vitamins in the fact that they are *not* a natural *group*. Each should be studied on its own merits as in Chapters XI to XVII.

In what follows in this chapter we follow the order carbohydrates, fats, and proteins as being, on the whole, the most logical progression from the simpler to the more complex.

CARBOHYDRATES

Sugars and starches, with a few related substances, are grouped under the name carbohydrates. This group name was suggested by the fact that these substances are composed of carbon, hydrogen, and oxygen, and that the hydrogen and oxygen are here in the same quantitative relation to each other as in water. Of special interest to the student of nutrition are the relationships between members of the three subdivisions of the carbohydrates as illustrated in the sections which follow.

Monosaccharides

The simplest of the carbohydrates, and the ultimate carbohydrate-units into which the more complex carbohydrates can be broken (hydrolyzed, as by digestion) are called monosaccharides. The significance of "mono" in the name is to emphasize their simplicity or "single-sugar-ness" of chemical nature (as contrasted with the disaccharides and polysaccharides to be mentioned below). Glucose, fructose, and galactose are the three monosaccharides of most importance in nutrition.

Glucose (also called dextrose, grape sugar, corn sugar, starch sugar) is widely distributed in nature, occurring in small amounts in the blood of all animals, and much more abundantly in many fruits and plant juices. It is especially abundant in grapes, of which it often constitutes 20 per cent of the total weight or more than half of the solid matter. Sweet corn, onions, and unripe potatoes are among the common vegetables containing considerable amounts of glucose. Pure dextrose made from cornstarch is now largely marketed as corn sugar; and it has been announced that so far as practicable corn sugar and cane sugar will receive equal treatment in the administration of the Federal Food Law.

Fructose (levulose, fruit sugar) occurs with glucose in plant juices, in fruits, and especially in honey, where it makes up about one-half of the solid matter. It is formed, along with an equal weight of glucose, when ordinary cane or beet sugar is digested.

Galactose is important because it is formed, along with an equal weight of glucose, when milk sugar is digested.

Disaccharides

The name *disaccharide* implies a substance each molecule of which can be broken down into two monosaccharide (simple sugar) molecules. The three nutritionally important members of this group of carbohydrates are sucrose (cane or beet sugar), lactose (milk sugar), and maltose (malt sugar).

Sucrose (saccharose, cane sugar, beet sugar), which upon digestion gives one molecule of glucose and one of fructose, is present in considerable quantity in the fruits and juices of many plants. The commercial sources of sucrose are the sugar beet, the sugar and sorghum canes, the sugar palm, and the sugar maple; but many of the common fruits and vegetables contain notable amounts. For example, sucrose is said to constitute at least half the solid matter of pineapples and of some roots, such as carrots.

The per capita consumption of the practically pure cane (and beet) sugar of commerce increased rapidly for a century in the United States (Fig. 3) until now it is estimated that on the average about one-tenth to one-seventh of our food calories are derived from this source. The question whether it is wise to take so much of a food which contributes none of the nutritionally important protein, mineral elements, and vitamins, may more profitably be discussed after the study of Chapters VI to XV.

Lactose (milk sugar) occurs in the milk of all mammals, usually constituting 6 to 7 per cent of human milk and 4.5 to 5 per cent of cows' and goats' milk. When digested it yields glucose and galactose in equal proportions.

Because lactose is regarded by some physicians and bacteriologists as markedly beneficial in maintaining a desirable state of the lower intestinal tract, many persons make a special effort to secure a liberal intake of this sugar, either through generous use of milk or by addition to their diet of pure lactose. As yet, the consumption

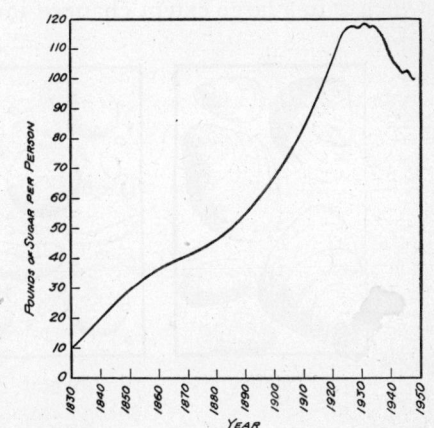

Fig. 3. Trend of the annual per capita consumption of refined sugar in the United States from 1830 to 1945.

of lactose in this country is far less than the amount which its dairy industry could very readily supply. The sweeter, more soluble form of this sugar is known as beta-lactose.

Maltose (malt sugar) occurs in germinating cereals, malt, and malt products. It also appears as an intermediate product when starch is digested in the body. Maltose, whether eaten as such or formed in the course of digestion, is not absorbed to any important extent, but is further broken down in the digestive tract, each molecule of maltose yielding two molecules of glucose.

Polysaccharides

Complex carbohydrates, each molecule of which represents many molecules of monosaccharide, are called *polysaccharides*.

Starch, the dextrins, glycogen ("animal starch"), cellulose, and the hemicelluloses, are the only members of this group which need be mentioned here.

Starch (whose ultimate digestion-product is glucose) is the form in which plants store the largest part of their reserve carbohydrate material, and is of great importance as a constituent of many natural foods. It occurs in the seeds, roots, tubers, bulbs, and to some extent in the stems and leaves of plants. It constitutes one-half to three-fourths of the solid matter of the ordinary cereal grains, when mature, and at least three-fourths of the solids of mature potatoes. Unripe apples and bananas contain much starch which is to a large extent changed into sugars as these fruits ripen;

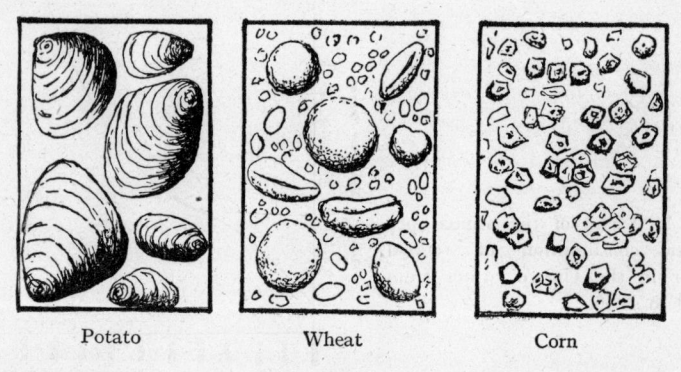

Potato   Wheat   Corn

Fig. 4. Granules of starches prepared from potatoes, wheat, and corn. In each case, the granules are magnified about 300 diameters.

while, on the other hand, young tender corn (maize) kernels and peas contain sugar which is transformed into starch as these seeds mature.

Starch granules of some typical plants are shown in Fig. 4. The differences in size, shape, and variability are significant both in identifying starches as to source (botanical species), and as affecting the ease and economy with which a starch can be separated from the materials which accompany it in nature. Thus cornstarch granules are fairly uniform in size and shape (Fig. 4) and can be washed (for removal of other substances naturally occurring in corn) with but little loss. In contrast, wheat starch contains many large and also many much smaller granules which (as they settle much more slowly) must be largely lost when the larger grains are purified by washing. This is one of the reasons that cornstarch is cheaper than correspondingly purified wheat starch. Another reason (in the United States) is the enormous size of our national corn crop—averaging about three times as many bushels of corn as of wheat. Norman Kennedy estimates (1949) that an average United States corn crop contains about 100,000,000,000 pounds of starch. In this country, much the greatest part of the corn produced is fed to farm animals.

Each molecule of starch contains many glucose units.

Starch granules are insoluble in cold water and apparently little affected by it; on warming, however, they absorb water and swell, passing eventually into a sort of semi-solution, and in this state they are very much more easily digested than is raw starch.

In digestion, the starch of the food is changed into smaller polysaccharides, the *dextrins,* and these into the disaccharide maltose. Since, as already indicated, maltose is further digested into glucose, it is as glucose that the large quantities of carbohydrates eaten in the form of starch become available to the body.

Glycogen is very similar in chemical composition to starch, and as it plays in some respects much the same rôle in animals which starch plays in plants, it is sometimes called animal starch. It occurs in many parts of the animal body, predominantly in the liver and the muscles.

Cellulose is familiar as a woody or fibrous material occurring in the cell walls of all vegetable tissues. It is a polysaccharide of glucose, more resistant than starch, and is only softened (not hydrolyzed) by cooking processes.

The hemicelluloses are polysaccharides which botanically resemble cellulose in belonging to the walls rather than to the contents of plant cells. Chemically, they are not so well defined as cellulose, and hemicelluloses from various sources have been reported to yield on hydrolysis different monosaccharides or mixtures of monosaccharides.

Usually a large proportion of the cellulose and hemicellulose of our food remains undigested and so gives bulk to the intestinal residue. This has some effect upon its regular movement. It is well to remember that individuals vary as to what constitutes sufficient bulk without too much roughage; and also that, not only indigestible matter, but fruits or their juices as well, may be efficient in promoting intestinal regularity.

FATS AND LIPOIDS

The Nature and Scientific Significance of the Fats

Fats are composed of the same three chemical elements as are the carbohydrates, namely, carbon, hydrogen, and oxygen, but in different proportions so that fats constitute a much more concentrated form of fuel than do carbohydrates.

The true fats are chemically triglycerides, i.e., the molecule of fat yields on digestion one glycerol and three fatty acid molecules.

The names applied to the individual fats generally indicate their fatty acid composition; as for example, *tristearin,* which contains three stearic acid radicles; *oleo-dipalmitin,* which contains one oleic and two palmitic acid radicles; *stearo-oleo-palmitin,* which has one radicle each of stearic, oleic, and palmitic acids.

The three fatty acids just named are the ones which occur most abundantly in food fats generally. Others are more characteristic of particular fats *e.g.,* the butyric acid of butter.

A number of the fatty acids are listed with their chemical formulae in the Appendix at the back of this book.

Typical fats are not soluble in water but can be dissolved in a *fat-solvent* such as ether, "petroleum ether," chloroform, or carbon tetrachloride. In the preparation of food fats, however, solvents are rarely used. Butter is, of course, obtained by churning; and most other fats are "rendered" either by pressing the fat out of the tissue, or by melting the fat and removing the residual tissue by settling or straining, or both.

The common commercial food fats have a wide variety of origins: butter from milk; lard, suet, and some margarines from meat fats; corn oil (maize oil) from the embryo of a cereal grain; peanut (arachis) and soybean oil from the seeds of leguminous plants; coconut oil, palm oil, and palm kernel oil from the seeds of palms; cottonseed and sesame oils from the seeds of other plants; olive oil from the flesh of a fruit.

While Italian cookery prefers olive oil as its chief fat, American households tend to follow the English, French, and German tradition of using butter as freely as income allows, with lard or a "lard substitute" as next choice, meaning by lard substitute a fat mixture or preparation of essentially the same plasticity and melting point as lard. Thus cottonseed oil as such finds relatively slight use in the American kitchen; but hydrogenated to the consistency of lard it finds a large sale as a cooking fat.

Liquid fats and those which melt at our body temperature are somewhat more readily and completely digested than those which are much harder. Fats in general tend, however, to slow down the digestive process; and the more so the greater the proportion of fat in the food as a whole.

Problems of fat supply, which became acute in the First World War and have continued to receive attention since, have led to a broadening of attitude of the consuming public toward food fats. Refined cottonseed oil, whether as such or hydrogenated to the consistency of a plastic fat like lard, has come to have a much more unquestioned place in the food supply than formerly; maize, peanut, and soybean oils have grown rapidly in acceptance as human food, particularly in margarine; and recently there has been described the preparation from Georgia pecans of a commercially practicable refined edible oil comparable with olive oil.

Some highly unsaturated fatty acid, such as linoleic, linolenic, or arachidonic, seems to be a nutritionally essential part of the diet. As the quantity which the food must furnish evidently need not be large, and as these nutritionally essential fatty acids appear to be widely distributed among common foods of various types, it seems permissible to assume that ordinary everyday dietaries will supply this need without any special planning.

Fat-like and Fat-soluble Substances

Fats are usually accompanied by *lipoids:* fat-like substances soluble either in fat solvents or in the fat itself. Some of these, including the *lecithins,* are closely related to fats in their chemical nature; others, such as the *sterols,* are "fat-like" rather in their physical properties than in their chemical natures. One will meet the lecithins again among phosphorus compounds, and the sterols in connection with the vitamins D.

Lipins and *lipids* are names sometimes used to cover both the true fats and the lipoids of all kinds.

The choice among fats as food is now largely (and very logically) influenced by the fact that some contain relatively much, and others practically none, of the important fat-soluble vitamin A, consideration of which is here deferred to Chapter XV.

Prominence of Fat in Some Everyday Food Problems

Scientifically it has been shown that fat* and carbohydrate are interchangeable as body fuel throughout a very wide range of proportions. In practice, there are certain facts, partly physiological and partly psychological, which tend to make the proportion of fat in the food a prominent factor in practical dietetics.

Fat is not only a food of high fuel value; foods also seem "richer" the more fat they contain, and correspondingly they "stay by" longer. The latter expression means chiefly that, other things being equal, the more fat a given meal contains the longer the time before it will have left the stomach. It is when the stomach is empty that the muscular contractions of its walls give rise to the "pangs" of hunger. Hence among the peoples of the Western World who have become accustomed to a fairly liberal use of fat in their daily food, any shortage of fat is felt both in the difficulty of getting the desired effects in cookery and in the fact that the low-fat meals leave the stomach more quickly so that there is more sensation of hunger before the next meal. When the physiological effect is further complicated by the anxiety accompanying a period of inadequate and uncertain food supply, the shortage of fat may become a real factor in impairment of morale.

In 1949 the Bureau of Human Nutrition and Home Economics of the U. S. Department of Agriculture published the results of a survey begun in the previous year upon fats and oils consumed by city families. Information was gathered from about 1,600 housekeeping families in 68 cities. Then four cities—Birmingham, Buffalo, Minneapolis-St. Paul, and San Francisco—taken as representative of different parts of the United States, were studied more intensively. *Table fats* were used in all four cities in total quantities of about 0.4 pound per person per week. *Other food fats* were consumed to the extent of about 0.4 pound to 0.7 pound per person per week. The largest per capita consumption of total fat was 1.10 pounds a week in Birmingham. "This reflects the prevalence in Birmingham of home baking of hot breads and of frying as a method of food preparation." Minneapolis-St. Paul used the smallest amount of total fat (0.79 pound per person per week) but the

---

* When, as in the case of the proteins, the fats, or the carbohydrates, the members of a related group admit of a generalized statement, the collective-singular form of the group name is commonly used.

largest amount of butter per person. Buffalo and San Francisco used amounts per person intermediate, both in total fats and in butter, between Birmingham and Minneapolis-St. Paul.

The art of dietetics as practiced in America and Europe tends to furnish from one-fourth to one-third of the total food calories in the form of fat. With much less than one-fourth there may be dissatisfaction for such reasons as mentioned above, while much more than one-third of the food calories in the form of fat may tend to give rise to sensations of excess.

When food is so rich in fat as to stay too long in the stomach, this organ may become fatigued or may even rebel. Here importance may also be attached to the way in which the fat is used in cookery. Fried foods are apt to come under special suspicion (1) that they may have been allowed to absorb too much fat, and (2) that irritating substances may have been formed in the fat by the heating to which it was subjected in the frying pan. Hence the advice to sear quickly the surface, especially of meat, and then lower the temperature so that the interior "cooks in its own juice." Clearly, too, a surface water-proofing of fat, such as will keep the food juices in, must also tend to keep the digestive juices out; so that the presence of fat retards the digestion of carbohydrates and proteins, and the more so the more the fat has been cooked into the rest of the food.

PROTEINS

Carbohydrates and fats are the chief sources of energy for the activities of the body but not the chief constituents of which the active tissues are composed. Muscle tissue, for example, contains but little carbohydrate, and often very little fat. The chief organic constituents of the muscles, and of the protoplasm of plant and animal cells generally, are substances which contain nitrogen and sulfur in addition to the carbon, hydrogen, and oxygen of which the carbohydrates and fats are composed. In 1838, the Dutch chemist Mulder separated and described a nitrogenous material which he believed to be the fundamental constituent of tissue substances and gave it the name *protein*, derived from a Greek verb meaning "to take the first place." While Mulder's chemical work did not prove to be of permanent value, the term which he introduced has been retained, and in the plural form, proteins, is now used as a group name for a large number of different but related nitrogenous organic compounds which are so prominent among the constituents of the tissues and of food that they may still be accorded some degree of preeminence by the student of nutrition.

Any typical protein molecule is very large and complex, composed essentially of a great number of comparatively simple units, the *amino acids*. When proteins are digested the amino acids are set free. Typically there are formed a number of intermediate products *proteoses, peptones, peptides* (corresponding to the dextrins and maltose in the digestion of starch) and ultimately the simple amino acids as final digestion products (corresponding to the monosaccharides which are the final products of the digestion of carbohydrates). Thus the relation of amino acid to protein is analogous to the relation of glucose to starch. There is, however, the important difference that the glucose molecules yielded by starch are all alike while the amino acid molecules yielded by proteins are of several different kinds.

Nutritional characteristics of the different kinds of amino acids will be studied in Chapter VI.

It is believed that in general the protein in each kind of tissue of each species of plant or animal is chemically distinct from the protein of every other tissue and species. When one considers that each molecule of protein may contain several hundred amino-acid units of as many as twenty-one different kinds, this almost unlimited number and diversity of the proteins in nature becomes in some measure understandable.

Plants synthesize their own proteins from inorganic materials obtained from the soil and air. Animals, on the other hand, must depend, for material from which to build their tissue proteins, upon the digestion products of the proteins of their food. Some of the amino acids may be formed in the body from other amino acids and so need not individually be furnished by the food proteins. Others, which contain characteristic chemical structures or groupings that the body cannot obtain from other sources or make for itself, must be supplied in some form in the nutriment. These latter, which are frequently designated as the *indispensable* or *nutritionally essential* amino acids will be discussed more fully in the study of protein requirements in nutrition and the relative merits of different foods in meeting these requirements (Chapters VI and XIX).

DETERMINATION OF PROTEINS, FATS, AND CARBOHYDRATES IN FOODS

Actual descriptions of the methods of food analysis lie outside the scope of this book. The purpose of the paragraphs which follow is simply to indicate enough of the general plan to give a reasonable feeling of acquaintance with the meaning of the percentages as used in subsequent chapters and as tabulated in the Appendix.

Protein.—Not only do all proteins contain nitrogen; they all contain not far from 16 per cent of nitrogen, and most foods contain only relatively insignificant amounts of other nitrogen compounds. Hence, to find the amount of total protein which a food contains, one may determine the amount of nitrogen and multiply this by 6.25.

Fat.—A weighed portion of the air-dry, finely ground, sample of food is dried until completely water-free; then extracted with water-free ether (or other fat-solvent), the solvent evaporated, and the fat weighed.

Carbohydrate.—While there are analytical methods by which each of the more important carbohydrates of our food may be determined individually when necessary, it is often considered sufficient to determine total carbohydrate "by difference," *i.e.*, by subtracting from the total percentage of organic matter in the food the percentages of protein and fat found as above. This of course involves determinations of water and ash in order that the total organic matter of the food may be known.

Water is determined by drying to constant weight, and **ash** by burning off the organic matter of the dry food and weighing the residue of mineral matter, both the operations and the interpretations requiring the observance of technical precautions the full discussion of which would lead us beyond the scope of this book.

Mineral elements and **vitamins** are important but are not among the more abundant nutrients in foods. Hence they are not discussed here but will be given full consideration in later chapters.

EXERCISES: for students, instructor, or both together

1. Why are the sugar cane and the sugar beet the two economically outstanding sources of the world's supply of sugar?

2. Using the library facilities available to you, prepare an account of one or more of the following: the growing and harvesting of sugar cane or sugar beets; the making of raw sugar from cane or beets; the refining of the raw sugar into the white crystallized sugar (granulated or domino sugar) of commerce; the present-day corn sugar industry.

3. Distinguishing between "sugar" and "sugar and sweets," compare present per capita sugar consumption of your country with that of others; and with those of 1900 and of 1925.

4. Examine food starches under the microscope.

5. What sugars and sirups are made from what starches on an industrial scale? To what countries and to what times does your answer refer?

6. Look up in one of the books listed below under Suggested Readings the starch contents and the sugar contents of potatoes and sweetpotatoes. (We do *not* write "white and sweet potatoes," because botanically the socalled sweetpotato is not a kind of potato. They belong not only to different species but to different genera. What are their scientific names?)

7. How do potatoes and sweetpotatoes differ with respect to other nutrient factors? Is more of nutritive value lost in the making of starch from one than from the other? (Use the index; also other books.)

8. Why have we an industry of hydrogenation of fats, which changes unsaturated into saturated fatty acids, when the "nutritionally essential" fatty acids belong to the unsaturated group?

SUGGESTED READINGS

ANDERSON, A. K.   1947   *Essentials of Physiological Chemistry*, 3rd Ed. (Wiley.)

BARKI, V. H., R. A. COLLINS, E. B. HART, and C. A. ELVEHJEM 1949   Relation of fat deficiency symptoms to the poly-unsaturated fatty acid content of the tissues of the mature rat. *Proc. Soc. Exptl. Biol. Med.* 71, 694–696.

BOGERT, L. J.   1949   *Nutrition and Physical Fitness*, 5th Ed. (W. B. Saunders Co.)

BOUTWELL, R. K., R. P. GEYER, C. A. ELVEHJEM, and E. B. HART 1941   The effect of hydrogenation on the nutritive value of the fatty acid fraction of butterfat and of certain vegetable oils. *J. Dairy Sci.* 24, 1027–1034.

BUREAU OF HUMAN NUTRITION AND HOME ECONOMICS   1949   Fats and oils consumed by city families: based on 1948 Food Consumption Surveys. U. S. Dept. Agriculture, *Commodity Summary* No. 2.

BUREAU OF HUMAN NUTRITION AND HOME ECONOMICS   1949b

Sugars and sweets in city diets, based on food consumption surveys of 1948. U. S. Dept. Agriculture, *Commodity Summary* No. 5.

HILDITCH, T. P., and H. JASPERSON 1944 The component acids of milk fats of the goat, ewe, and mare. *Biochem. J.* 38, 443–447; *Nutr. Abs. Rev.* 15, 41–42.

HOAGLAND, R., and G. G. SNIDER 1941 Nutritive properties of steam-rendered lard and hydrogenated cottonseed oil. *J. Nutrition* 22, 65–76.

HUGHES, O. 1940 *Introductory Foods.* (Macmillan.)

JACK, E. L., and J. L. HENDERSON 1945 The fatty-acid composition of glyceride fractions separated from milk fat. *J. Dairy Sci.* 28, 65–78; *Nutr. Abs. Rev.* 15, 41.

JUSTIN, M. H., L. O. RUST, and G. E. VAIL 1940 *Foods: An Introductory College Course,* Revised Ed. (Houghton Mifflin.)

MAYNARD, L. A., and E. RASMUSSEN 1942 Influence of dietary fat on lactation. *J. Nutrition* 23, 385–398.

PRESCOTT, S. C., and B. E. PROCTOR 1937 *Food Technology,* Chapters VII, XXI. (McGraw-Hill.)

SHERMAN, H. C. 1948 *Food Products,* 4th Ed., Chapters I, XII, and XIII. (Macmillan.)

SINCLAIR, R. G. 1940 Growth of rats on high-fat and low-fat diets, deficient in the essential unsaturated fatty acids. *J. Nutrition* 19, 131–140.

STANLEY, L., and J. A. CLINE 1950 *Foods: Their Selection and Preparation,* New Ed. (Ginn and Co.)

STEWART, J. J., and A. L. EDWARDS 1948 *Foods: Production, Marketing, Consumption,* 2nd Ed. (Prentice-Hall, Inc.)

WILLIAMS, R. J., and E. BEERSTECHER, JR. 1948 *Introduction to Biochemistry,* 2nd Ed. (Van Nostrand.)

III

WHAT HAPPENS TO FOOD
IN THE BODY:
DIGESTION AND METABOLISM

What we have now to consider is how the foodstuffs studied in the preceding chapter are brought into the actual nutritional service of the body.

Digestion is the general name for the processes by means of which the carbohydrates, fats, and proteins of the food are brought by the body into forms fitted for absorption from its digestive tract into its true interior,—the blood and lymph, the spinal fluid, and the organs and tissues.

Metabolism (derived from a Greek word the literal meaning of which is merely "change") is used by the science of nutrition as a general name for the changes which the digestion-products undergo from the moment of their absorption until they have reached the end products of the nutritional process.

The same terms thus applied to the food as a whole may also be applied to a single kind of nutrient, as when we speak of the digestion and metabolism of carbohydrate; or of fat; or of protein.

Digestion

The process of digestion of the food as a whole may be said to have four general effects: (1) it brings the digestible constituents of food into fluid form; (2) it changes the more complex sugars and the starches into sugars of the simplest type, "monosaccharides"; (3) it changes fats into a mixture of glycerol and fatty acids; (4) it changes proteins into a mixture of amino acids.

The significance of these digestive changes is of a two-fold kind.

It facilitates the absorption of the nutrients; and it results in their being absorbed in the form of their simplest "building-blocks," from which the body tissues can reconstruct carbohydrates, fats, and proteins according to their own patterns.

Or instead of rebuilding the digestion-products of the foodstuffs into the corresponding tissue-stuffs, the body may use the digestion-products as fuel.

Enzymes

The changes which the foodstuffs undergo in digestion and metabolism are facilitated and greatly hastened by the presence (in the digestive juices and in the active cells) of substances known as enzymes.

Fig. 5. Crystals of pepsin. Contrast with trypsin, shown in Fig. 6. Both are representative digestive enzymes, isolated in crystalline condition, both typically protein in their chemical nature, but of very different crystalline form. (Courtesy of Dr. J. H. Northrop.)

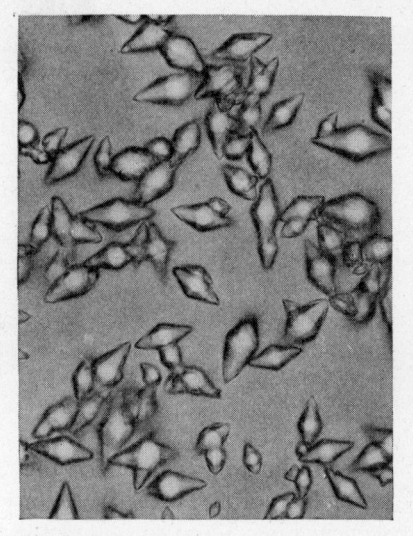

By definition, *enzymes* are catalysts formed in living cells; and *catalysts* (or *catalytic agents*) are things that "act by contact," or more particularly they are things which act very significantly in bringing about chemical changes without themselves being used up in the reaction.

In theory, such a catalyst is regarded as speeding-up a change which would otherwise go on only slowly. In practice, the enzyme may make all the difference between a rapid rate of change and a rate which is infinitely slow. Hence one often speaks *as if* the enzyme were responsible for initiating the reaction which it catalyzes.

Thus the enzymes are characterized by their ability, even in very small amounts, to accelerate changes in other substances. The typical enzymes are *specific* both as to the substance on which each acts, often called its *substrate,* and with regard to the nature of the change which they catalyze.

Furthermore, enzymes formed in different organs of the body are apt to be at least slightly different in their own chemical nature,

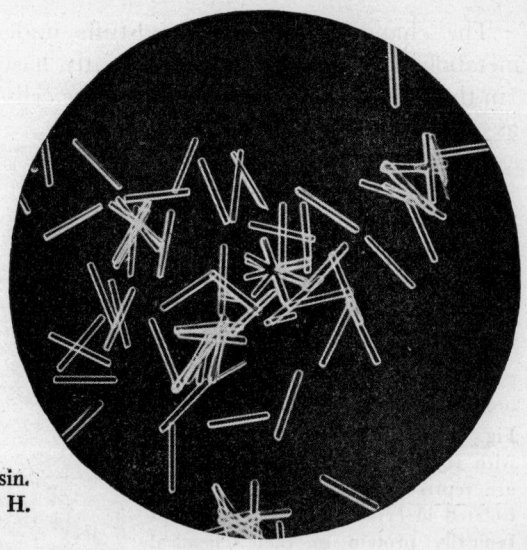

Fig. 6. Crystals of trypsin. (Courtesy of Dr. J. H. Northrop.)

even in those cases in which they act in the same manner upon the same substrate. This is true, for example, of pepsin and trypsin as seen in Figs. 5 and 6; and of two enzymes which both take part in the normal digestion of starch, and which will serve to illustrate the modern system of naming enzymes.

By this system the name of an enzyme is constructed from the name of the substance upon which it acts, with the suffix *-ase;* and the noun thus formed is preceded by an adjective indicating the source of the enzyme. Thus in the present example, as the classical name of starch is *amylum,* the starch-digesting enzymes are called *amylases.* The one contained in saliva is called *salivary amylase* and the one in pancreatic juice is called *pancreatic amylase.*

Enzymes which digest fats are called *lipases;* those which digest proteins are called *proteases.*

There are, however, several important instances in which names assigned before this plan of nomenclature had been decided upon still continue in common scientific use, as, for example, *pepsin* for what according to the formal system would be called *gastric protease*.

In this chapter, we shall be chiefly concerned with the enzymes which act upon food in its course through the alimentary tract. Most of these are *hydrolytic* enzymes, *i.e.*, they accelerate processes in which the elements of water enter into the process of splitting of the foodstuff into its digestion products. The most thoroughly studied of these digestive enzymes have all been found to be typical proteins. In Figs. 5 and 6 are shown crystals of two typical digestive enzymes, pepsin and trypsin, prepared in a purified condition by Northrop and his coworkers.

A tabular summary of the best-known digestive enzymes is given in the Appendix.

For our present purpose the essential point is that the digestive enzymes (sometimes called "digestive ferments") result in the breaking down (by hydrolysis) of the carbohydrates, fats, and proteins of the food into digestion-products which (1) are more soluble and diffusible and thus more available to the body cells, and (2) are simple enough to be readily used as building-stones in the chemical architecture of the body substances, "tissue" or "regulatory," or to function readily as fuel for the support of the energy needs of nutrition.

The Course of the Food through the Digestive Tract

The digestion of foodstuffs may perhaps best be studied by first tracing the course of the food as a whole through the digestive tract and then taking up in turn the fate of the carbohydrates, the fats, and the proteins, both in digestion and after absorption.

The digestive apparatus includes the *alimentary tract*,—essentially a tube about 30 feet long in a grown person,—and the *glands* whose secretions are poured into the alimentary tract and assist in the changes taking place there. The general features of the arrangement of the digestive tract are familiar to almost everyone, and are shown diagrammatically in Fig. 7. As will appear in the discussion which follows, this system of organs is specifically adapted to perform efficiently both the *mechanical* or *physical functions* of grinding and shaking the food-masses until finely divided and thoroughly mixed with the digestive juices; and also the *chemical functions* of providing digestive enzymes and surrounding them with conditions favorable to their activity.

In the course of normal digestion these functions in the different parts of the digestive system are coordinated partly through the nervous system and partly by the sending ahead of "chemical messengers" (hormones) to prepare the digestive apparatus for the oncoming food material. Thus, the taste of food (or often even the thought of it) may initiate the secretion of digestive juices not only in the mouth but also in the stomach. And as soon as the

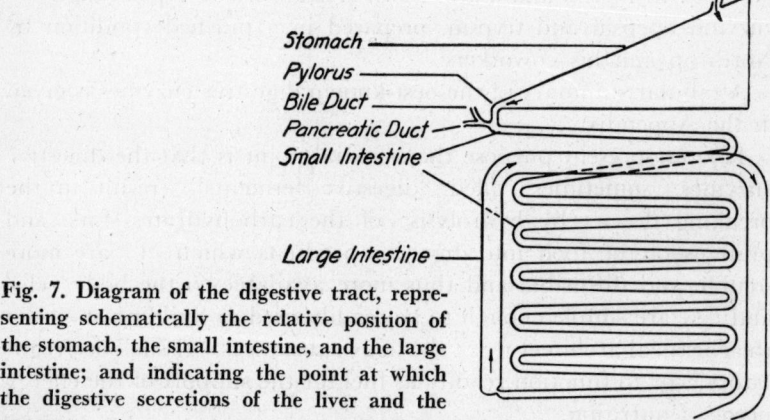

Fig. 7. Diagram of the digestive tract, representing schematically the relative position of the stomach, the small intestine, and the large intestine; and indicating the point at which the digestive secretions of the liver and the pancreas enter.

stomach begins to allow the passage of the partially digested food mixture into the small intestine, a chemical messenger (called *secretin*) is sent from the intestinal membranes by way of the blood stream to the pancreas and liver, exciting these organs to increased production of secretions which are discharged into the small intestine and assist in the digestive processes there.

As indicated by the heading of this section, what follows is an account of what goes on in the successive organs of the digestive tract. The description refers, first, to the mechanical handling of the food-mass as a whole and, second, to the chemical changes which occur in the carbohydrates, the proteins, and the fats of the food. These are, of course, the physical and the chemical aspects of what the digestive tract does to the food.

As one follows the course of the food through the digestive tract it should be with two aspects of thought in mind: How should the person treat the digestive system, especially as to what is swallowed and in what circumstances; and what service may then be expected from the digestive system.

The scope of this book does not include the study of disorders. The following outline therefore presumes that we are dealing with a well-treated and well-behaved digestion.

In the mouth the food should be not merely softened and lubricated so that it can be swallowed easily; it should be chewed thoroughly to reduce it to particles of the smallest size and to mix the saliva intimately through every bit of the food mass. Only when the food has been chewed until reduced to very small particles can the different digestive juices act upon it to best advantage. In the mode of attachment of the jaw and in the strength of its muscles, we are provided by nature with an ample and efficient mechanism for the proper chewing of our food. But nature has made chewing a voluntary act; thus leaving it to our own intelligence and will to determine the thoroughness with which this first act of the digestive process shall be performed. Such rules as that one should chew a given number of times upon each mouthful may be helpful, but are too mechanical to satisfy one who takes an intelligent interest. A more rational though perhaps somewhat more extreme rule is that each mouthful should be chewed as long as any taste can be perceived or until swallowing is entirely unconscious. It is a mistake to suppose that such thorough chewing greatly reduces the amount of food required; but for other reasons it is an excellent habit.

While the food is in the mouth, the several groups of salivary glands pour out their secretion upon it. This saliva is the only digestive juice which ordinarily comes directly under our observation, and perhaps because it is familiar we are apt to underestimate its significance. We say that a tempting dish "makes the mouth water," and are apt to think of this as a property of the food rather than as an important first step in digestion. The actual part played by the saliva in the process of digestion is much greater than was formerly supposed. The saliva has no appreciable action upon proteins or fats but does digest starches and dextrins by means of an enzyme known as ptyalin (or more recently as salivary amylase) which is active in approximately neutral solutions. Although relatively little chemical change in the food actually takes place in the mouth, under favorable conditions the salivary amylase may continue to act on food carbohydrates in the stomach for some time before the acid gastric secretion reaches it in sufficient amount to halt its activity.

To end a meal with (or to follow a meal by) the eating of raw fruit or celery, when one can conveniently arrange to do so, is an excellent habit for several reasons. The discussion of the ultimate nutritional benefit belongs to later chapters; but some of the more immediate advantages should be noted here. The combined mechanical action of the vegetable fiber and chemical action of the mild fruit acid leave the mouth in the best possible condition with a sensation of savory cleanliness and toning up which is well worth while in itself; and which also sends nerve impulses and chemical messengers which greatly aid the successive steps in the digestive process.

In the stomach, the food is stored for a longer or shorter time depending largely upon the size and character of the meal. The walls of the stomach are so elastic that, as expressed by Howell, there is "never any empty space within; its cavity is only as large as its contents, so that the first portion of food eaten entirely fills it and successive portions find the wall layer occupied and are therefore received into the interior." There is thus no general circulation and mixing of the stomach contents during or immediately following a meal. This was well illustrated in an experiment in which a rat was fed a liberal meal in three courses, each food of a different color. This animal was then killed, frozen, and the stomach contents examined. The food which had been eaten first lay next to the wall of the stomach and filled the part of the stomach which connects with the intestine, while the food last eaten lay in the interior of the stomach contents near the point at which it had been pushed into the stomach by the act of swallowing. Fig. 8 represents somewhat diagrammatically the relative position of food portions in the stomach during normal digestion according to the sequence in which they were eaten.

Not much nutriment is actually absorbed from the stomach, although some such absorption occurs in the case of such things as the monosaccharides and the soluble salts of the food which as swallowed are already in the forms in which they will be absorbed. A larger factor, in the quickness with which nutriment is absorbed in any important quantity, is the promptness of its passage through the stomach and into the small intestine whose wall is a much more effective absorbing surface.

As all food-masses should be thoroughly moist throughout when they are swallowed, and in the stomach are further wetted by the gastric juice, the water (or solution of foodstuffs in water) which is swallowed as such during a meal need not soak into the whole foodmass in the stomach but may (and largely does) find its way along the "lesser curvature" of the stomach wall* from the esophagus to the pylorus, and thus pass more quickly into the small intestine than does the bulk of either the protein, the fat, or the carbohydrate of the ordinary solid food.

Fig. 8. Diagram of the stomach and the status of its contents during digestion. The position of the food last swallowed is here indicated by the speckled area, that of the intermediate portion of food by the horizontal shading, whereas the food first eaten, which has been pushed into the pyloric region and there thoroughly mixed with the gastric juice, is represented by the cross-hatched shading. The stomach wall is thicker and much more muscular from the region of the transverse band to the pylorus, while the wall of the fundus is relatively thin, passive, and elastic.

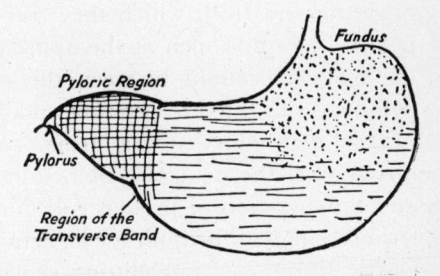

As in the case of any other organ, a detailed study of the functions of the stomach would involve a knowledge of its structure. Omitting all but what is essential to our present purpose, we may speak of the stomach as consisting of: (1) a larger part called the *fundus* or *cardiac region,* into which the food is received when swallowed, and which is very elastic and becomes distended as the stomach stretches to accommodate more food; and (2) the *antrum* or *pyloric region,* a much smaller part, conical in shape, and ending in the *pylorus,* the muscular valve which connects the stomach with the small intestine. A region of especially thick circular muscle fibers known as the *transverse band* is considered as marking the boundary between the cardiac and the pyloric regions of the stomach. (Fig. 8).

By mixing some harmless mineral substance such as bismuth

* The shape and position of the stomach are such that Fig. 8 may be regarded as about equally representative of a vertical or a horizontal section.

subnitrate with the food it becomes possible to observe the contour and movements of the food mass in the digestive tract by means of the x-ray. In this way it was shown that only in the pyloric region are the food masses and the gastric juice actively mixed by muscular contractions (See Fig. 8); in the fundus the swallowed masses of food and saliva remain comparatively undisturbed, so that in this part of the stomach the salivary digestion of starch may continue for a relatively long time.

In the region of the transverse band there is, during digestion, a rather copious secretion of strongly acid gastric juice, and it is in this same region that waves of muscular constriction are seen to originate and from which they travel toward the pylorus. But the pylorus does not open at the approach of each of these waves and the material caught between the muscular wave and the closed pylorus is subjected to pressure and to an eddying movement which mixes it and reduces it to a creamy *chyme*. As the food thus becomes mixed with the acid secretion, salivary digestion of starch ceases; and the digestion of protein is begun by the enzyme *pepsin,* which requires an acid medium for its activity. There is also present in the gastric secretion a fat-splitting enzyme *(gastric lipase),* but its activity under the conditions usually prevailing in the stomach is rather limited. The flow of gastric juice is affected by many factors, prominent among which are appetite for the food, pleasurable sensations when the food is being chewed, freedom from emotional tension, and the presence in the stomach of certain substances including water, dilute acids, fruit and meat juices, and many other food constituents which have stimulating effects upon gastric secretion. This fact affords sound scientific justification for the common practice of beginning a meal with a dilute (watery) yet stimulating first course such as soup or fruit.

The free hydrochloric acid of the gastric juice has not only a digestive but also an antiseptic function, for this acid is a fairly efficient germicide. If the food, by thorough chewing, has been broken into very small particles so that any bacteria which it contains are freely exposed to the gastric juice, the latter will afford a much more effective protection against the passage of objectionable bacteria through the stomach into the intestine than is possible when some of the food particles are too large to be completely permeated by the acid during the time that the acid chyme remains in the stomach.

At intervals the pylorus opens and permits the passage of chyme into the small intestine. As the food in the pyloric region is thus gradually passed out of the stomach, fresh portions of the food mass in the fundus are pressed into the antrum by the muscular tension of the stomach wall.

Thus, while the dividing line is not sharp nor prominent there is a fairly distinct difference both in structure and in function between the two regions of the stomach: In the thin-walled elastic fundus the food mass is held quietly in storage and salivary digestion of starch continues; in the thick-walled antrum with its peristaltic waves of muscular constriction the food is mixed with the gastric juice, salivary digestion ceases, peptic digestion of proteins begins, and the food is more or less thoroughly disinfected by the free acid of the gastric juice.

The stomach as a whole may therefore be said to have four main functions. It serves: (1) as a storage reservoir receiving food in relatively large quantities, say three times a day, and passing it on to the intestine in small portions at frequent intervals; (2) as a place for the continuation of the salivary digestion of starch; and (3) for the beginning of the digestion of proteins and perhaps fats; and finally (4) as a disinfecting station of somewhat doubtful and variable value since the food is subjected to the acidity of the gastric juice for a relatively short time in the pyloric region, and the degree of contact of acid with bacteria must depend largely upon the size of the food particles at this stage of digestion.

The length of time spent by food in the stomach depends in part upon the proportions of carbohydrate, protein, and fat eaten. In experiments where each is eaten separately, protein food stays longer in the stomach than carbohydrate; fat longer than protein; and mixtures of fat and protein longest of all. In a mixed diet, then, the greater the proportion of fat the longer the food stays in the stomach. This action of fat may be either disadvantageous or advantageous according to circumstances. Excessive fat may retard digestion unduly and lead to discomfort; on the other hand, too little fat may result in such early emptying of the stomach that hunger pangs are felt too shortly after the meal is eaten.

In the small intestine, the food, which (as we saw) has already been reduced to a liquid chyme, is subjected to the simultaneous action of three different secretions, the bile, the pancreatic juice, and the intestinal juice (or *succus entericus*). These three secretions all contain alkaline salts which quickly overcome the acidity of the chyme so that the intestinal contents as a whole are normally alkaline. The bile does not seem to exert any direct digestive action but by its solvent and dispersive action on fats and fatty acids it not only assists the fat-splitting enzymes to come into more effective contact with their substrate, but also facilitates the absorption of the fatty acids formed as the result of their activity. Pancreatic juice contains digestive enzymes for each of the three groups of foodstuffs—proteins, fats, and carbohydrates. The intestinal juice takes part in the digestion of both proteins and carbohydrates. For fuller information regarding the specific enzymes involved, Appendix B may be consulted.

In the upper part of the small intestine there occurs a special sort of muscular contraction which quickly emulsifies the fat by shaking it back and forth with the alkaline juices and bile, at the same time promoting the digestion of all of the foodstuffs by bringing them into intimate association with their digestive enzymes and facilitating absorption by constantly pressing fresh portions of the digesting mixture against the intestinal wall. In addition to this peculiar movement which is characteristic of the upper part of the small intestine, there occurs throughout its length a succession of peristaltic waves of muscular constriction which force the food mass against the absorbing surface and move it onward along the digestive canal. In the wall of the small intestine there are many cross-folds and innumerable tiny projections (*villi*) extending, like the fingers of a glove, into the central cavity (the *lumen*), which enormously increase the area of surface with which the digested food mixture comes into contact and facilitate the transfer of digestion products from the lumen of the intestine to the circulating fluids of the body, the blood and the lymph. For, in addition to the reasons already suggested, every wave of muscular pressure tends to force the blood and lymph from the villi onward into the body to be replaced by fresh blood and lymph from the general circulation (and with renewed avidity for the digestion products) as soon as the muscular wall relaxes again. The small intestine, with its abundance of enzymes and exceptionally favorable mechanical conditions, is thus well adapted to the processes of digestion and absorption and it is here that the greater part of the digestion products of the three major groups of organic foodstuffs are absorbed. From observations on a patient whose digestive processes were apparently normal it was found that 85 per cent of the protein of the food had been absorbed before the food left the small intestine.

In the large intestine, the digestive juices continue to act upon the remnants of the foodstuffs and a further absorption of digestion products takes place, along with a very marked absorption of water. The material remaining unabsorbed gradually becomes more solid and takes on the character of feces. A comparatively long time (often 18 hours or more) may normally elapse between the entrance of the digestion mixture into the large intestine and the elimination of the residual material from the body.

Fate of the Individual Foodstuffs in Digestion and Metabolism

The changes which some of the more prominent organic constituents of the food undergo in digestion and after absorption may now be considered individually. As a detailed treatment of the processes of intermediary metabolism would involve a somewhat technical knowledge both of organic chemistry and of physiology and require more space than is available here, we shall outline only those aspects an understanding of which is requisite to the purpose of this book, that is, the adaptation of food to the service of the body.

Absorption and Metabolism of Carbohydrates

The carbohydrates of the food, having been brought by the digestive processes to the form of monosaccharides, are taken up from the lumen of the intestine by the cells of the intestinal mucosa and passed, so to speak, into the "physiological interior" of the body. Most of the absorbed carbohydrate is transported from the intestine to the liver by way of the portal vein. In the liver, much of the carbohydrate is removed from the blood stream, glucose, fructose, and galactose each being converted into the polysaccharide *glycogen* for storage in that organ.

The glycogen which has been stored in the liver is subsequently split to yield glucose and this glucose is supplied to the blood to replace the carbohydrate which has been removed from it by other tissues of the body. The liver thus functions to maintain nearly constant the level of glucose in the blood of the general circulation.

The concentration of carbohydrate in the liver, on the other hand, is subject to enormous variations, reaching as high as 10 per cent of the weight of the liver after an abundant meal and falling to nearly nothing when no carbohydrate food has been taken for some time.

The carbohydrate stored in the liver after a meal is thus usually converted into glucose and passes into the blood stream before the next meal, but still the glucose content of the blood remains small and nearly constant. This indicates that the glucose of the blood must be quite rapidly used, and, from the standpoint of our present study, the immediate question is, What becomes of the glucose which the blood carries away from the liver? Investigation shows that this glucose disappears chiefly in the muscles. There, glucose is converted into glycogen, which may reach a concentration of two per cent of the weight of the muscle. This glycogen plays a part in the complicated chain of chemical reactions through which energy is released for muscular work.

Other active tissues of the body also withdraw glucose from the circulation, oxidizing it directly or indirectly as fuel for the various kinds of work which they perform.

Carbohydrate in excess of what is immediately burned and of what is stored as glycogen is converted into fat, which is a much more concentrated form of fuel and which can be stored in much larger quantity than can glycogen. Thus, under the most favorable conditions of feeding and rest, the maximum amount of glycogen stored in the entire adult body is only about two-thirds to one pound, no more carbohydrate than is frequently taken in one day's food, and only about enough, if it were the sole source of energy, to support the body for one day. Whereas, it is a matter of everyday observation that the storage of fat may reach many pounds; and a well nourished individual carries in his body enough fat to serve him as fuel for a month or more.

Digestion of Fats

Before it can be absorbed from the intestinal tract, the fat of the food apparently must be split into its components, glycerol and fatty acids. This cleavage takes place through the action of fat-splitting (lipolytic) enzymes known as *lipases*. There is a lipase in the gastric secretion, but this can effectively digest only fat which has been eaten in a highly emulsified (finely subdivided) condition. The remainder of the fat, after becoming thoroughly emulsified in the small intestine by the vigorous agitation with bile and alkaline salts to which it is there subjected, is digested by the lipase in the pancreatic juice.

Absorption and Metabolism of Fats

The fatty acids and glycerol which are formed in the digestion of fat recombine into fat in the process of being transferred through the cells lining the intestinal tract. This fat passes mainly into the lymph vessels (rather than the blood vessels) and is finally poured with the lymph into the blood, without first having been through the liver. This results in a rise in the fat content of the blood of the general circulation which may be more marked than the increase in glucose concentration following absorption of carbohydrate. The fat thus distributed through the body may be burned in the muscles and other active tissues as a source of energy for muscular and other forms of work; or, if not needed at once as fuel, it may be deposited as body fat, a stored fuel ready to be drawn upon when needed.

Regarded as sources of energy, the functions of fat and carbohydrate are essentially the same, although the utilization of carbohydrate for the performance of muscular work appears to be slightly more efficient than that of fat. Furthermore, as we have seen, the body can change carbohydrate into fat to an almost unlimited extent. To what degree the body can change fat back into carbohydrate, we do not know with certainty. But since, within wide limits, fat serves the same purposes as carbohydrate, our study of the uses of the foodstuffs in nutrition does not necessitate an answer to this latter question.

The fact of the essential interchangeability of fat and carbohydrate in the support of body work greatly simplifies dietary calculations, since in many cases where we deal with the energy values of foods we need not stop to consider separately how much of the energy comes from fat and how much from carbohydrate. But this fact does not justify an attitude of total indifference toward fat as a dietary constituent, for, as already mentioned in Chapter II, fat has important specific properties.

A part of the fatty acids obtained from the fat of the diet or synthesized from carbohydrate is utilized in the formation of constituents of many of the active tissues of the body. To this limited extent at least, the fats may be regarded as tissue-building materials.

However, most of the fat of the well nourished body represents reserve fuel, and as such is deposited in the metabolically inactive adipose (fat-storing) tissues. This storage of fat may occur in many regions of the body, but is particularly marked just below the skin, where a layer of fat of variable thickness may usually be found. Stored fat is also present between the muscles and surrounding the internal organs. Fat thus deposited, although of principal significance as a reserve source of energy, may also serve the body as a mechanical protection against shocks and bruises, as a comparatively impervious blanket against the cold, and as a packing and support for certain of the organs, notably the kidneys.

Usually the nature of the fat found in the body is more or less characteristic of each species or group of closely related species. Herbivora contain as a rule harder fats than carnivora, land animals have harder fat than marine animals, and all warm-blooded animals have fats of higher melting points than those found in fishes. The nature of the body fat may also be affected by the diet. Under many conditions of feeding, the major part of the body fat may be made from carbohydrates. If, however, much of the body fat is formed from fatty acids present in the food, and if these differ markedly either in kind or in relative proportions from the mixture of fatty acids usually occurring in the fat of that species of animal, these differences may be reflected to some extent in the kind of fat deposited in the body.

Nevertheless, although the body fat may thus differ somewhat in its chemical character, its nutritive value appears to be essentially the same. In either case, the fat thus stored may be drawn upon for use as fuel at any future time when the energy requirements of the body demand it.

Digestion of Proteins

The saliva does not digest protein; and so long as the swallowed food remains in the muscularly inactive region of the stomach and unmixed with the gastric juice, the protein is unchanged. Little by little however, as explained earlier, the food becomes mixed with the gastric juice, which contains hydrochloric acid and the proteolytic enzyme, pepsin. Together, these attack the protein of the food, changing it into the somewhat simpler, but still very complex, proteoses and peptones. The proteoses and peptones pass into the small intestine where they (and any protein which may have escaped the action of pepsin) are exposed to a whole battery of other proteolytic enzymes, of which one group, formerly designated as "trypsin" (but now known to consist of at least three distinct enzymes), is provided by the pancreas. Another group, originally referred to in the singular as "erepsin" (but actually consisting of at least two enzymes), is secreted by the intestinal mucosa. Acting cooperatively in the small intestine, these numerous separate enzymes complete the cleavage (hydrolysis) of the protein, proteoses, and peptones received from the stomach, into their ultimate component units, the amino acids.

Absorption and Metabolism of Amino Acids

It is now believed that the hydrolysis of proteins to amino acids in the digestive tract is, in normal conditions, practically complete. The protein digestion products are absorbed, mainly from the small intestine, into the blood stream, and distributed as amino acids to the various tissues of the body. The amino acids, having been withdrawn from the blood stream by the tissues, may be used by them in various ways. (1) Part may be reassembled as building stones to form new protein in the proportions and according to the specific pattern characteristic of the tissue in question. (2) Some may be assimilated to take the place of fragments of body protein which are being broken down in the wear-and-tear processes which always go on in living cells. (3) Certain of them may be utilized in the synthesis of substances (some protein in nature, others of simpler composition) such as certain hormones and enzymes, which have essentially body-regulating rather than structural functions. (4) The remaining are broken down ("deaminized") into a nitrogenous fragment, which is eliminated from the body chiefly in the form of urea, and a non-nitrogenous residue, which is either burned as fuel, or converted into carbohydrate or fat. In serving as fuel, the protein is utilized interchangeably with carbohydrate and fat, since its energy may be converted into muscular work, internal activity, or heat.

An excellent account of the physiological fate of the amino acids is that given by Van Slyke. See Suggested Readings below.

In the growing child, there is extensive construction of new tissue and an important fraction of the food protein may be required to meet this need. Once the individual has achieved his full growth, however, there is little or no further accumulation of protein (except in special cases as, for example, in pregnancy, or during recovery after a severe wasting disease, where actual construction or reconstruction of body tissues is involved, or when, as the result of increased muscular exercise, a real enlargement of the muscles occurs). It is therefore ambiguous and may be misleading to state that the amino acids resulting from digestion of food protein may be used for purposes of tissue repair *or* be burned as fuel; for that fraction which is used in the upkeep or repair process is in general *not added* to the body's store but simply *exchanged* for an equal amount of material which is being broken down and burned.

Summary of the Fate of Foodstuffs

Carbohydrate may be
    Burned to yield energy: (a) for external muscular work; (b) for internal activity; (c) for heat
    Stored as glycogen
    Changed into fat

Fat may be
    Burned to yield energy: (a) for external muscular work; (b) for internal activity; (c) for heat
    Stored as fat
    Used in formation of tissue lipids
    Possibly to some extent changed into carbohydrate

Protein may be
    Used in building or repair (upkeep) of protein tissue
    Used in formation of certain hormones, enzymes, and other body regulators
    Deaminized and
        Burned to yield energy: (a) for external muscular work; (b) for internal activity; (c) for heat
    Changed into carbohydrate
    Changed into fat (possibly through carbohydrate).

Thus carbohydrates, fats, and proteins all serve as fuel to yield the energy of muscular and other forms of work, or to keep the body warm, and any or all of them when present in quantities more than sufficient to meet immediate needs may contribute to the production of fat which is the body's chief form of stored fuel and which is utilized in just the same way whether formed from the carbohydrate, the protein, or the fat of the food.

The body has very great power to convert one foodstuff into, or use it in place of, another; and so to economize its resources in this respect that the total energy value of the food is used to meet the total energy requirement of the body. This is of much practical importance in the planning of high and of low calorie diets. In the next chapters we shall consider the more quantitative aspects of the problem of balancing the potential energy represented by the different items of the diet against the bodily expenditure of energy in its various forms.

EXERCISES

1. Using data tabulated in the Appendix, compute the number of grams (a) of protein, (b) of fat, (c) of carbohydrate, consumed on each of the days for which you previously recorded your food consumption. Refer, if needed, to *Rose's Laboratory Handbook for Dietetics*, revised by Taylor and MacLeod (1949).
2. What significance do you attribute to the daily variations?
3. If your record contains any food too rare or of too artificial a nature to be included in the appended reference tables, either make adequate inquiry as to its nature and composition* so as to be able to complete your calculation, or amend your proposed "dietary" by the substitution of some food whose composition is better known.

SUGGESTED READINGS

ANDERSON, A. K.   1947   *Essentials of Physiological Chemistry*, 3rd Ed. (Wiley.)

BLOOR, W. R.   1939   Fat transport in the animal body. *Physiol. Rev.* **19**, 557–577.

BOGERT, L. J.   1949   *Nutrition and Physical Fitness*, 5th Ed. (W. B. Saunders Co.)

* See, for example, the extensive table of nutritive values of cooked foods in the Appendix of Rose's *Feeding the Family*, 4th Edition (1940).

Burr, G. O., and R. H. Barnes   1943   Noncaloric functions of dietary fats. *Physiol. Rev.* **23,** 256–278.

Cannon, W. B.   1936   *Digestion and Health*. (Norton.)

Cannon, W. B.   1939   The importance of emotional attitudes for good digestion. *J. Am. Dietet. Assoc.* **15,** 333–344.

Cannon, W. B.   1939b   *The Wisdom of the Body,* Revised Ed. (Norton.)

Chaney, M. S., and M. Ahlborn   1949   *Nutrition,* 4th Ed. (Houghton Mifflin.)

Crandall, L. A.   1939   *An Introduction to Human Physiology,* 2nd Ed., Chapters X–XIV. (W. B. Saunders Co.)

Fantus, B., G. Kopstein, and H. R. Schmidt   1940   Roentgen-ray study of intestinal motility as influenced by bran. *J. Am. Med. Assoc.* **114,** 404–408.

Longenecker, H. E.   1944   Fats in human nutrition. *J. Am. Dietet. Assoc.* **20,** 83–85.

McKibbin, J. M., R. M. Ferry, Jr., and F. J. Stare   1946   Parenteral nutrition. II. Utilization of emulsified fat given intravenously. *J. Clin. Investigation* **25,** 679–685.

Review   1949   Utilization of fat administered intravenously. *Nutr. Rev.* **7,** 179–180.

Rose, M. S.   1940   *Feeding the Family,* 4th Ed., Chapter II, "The care of the digestive mechanism." (Macmillan.)

Stare, F. J., G. V. Mann, R. P. Geyer, and D. M. Watkin   1949   The need of fat in intravenous feeding. *J. Am. Oil Chem. Soc.* **26,** 145–147.

Van Slyke, D. D.   1942   Physiology of the amino acids. *Science* **95,** 259–263.

Wu, H., and D. Rittenberg   1949   Metabolism of *l*-aspartic acid. *J. Biol. Chem.* **179,** 847–856.

IV

ENERGY ASPECTS OF NUTRITION

Introductory Explanations

Every act and moment of life involves, in terms of formal physics, a *transformation,* or, in everyday terms, an *expenditure, of energy.*

We are fully aware of spending energy when we do active muscular work. When we rest, energy expenditure diminishes but does not stop. For, when you have relaxed as completely as you can, your body still has internal work to do. The muscular work of the heart and the work of the muscles of respiration involve significant amounts of energy within every minute; and the resting muscles still possess some degree of tension (tone or *tonus*), the maintenance of which requires a considerable energy transformation or expenditure. The internal work of the body must go on so long as life continues. It is difficult to measure any one of the forms of internal work separately from the others; but it has been estimated that the heart alone (even when the person is lying perfectly quiet) does an amount of work *each hour* equivalent to the lifting of the entire body about 100 feet into the air; and the work of breathing usually involves a considerably larger expenditure of energy; while the amount of energy expended in maintaining the tension or tonus of the muscles is larger still.

The energy which the body "spends" appears so largely in the form of heat, that the science of nutrition finds it convenient to express energy measurements in terms of the heat unit, the Calorie.

Physics makes use of two such heat units, one a thousand times greater than the other; and for brevity distinguishes the greater Calorie by writing it with a capital C while writing the lesser calorie with a small initial letter. The energy transformations in our bodies are always of such magnitude as to make the larger unit the more convenient, and it is practically always used in speaking or writing of the energy aspect of nutrition. As a technical term belonging primarily to physics, it should be written as the physicists write it, Calorie. But some writers and editors, growing weary of frequent use of the capital, have decided that in nutrition books there is no real danger of confusion if the existence of the lesser unit be simply ignored and the initial capital dispensed with in referring to the greater calorie inasmuch as this is the only one which need be used in nutritional discussions.

Hence in writings on nutrition the unqualified word, "calorie," will presumably mean the same as *Calorie, i.e.,* the greater calorie (or kilogram-calorie or kilo-calorie) which is *the amount of heat which raises the temperature of one kilogram of water through one degree centigrade.*

In this book the Calorie is given an initial capital in those cases (only) in which an explicitly quantitative statement is being made.

As a help in relating the scientific unit to our everyday measures, it may be noted that this is almost the same as the amount of heat which raises the temperature of one pound of water through four degrees Fahrenheit—or of four pounds of water through one degree Fahrenheit.

And it may also be helpful to remember that 100 Calories is about the amount of energy spent by a normal adult sitting (not *too* completely relaxed!) in a lecture-room or study chair for one hour.

While the unit of energy used in discussions of food values and nutritional needs has a direct and well-established physical definition, the word *energy* does not always stand simply for the mechanical concept to which the physical definition applies.

It is a current statement that: "Energy is the ability to do work."

But as applied to our body and its nutritional needs, this short definition may have a double meaning, which, while it should not seriously mislead a student well-grounded in even elementary physics, is in fact confusing to many people. For our bodily "ability to do work" implies, in the literal everyday meaning of the words, *both* a supply of available fuel and a properly built and conditioned "mechanism" for the transformation of the potential fuel value into the effective activities of muscles and other bodily organs. It is to the first of these that we refer when we speak of the energy aspect of nutrition and the energy values of foods; but it is to the second that we are usually referring when we say that we "feel full of energy" or that we "lack energy." Thus the energy value of foods as expressed in Calories is energy in the purely fuel or merely mechanical sense; while our *fitness* is, or is directly related to, our state of being energetic in the colloquial or psychological sense.

Mental work may cause fatigue without any corresponding energy expenditure.

The difference finds frequent illustration in the daily lives of students and teachers. Usually at the end of a lecture-hour both the students and the teacher will be tired, fatigued, "lacking in energy," more or less depleted of their "ability to do work"—though probably no one "spends" (transforms) more than 100–150 Calories of energy in an hour in a classroom. If, then, after the lecture one goes for a walk one will probably spend twice as much energy (in the mechanical or calorie sense) in an hour, yet return feeling rested and energetic. A feeling of fatigue may be directly related to one's bodily condition without being proportional to expenditure of energy in the physical or mechanical or calorie sense. As one usually speaks, "lack of energy" will generally be due to some suboptimal condition of one's bodily chemistry or internal environment; but not necessarily as the result of too much muscular work and energy metabolism—perhaps as a result of too little!

In this connection we might mention the hypothesis that each normal member of any given species has as a natural birthright the ability to spend about a certain total amount of energy in the course of a natural life time, so that the more energy one spends per year the fewer years he should expect to live. In an empirical form this hypothesis is a tradition of army teamsters who say, "There is so much work in a mule; you take it out of him faster or more slowly according to how hard you work him." Rubner, an influential expert in nutrition, held much the same idea as a formal scientific hypothesis. But to speak of how "hard" one works involves much the same ambiguity as to speak of energy as ability to do work. No doubt some human lives are shortened by excessive muscular work; but one may also shorten his life by working so "hard" at a sedentary occupation that he gets too little muscular exercise. In so far as one's work influences the length of one's life, it is probably not so much through rate of energy expenditure *per se* as through the effect upon the body's internal environment which may be unfavorably influenced either by overtaxing the muscles or by leaving them stagnant too much of the time.

Internal environment as a factor in nutritional well-being can be more clearly apprehended after we have studied the mineral elements and the vitamins as factors in nutrition. But meanwhile some ambiguities may be avoided if what has been suggested is kept in mind throughout the study of the energy aspects of nutrition and food values.

The Council on Foods of the American Medical Association includes among its general rules regarding advertising that the advertiser should correctly inform the public as to energy values of foods in such carefully chosen terms as clearly to distinguish between "the caloric and the popular" senses of the word *energy,* which distinction, the Council declares, "must be recognized and observed."*

The Council also admonishes the advertisers of food products to "take cognizance of the fact that limitation of the energy intake is essential for reduction of body weight. There are no foods that burn up body fat."

The use of the Calorie as a convenient energy unit does not imply that the body is a heat engine, though this faulty analogy has been used in the past.

At the end of the nineteenth century, some teachers thought that a reasonably satisfactory approach to the essentials of nutrition as then known could be made in terms of protein and calories, and by way of the steam engine as an analogy. The protein of the food was pictured as the building material of the "mechanism"; and the energy value of the food, as corresponding with the calorific value of the fuel burned in the engine.

But the body is so emphatically *not a heat engine* that to liken it to a steam engine is now realized to be misleadingly inadequate. Less inadequate, as well as more modern, is the analogy of the *gasoline engine* of an automobile or a motorboat; for in such a motor, as in the body, the heat is a by-product or end-product and not (as in the steam engine) the means through which the potential or chemical energy of the fuel is transformed into useful work.

If, then, one desires to compare the body with an automobile en-

---

* Council on Foods 1939 Accepted Foods and Their Nutritional Significance, p. 23. (American Medical Association, 535 North Dearborn Street, Chicago.)

gine, the protein and some of the mineral elements correspond to the structural material of the motor; other mineral matters, including water, correspond to the lubricants; such organic foods as the carbohydrates and fats and the non-nitrogen derivatives of the proteins are the fuel; and the vitamins correspond to the ignition sparks, whose own energy value is insignificant, but without which this kind of engine cannot run, however abundant its fuel and however appropriate its structural materials and its lubricants.

Throughout the present discussion of the energy aspect of nutrition, we shall be assuming (unless otherwise specifically stated) that the other nutritional requirements are being sufficiently supplied to meet normal needs, and that we are dealing with physiological rather than pathological conditions.

When one speaks of the amount of food required, it is usually the body's energy requirement, the *number of Calories needed per day*, which *first* comes to the mind of the systematic student of nutrition; for to any extent that the intake of fuel is inadequate, the body must burn some of its own substance as fuel to meet its energy needs. Hence, generally speaking, the economy of other nutritional assets is fundamentally conditioned by the meeting of the body's energy requirement.

For the purpose of the present brief study of the body's energy needs, we may start with an average-sized healthy man at rest. Such a man, sitting comfortably in a chair, will as already mentioned spend about 100 Calories of energy per hour.

Methods of Measuring Energy Metabolism

Atwater-Rosa-Benedict respiration calorimeter and its successors.—At the turn of the century, the outstanding news in nutrition was that about "the man in the copper box," *i.e.*, the experiments with human subjects in the respiration calorimeter which had been developed and brought into successful use by Atwater, Rosa, and Benedict. (Figs. 9 and 10 are photographs of the exterior and interior of the original Atwater-Rosa-Benedict respiration calorimeter; while in Fig. 11 is shown a considerably later modification of this apparatus in use at present in the Russell Sage Institute of Pathology.)

The respiration calorimeter, as the name implies, is both a respiration apparatus for the chemical determination of the oxygen consumed and the carbon dioxide and water produced in the respiratory exchange, and a calorimeter for the direct measurement of the heat given off by the body.

The measurements were brought to a very high order of precision; and upon averaging the results of a large number of such experiments it was found that the energy metabolism computed from the data of the respiratory exchange and that measured

Fig. 9. Outside view of the original Atwater-Rosa-Benedict respiration calorimeter.

directly as heat (or as heat plus external muscular work) agreed within a small fraction of one per cent. This finding resulted in general acceptance of the view that energy metabolism may be measured either by direct calorimetry (the man living in a calorimeter) or by the "indirect calorimetry" of computation from the chemically determined data of the respiratory exchange.

As a further development justified by this finding, there have also been devised several forms of simplified respiration apparatus (Figs. 12–14) which while measuring the energy metabolism do so without the need of such elaborate procedures. Thus it has now become practicable to measure the rate of energy metabolism of students in the classroom, patients in the clinic, and representatives of different races as encountered by field anthropologists in various parts of the world. These recently developed outfits, so much more

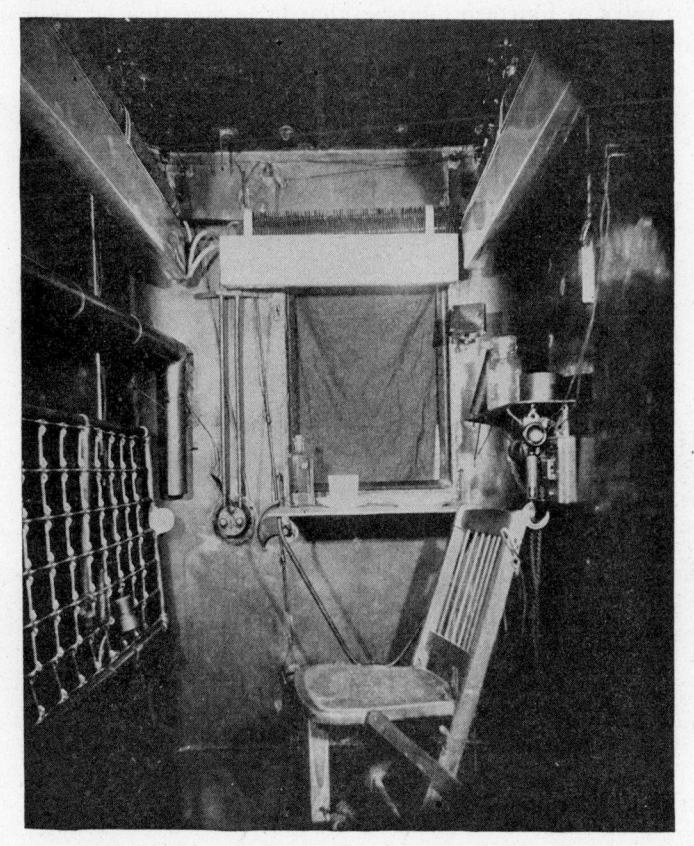

Fig. 10. Inside view of the original Atwater-Rosa-Benedict respiration calorimeter.

portable and less expensive than those previously available, are also adaptable to the measurement of the energy metabolism of people of widely varied ages and occupations. Hence the somewhat wide-ranging discussions of this and the following chapter can be based almost entirely upon quantitative measurements of actual cases, and usually of many cases of a kind.

Basal Energy Metabolism

The basal energy metabolism (or basal metabolic rate) is a term often applied to the rate of expenditure of energy by a person awake, lying still, and who has taken little if any food during the past twelve or fourteen hours so that little digestion or absorption of food material is taking place at the time of observation (*i.e.*, in

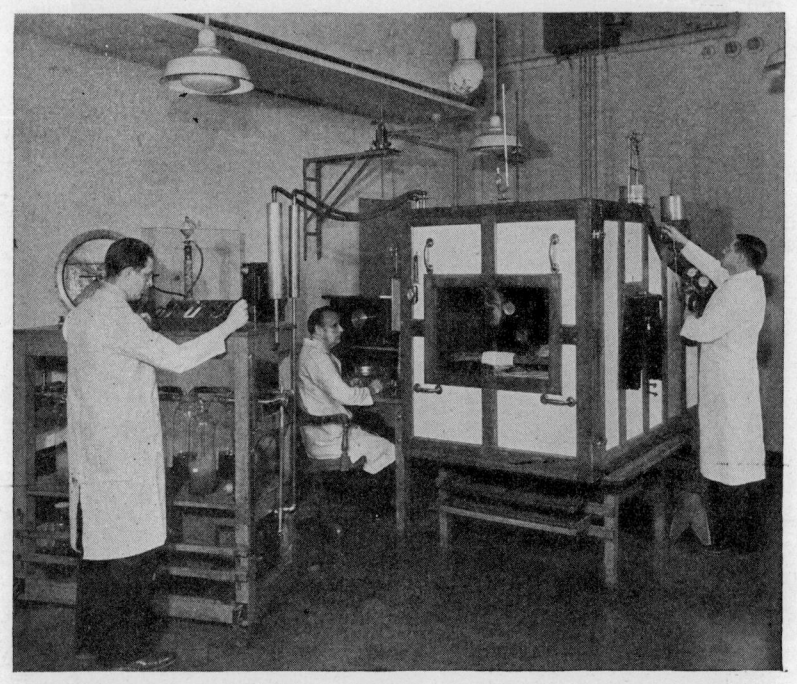

Fig. 11. The respiration calorimeter now in use at the Russell Sage Institute of Pathology. (Courtesy of Dr. E. F. DuBois.)

the "post-absorptive" state). This is often measured as a step in diagnosis in modern medicine.

In healthy grown people this basal energy metabolism averages just about one Calorie per kilogram of body weight per hour. This is supposedly the minimal rate of expenditure of the normal man or woman when awake. During sleep the energy output is less, but when sitting erect it is more, while standing involves a still further expenditure of energy. A normal man, therefore, however sedentary he may be, is almost sure to expend in the course of the 24 hour

Fig. 12. Apparatus for the study of energy metabolism in walking. In this and in the types of apparatus shown in Figs. 13 and 14, the heat production is not measured directly, but the energy metabolism is computed from observations on the respiration, usually of the amount of oxygen consumed. The external muscular work which the subject here performs in walking is measured mechanically. (Courtesy of Dr. F. G. Benedict.)

day somewhat more than 24 times his *basal* hourly number of calories.

Moreover in any case the basal rate could be maintained throughout the day only by fasting. Eating is always followed by an increase in the rate of heat production, the extent of the in-

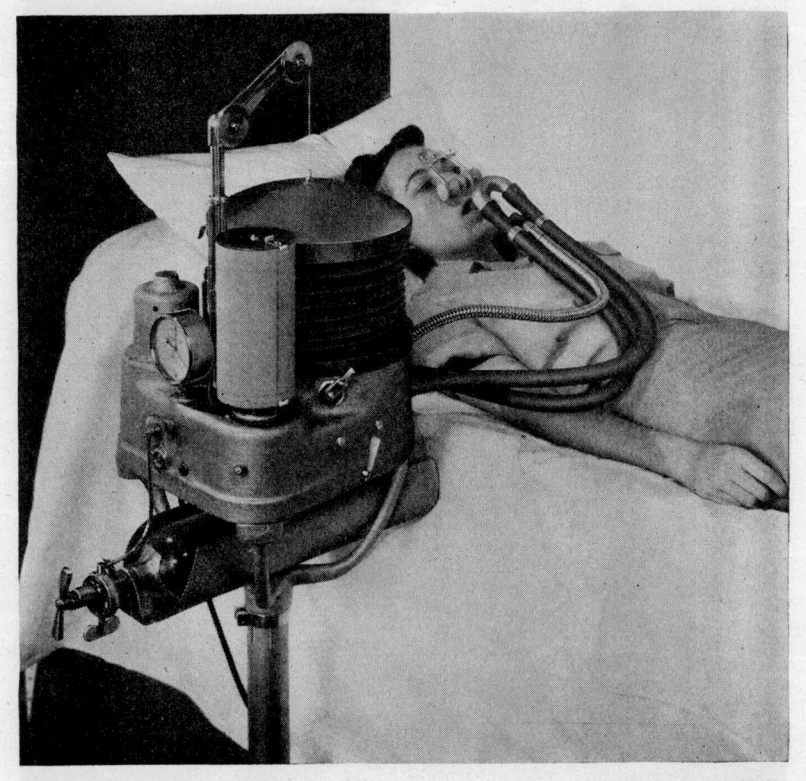

Fig. 13. A simple form of portable respiration apparatus. (Courtesy of the Sanborn Company.)

crease depending upon both the character and the amount of food eaten, as explained below.

For a very full and expert account of the measurement and interpretation of the basal metabolism with special attention to its medical aspects, the reader is referred to DuBois' *Basal Metabolism in Health and Disease;* and for a concise but liberally illustrated account, to Rose's *Foundations of Nutrition*. With such authoritative and up-to-date discussions so conveniently available, we here need merely mention any of the factors affecting the basal metabolism which are not themselves essentially nutritional. We do not here enter at all upon the discussion of pathological conditions; and the somewhat vexed question as to whether there is "a racial factor" need be mentioned only so far as to point out that if a truly racial factor exists it must be a vanishingly small one, when its very existence is still a subject of debate after such long and widespread investigation.

Benedict has concluded that the basal metabolism of an individual may be considered as quantitatively determined by: (1) the total mass of active protoplasmic tissue; and (2) the total stimulus to cellular activity existing at the time the measurement of the metabolism was made. Age, under such a generalization, becomes one of the factors causing variations in the stimulus to cellular activity.

The difference between boys and girls, in their basal energy metabolism per unit of weight or surface, is small in the early years but considerable in their teens; after which the difference diminishes to something like six per cent as between women and men, the latter having the higher rate.

Body Weight, Surface Area, and Energy Metabolism

Although loss of heat from the surface of the body is usually rather an end-result than a cause of energy metabolism, yet measurement seemed several years ago to have established empirically that energy metabolism is quantitatively more nearly proportional to body surface than to body weight. Much use has been made of the "surface area relationship" and some authorities treat it as more systematic to express measurements of energy metabolism in terms of Calories per square meter of body surface, than per kilogram of body weight.

Inasmuch as among normal grown people the ratios between their weights and the ratios between their surfaces are not very different, and since any comparison of children with adults requires consideration of the age factor anyway, we have arranged the present text so that data presented either in terms of surface or of weight may be used without the necessity of converting one into the other.

What Determines the Rate of Energy Metabolism in a Given Normal Individual at Rest?

While there is a never-ceasing exchange or transformation or metabolism of energy in every living body, the *rate* of this energy metabolism is not constant. It differs between individuals, and in the same individual from time to time.

There is, as yet, no neat, simple, comprehensive answer to the question, what determines the rate of energy metabolism; but several factors have been studied quantitatively, so that we have

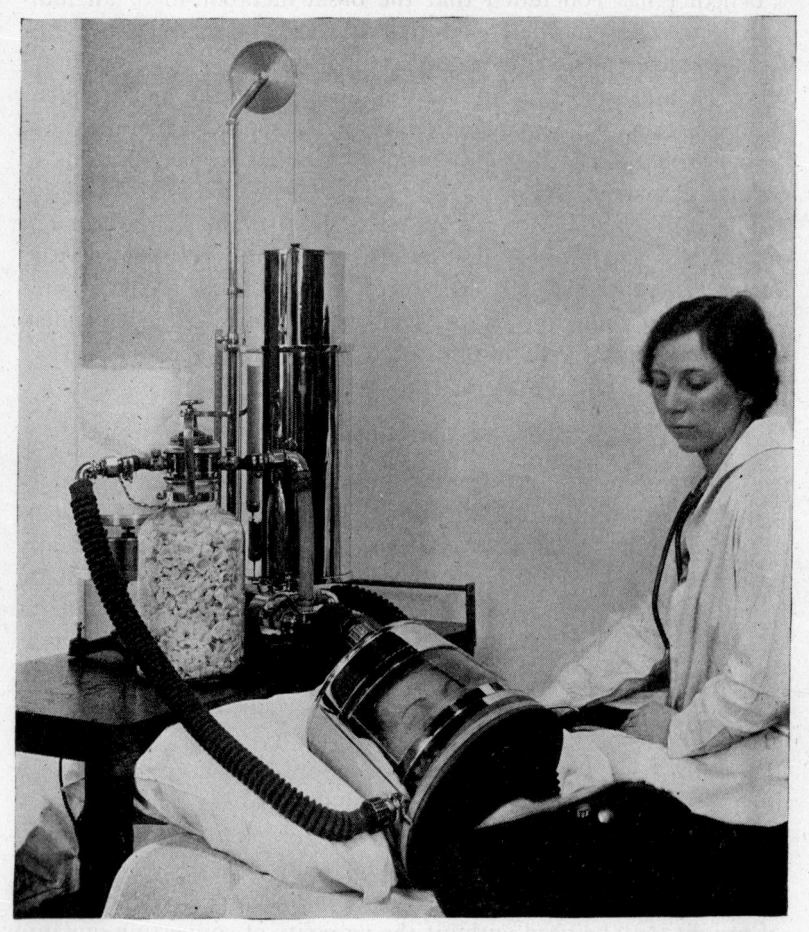

Fig. 14. The Benedict helmet form of respiration apparatus. (Courtesy of Drs. F. G. Benedict and T. M. Carpenter.)

well-established information as to which are of major, and which of relatively minor, influence.

Thus to speak of two everyday, voluntary factors we may say that for all ordinary conditions the amount of exercise that one takes has more influence in determining the rate of energy metabolism than does the amount of food one takes. A healthy person living with a minimum of muscular activity and eating enough food for maintenance may be metabolizing, say, 1600 to 2000 Calories per 24 hours. This rate of energy metabolism per day can easily be increased one hundred per cent by exercise, while to double the food intake will not increase the 24-hour energy metabolism by more than about ten or fifteen per cent.

But while the food intake is not a major influence in determining the rate of energy exchange in the body, still it has a measurable effect; and it is not the same for the different groups of foodstuffs, nor proportional to their fuel values. In other words food intake does act appreciably to increase the rate of energy metabolism, and this "dynamic" action is "specifically" greater for some of the organic foodstuffs than for others.

Specific dynamic action of the foodstuffs.—In the quantitative study of this relationship, by Rubner and by Lusk independently, it was found that when enough food-calories for maintenance were fed, in the form of a single foodstuff at a time, the 24-hour metabolism was increased over that of fasting: 6 to 7 per cent by carbohydrate; 4 to 14 per cent by fat; 30 to 40 per cent by protein. Another way of expressing these same experimental observations is to say that less than one-tenth of the energy value of the carbohydrate of the food, probably about one-tenth of the energy value of the fat, and about one-third of the energy value of the protein spends itself in its specific dynamic effect of increasing the rate of energy metabolism of the body as a whole and for the 24-hour day as a whole. In some experiments fat has shown a higher and in others a lower effect than carbohydrate, and the number of quantitative comparisons has not been large enough to justify statistical interpretation. What is really "specific" is the higher "dynamic effect" or output of "waste heat" which results from protein as compared with either fat or carbohydrate. A large amount of investigation and discussion has been devoted to this specific dynamic action of proteins and of their individual amino acids without any very clear-cut or scientifically significant outcome as yet. The practical significance thus far apparent is that protein is relatively less efficient and more heating as fuel for either the internal or external activities of the body than is carbohydrate or fat. This greater production of heat in proportion as protein is more largely used as fuel may be a source of comfort when one is exposed to severe cold, or of discomfort in hot weather; but usually it is not of great importance, because protein constitutes only about a tenth of the food-fuel of a normally-balanced diet. The exceptionally accurate measurements of Atwater and Benedict showed only 9 per cent of the total food calories expended in the "dynamic action" of the body's direct response to the intake of a mixed diet.

The influence of the habitual level of food intake.—Aside from the immediate specific dynamic effects of the foodstuffs, to what extent does the habitual general level of intake of food calories influence the habitual rate of energy metabolism?

Benedict and his coworkers, studying a group of 12 healthy young men who voluntarily accepted much-reduced rations during the First World War, found that when such undernutrition had reduced the body weight by 12 per cent it had reduced the rate of energy metabolism of the body at rest by 18 per cent. Whether this was an advantageous economy is doubtful. The men remained healthy and able to do their accustomed work, but there appeared to be some lowering of spontaneous vitality.

There are also well authenticated cases of underweight with relatively high energy metabolism which are interpretable in terms of simple absence of adipose tissue and consequent higher percentage of metabolically active lean tissue in the body, as in the lean school children found by Blunt to have rates of energy metabolism *per kilogram of body weight* from 16 to 24 per cent higher than children of average fatness. That in this case the measured difference in metabolic rate seems somewhat larger than the probable difference in body composition would account for, is easily explainable by the probability of higher muscular tone and perhaps greater thyroid activity in the thinner children. We shall return to the discussion of the thyroid in the chapter on iodine.

Talbot, also, has shown that undernutrition may result in either an increase or a decrease of the basal metabolic rate, according to circumstances.*

---

* Talbot, F. B. 1938 Basal metabolism of undernourished girls. *Am. J. Diseases of Children* **56**, 61–66.

Regulation of Body Temperature

As warm-blooded animals we have evolved life processes which depend upon the maintenance of a fairly constant body temperature, and this is above that of our ordinary surroundings. To what extent, then, is the energy aspect of our metabolism a *direct* expenditure for the mere purpose of keeping the body warm? Certainly much less than is often supposed.

When we are comfortably clothed and housed, our body temperature is maintained, chiefly or wholly, by the heat which is produced as a by-product of the work which the life processes involve anyway. And the heat-regulating center in the brain, acting through the nervous and circulatory systems, is able to conserve this resource by constricting the arterioles in the skin and thus diminishing the heat-loss from the surface. This is called *physical regulation,* while an increase of oxidation (burning of fuel foodstuffs) for the direct purpose of producing heat as such to keep up body temperature is called its *chemical regulation.*

For most of us in ordinary daily life, our physical regulation suffices. Only at about the point at which we feel uncomfortably chilly, or at which shivering begins, is the chemical regulation (burning merely for heat) called into play. In fact it appears significant of the body's habitual dependence upon physical regulation that when increased oxidation is needed to maintain temperature the mechanism of muscle activity is still employed, namely, shivering as an involuntary form of muscular work whose function is merely to increase heat production.

The fact that physical regulation very nearly suffices for most of us during most of the time does not mean that the burning of foodstuffs for heat remains at complete zero, for anyone. And such use of food energy value for body heat may be a larger factor in children whose muscles are not yet fully developed, and in the aged whose muscle-tone is declining, than in robust young adults. Extreme thinness also may so increase the loss of heat from the body surface as to increase the calorie requirement.

Here as elsewhere the study of nutrition calls for a judicially balanced habit of thought. Need of heat as such for the maintenance of body temperature may at some times and for some people be a real factor in the energy requirement; but the body is not a heat engine, it usually gets enough heat in the course of doing its work, and one should not be misled by the fact that for convenience we count energy values in terms of calories.

Energy Values of Foods in Relation to the Metabolism of Energy in the Body

We saw in the last chaper that carbohydrates, fats, and the non-nitrogenous cleavage products of proteins all serve as fuel in the body. We know also that, throughout a very wide range (though not quite to an unlimited extent), the body can use these different fuel foodstuffs interchangeably in meeting its energy needs. And we have seen also how, though the body is not a heat engine, yet the Calorie serves as a convenient unit for expression and comparison of food energy values and the body's energy requirements.

The energy values of many pure foodstuffs have been determined by burning weighed specimens in compressed oxygen in calorimeters so arranged as to permit the energy liberated to be very accurately measured as heat (see Fig. 15). Thus one gram of pure dry starch yields 4.22 Calories, one gram of pure cane sugar, 3.96 Calories.

Averaging the results for each group of foodstuffs, correcting in all cases for average losses in digestion, and in the case of protein correcting further for the fact that oxidation in the body is less complete than in the oxygen-charged bomb, we obtain the following physiological fuel values:

Carbohydrate 4.0 Calories per gram or 1814 Calories per lb.
Fat......... 9.0   "   "   " 4082   "   "
Protein...... 4.0   "   "   " 1814   "   "

It is worthwhile to remember that the values 4.0, 9.0, and 4.0 were *not* obtained by "rounding off" the German estimates of 4.1, 9.3, and 4.1. The German experiments were with dogs fed upon diets which yielded less than average amounts of intestinal residue. The Atwater and Bryant averages of 4.0, 9.0, and 4.0, based upon larger numbers of experiments, made with men, and in which the diets were much more representative of normal human food supplies, are therefore the more accurate of the two sets of factors. Repeated reinvestigation and critical scrutiny has brought no significant modification of these as the most accurate *average* factors for use in the calculations of human food values and nutritional needs. (That the most accurate are also the most convenient is only an incidental advantage, not the reason for their adoption and continued use.)

With some foods of less than average digestibility, a downward revision of the Atwater factors may improve the accuracy of the

Fig. 15. The Atwater bomb calorimeter for determining the energy values (heats of combustion) of foods. It consists essentially of a heavy steel bomb, A, with a platinum or gold-plated copper lining and a cover held tightly in place by means of a strong screw collar. A weighed amount of sample is placed in a small platinum cup, B, the bomb is then charged with oxygen to a pressure of at least 20 atmospheres, closed, and immersed in a weighed amount of water, C. The water is constantly stirred and its temperature determined at intervals by means of an extremely accurate and sensitive thermometer, D. The sample is ignited by means of an electric fuse, E, and, on account of the large amount of oxygen present, undergoes rapid and complete combustion. The heat liberated is communicated to the water in which the bomb is immersed, and the resulting rise in temperature is accurately determined. After appropriate corrections have been made for loss of heat by radiation, heat arising from accessory oxidations (the oxidation of the iron wire of the fuse, etc.), the number of Calories arising from the combustion of the sample is computed from the rise in temperature of the water surrounding the bomb and the heat capacity of the apparatus.

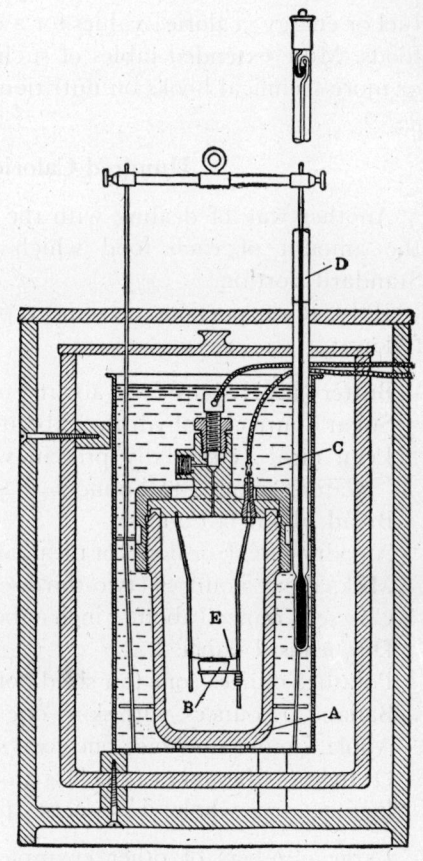

findings. See Maynard (1944) and Merrill and Watt (1948) in the list of suggested readings below.

In most cases it is customary to treat all nitrogenous matter involved in human dietary calculations as if it were protein. Only insignificant errors are ordinarily involved in this simplifying assumption. Using the accepted fuel values for protein, fat, and carbohydrate, respectively, one may readily compute the energy values corresponding to a given food analysis, whether of an individual specimen or an average of many specimens of a given kind. In Appendix C of this book there are given such average analyses and fuel or energy (calorie) values for a considerable number of typical foods. More extended tables of such data may be found in larger or more technical books on nutrition and in Government bulletins.

Hundred-Calorie Portions

Another way of dealing with the fuel value of foods is to treat the amount of each food which furnishes 100 Calories as a Standard Portion.

100-Calorie portions of some typical articles of food weigh as follows:

Butter (nearly pure fat), about $\frac{1}{2}$ ounce
Sugar (pure carbohydrate), about 1 ounce
Lean meat (essentially protein with three times its weight of water), about 3 to 4 ounces
Bread, about $1\frac{1}{3}$ ounces
Any dry cereal, or flour, or meal, about 1 ounce
Milk, about 5 ounces (two-thirds of a glass)
Cheese, $\frac{4}{5}$ ounce (about 1 inch cube)
Dry beans, 1 ounce
Potato, 5 ounces (one fair sized potato)
Banana, $5\frac{1}{2}$ ounces, with skin (one average sized)
Apple, 7 ounces, whole (one good sized apple)
Orange, 9–10 ounces (one large, or two small)
Prunes, dry, whole, $1\frac{1}{3}$ ounces (four average sized prunes).

Large numbers of other examples, including many of cooked foods and "made dishes," may be found in Rose's *Laboratory Handbook for Dietetics,* and in both the text and the Appendix of her *Feeding the Family.*

Familiarity with 100-Calorie portions continues to be found helpful to the gaining of a good grasp of the relative energy (calorie) values of different types of food. Hence it holds an honored place in the learning of food values, even though, both in institutional dietetics and in everyday home practice, foods are generally served either in 100-gram portions or in other conventional "standard" servings. The general food composition table at the back of this book is in terms of nutrients per 100 grams of edible food.

More Specific Factors for Calculating Calorie Values of Foods

The general factors introduced by Atwater and Bryant in 1899 —4, 9, 4 Calories per gram for protein, fat, and carbohydrate, respectively—served satisfactorily for nearly 50 years, but called for more discrimination when used in special conditions arising from the Second World War. In May 1947, the Food and Agriculture Organization of the United Nations proposed definite revisions in a bulletin entitled "Energy-yielding Components of Food and Computation of Calories." In 1949, Taylor and MacLeod explained the situation in pages 206–208 (including Table 35A) of the Fifth Edition of *Rose's Laboratory Handbook for Dietetics*. In October 1949 there appeared a 56-page bulletin entitled, "Food Composition Tables for International Use," a report prepared by Charlotte Chatfield, Nutrition Division of the Food and Agriculture Organization of the United Nations. In June 1950, the U. S. Department of Agriculture issued its "Agriculture Handbook No. 8" which includes composition data for 751 foods, all calorie values for which are computed by the "more specific factors." This publication, according to its title page, "supersedes Miscellaneous Publication 572." How rapidly the "more specific" (but also more complicated) calculation will actually supersede the use of the "Atwater factors" (and the current statements based on them) in teaching and in practical dietetics will of course be determined by the test of time. As both will probably be more or less current for the next several years, results of the two methods of calculation are given in parallel columns in Table 40 in Appendix C of this book. As applied to American and West-European dietary data the newer factors yield only slightly different results from those of the Atwater factors.

The differences between findings are not in all cases strictly due to the difference in factors alone; in some cases natural variations, errors of sampling, analysis, or interpretation also play a part. But these latter causes of variation are not so frequent nor so large (in our opinion) as to invalidate the general effect of the comparison of these parallel columns.

EXERCISES: for the student, the teacher, or both working jointly, according to circumstances

1. (*a*) How many Calories did each of your recorded dietaries (daily food intakes) furnish?
(*b*) What was the percentage distribution of each day's total Calories, as between protein, fat, and carbohydrate?
(The use of *Rose's Laboratory Handbook for Dietetics* may greatly facilitate these calculations.)

2. Choose from twelve to forty foods* and (*a*) compute for each the percentage distribution of its Calories as between protein, fat, and carbohydrate, (*b*) arrange them in three lists in the order of the relative prominence of protein, fat, and carbohydrate, respectively (as thus computed with reference to distribution of the calories).

3. What is the total calorie value for each of these foods, per 100 grams of edible portion?

SUGGESTED READINGS

BENEDICT, F. G. 1928 Basal metabolism: The modern measure of vital activity. *The Scientific Monthly* **27**, 5–27.

DuBois, E. F. 1936 *Basal Metabolism in Health and Disease*, 3rd Ed. (Lea and Febiger.)

FORBES, E. B., R. W. SWIFT, R. F. ELLIOTT, and W. H. JAMES 1946 Relation of fat to economy of food utilization. I, II. *J. Nutrition* **31**, 203–212, 213–227.

MACLEOD, G., and C. M. TAYLOR 1944 *Rose's Foundations of Nutrition*, 4th Ed. (Macmillan.)

MAYNARD, L. A. 1944 The Atwater system of calculating the calorific value of diets. *J. Nutrition* **28**, 443–452.

MERRILL, A. L., and B. K. WATT 1948 Physiologic energy values of wheat. *J. Am. Dietet. Assoc.* **24**, 953–956.

ROSE, M. S. 1940 "Fuel for the human machine," "Sources of body fuel," "Measurement of the fuel value of food," and "Measurement of the fuel requirements of the body," in Chapter I of *Feeding the Family*, 4th Ed. (Macmillan.)

SHAFIROFF, B. G. P., J. H. MULHOLLAND, E. ROTH, and H. C. BARON 1949 Oxygen consumption studies with intravenous infusions of the combined fat emulsions. *Proc. Soc. Exptl. Biol. Med.* **71**, 102–106.

---

* This exercise and the similar ones suggested at the ends of some of the subsequent chapters are intended to develop familiarity with the relative values of different foods as sources of different nutritive factors. It is suggested that your selection of foods include at least one from each of the ten groups shown in Chapter XIX and preferably several from some of the groups.

ND# V

HOW TO MEET THE ENERGY NEED AND HAVE THE BODY WEIGHT YOU WANT

As explained in the preceding chapter, we and other living things "trade" in energy. It is chiefly because we see "expenditures" of energy, as in motion or in the giving off of heat to its surroundings, that we consider an object to be alive. Every living thing, then, is always "spending" energy, or, in more precisely scientific terms, is engaged in processes which involve transformations of energy. The total energy intake required to meet all these expenditures we commonly speak of as the energy need or energy requirement of the body. Having sketched the scientific foundations of this subject in Chapter IV, we now take up its everyday functioning.

Activity, age, and size are the outstanding factors in determining the amount of energy needed by a healthy person under ordinary conditions of life.

Mental and Muscular Activity as Factors in Energy Metabolism

Soon after the satisfactory development of their respiration calorimeter (noted in Chapter IV), Atwater and Benedict arranged to have 22 college students (separately) take mid-year examinations in this apparatus, so that the energy metabolized while performing this mental work could be measured and compared with that shown by the same person for a parallel period at the same time of day, in the same physical posture and surroundings, but with no mental work to do. There was no marked or constant difference in the results. Some students showed a slightly higher, and some a slightly lower, energy metabolism while taking the examination than in a period of equal length with parallel physical conditions without mental demand. If the mental work increased energy metabolism in the brain, the quantitative effect was so small as to be lost in the unavoidable fluctuations that occurred in the muscles. Even the brainiest person has many-fold more pounds of muscle than of brain, and spends many hundreds of Calories per day in muscular tension or tone. That some students spent more energy during their examination was probably mainly because their muscles as well as their minds were more tense during the ordeal than on the day of rest. And that some other students showed decreased energy expenditure during the examination-period was probably because they were so well-prepared and self-disciplined that the more they concentrated their minds upon the examination-questions the more completely their muscles relaxed.

The factor of muscular tension was probably more perfectly controlled in the later experiments of Dr. and Mrs. Benedict. In repeated experiments the Benedicts were able to demonstrate an increase of energy metabolism during periods of mental work. But the difference was so slight that they decided to make clear its smallness by reporting that the extra energy involved in an hour of mental work was no more than is furnished by half a peanut.

Thus the contrast between mental and muscular work is very pronounced, so far as its quantitative effect upon energy metabolism is concerned.

In the healthy adult, muscular activity is usually the largest variable factor in determining the rate of energy expenditure.

The average-sized man who spends about 100 Calories per hour when sitting still will (for the time being) approximately double this rate of expenditure if he simply strolls around the room, or treble it if he walks vigorously.

Moderate use of large muscles may easily involve a greater expenditure of energy than does the most intense use of a set of much smaller muscles. Thus the slowest walking will probably involve a larger output of calories per hour than the fastest typewriting.

Typical findings of energy metabolism per hour in healthy grown people differently occupied are shown in Table 1 (based on that of Dr. M. S. Rose).

Total Energy Requirement of Adults

By the use of such data as those in the accompanying Table 1, the probable food requirement for a person of 70 kilograms (154 pounds) may be calculated very simply, as, for instance, in the following example:

8 hours of sleep at 65 Calories	= 520 Calories
2 hours' light exercise* at 170 Calories	= 340 Calories
8 hours' carpentry work at 240 Calories	= 1920 Calories
6 hours' sitting at rest at 100 Calories	= 600 Calories

Total food requirement for the carpenter, per day, 3380 Calories

It may be of interest at this point to make a similar calculation for one's own case, and compare the outcome with the estimates for typical occupations below.

For a healthy grown person of normal physique but materially larger or smaller than 154 pounds (70 kilograms) weight, similar calculations can be based upon the data in the per-kilogram or per-pound columns of Table 1. Among such people, at least, the differences between their relative weights and their relative surface areas are not so large as to demand the figuring of the data to a surface-area basis.

Neither is it necessary for everyday purposes to make any further difference in energy allowances for men and for women than simply to credit each with his or her actual bodily size and occupation.

The Recommended Allowances of the National Research Council (the "yardstick" explained in Chapter I) include total food energy for average normal adults as follows: Women (actual body weight 56 kilograms or 123 pounds)

sedentary,	2000	Calories per day
moderately active,	2400	" " "
very active,	3000	" " "

Man (actual body weight 70 kilograms or 154 pounds)

sedentary,	2400	Calories per day
physically active,	3000	" " "
with heavy work,	4500	" " "

* Going to and from work, for example.

TABLE 1. *Energy Expenditure per Hour Under Different Conditions of Muscular Activity*

Form of Activity	Calories per Hour		
	Per 70 Kilograms	Per Kilogram	Per Pound
Sleeping	65	0.93	0.43
Awake lying still	77	1.10	0.50
Sitting	100	1.43	0.65
Reading aloud	105	1.50	0.69
Standing relaxed	105	1.50	0.69
Hand sewing	111	1.59	0.72
Standing at laboratory work	115	1.63	0.74
Knitting	116	1.66	0.75
Dressing and undressing	118	1.69	0.77
Singing	122	1.74	0.79
Driving automobile	133	1.90	0.86
Typewriting rapidly	140	2.00	0.91
Dishwashing	144	2.06	0.93
Ironing	144	2.06	0.93
Laundry, light	161	2.30	1.04
Sweeping	169	2.41	1.09
Walking, 2.6 miles per hour	200	2.86	1.30
Carpentry, metal working, industrial painting	240	3.43	1.56
Bicycling, moderate speed	245	3.50	1.59
Dancing, waltz	280	4.00	1.82
Walking, 3.75 miles per hour	300	4.28	1.95
Dancing, foxtrot	336	4.80	2.18
Walking down stairs	364	5.20	2.36
Horseback riding, trot	371	5.30	2.40
Sawing wood	480	6.86	3.12
Swimming	500	7.14	3.25
Running, 5.3 miles per hour	570	8.14	3.70
Walking, 5.3 miles per hour	650	9.28	4.22
Walking up stairs	1100	15.8	7.18
Rowing in race	1190	17.0	7.65

This last figure provides for a man who works full time at an occupation employing highly developed large muscles.

The allowance of 3000 Calories per day for men formerly described as "moderately," and now as "physically" active, has been, and is, much used as a starting point in dietary calculations. As an obviously conventional *base line* or *bench mark* its convenience does not depend upon how closely it corresponds to the *average* need of the majority of the normal adults of the population. Doubtless the 2400 Calories which is the conventional Recommended Allowance for moderately active women and for sedentary men is near to the actual need of a larger proportion of the population. For it is probably true that women now take more exercise than formerly and that women in commercial work are often less sedentary than the men working in the same offices, and many women do housework in addition to the duties of full-time employment outside of the home. Meanwhile it is a steadily decreasing proportion of men who are engaged in physically active toil, and this trend will doubtless continue with the increasing use of labor-saving machinery.

But (as we saw in Chapter IV) one's feeling of fatigue may bear but little relation to the number of calories spent. One may be greatly fatigued by a day of either hand- or type-writing; but it may not involve as much energy expenditure as a day of recreation.

For guidance in the practical planning of food to meet the needs of people of different ages and types, and at different cost levels, Rose's *Feeding the Family* is especially recommended.

Exercises in the planning and evaluation of dietaries from the viewpoints of different aspects of nutrition are suggested at the ends of several of the chapters of the present book. If at this stage you are undertaking an exercise in which only the calories of the diet are specified, it is nevertheless well to realize even from the start that every dietary should be well-balanced with respect to other nutritional essentials also.

Table 2 shows 24-hour energy requirements for men of 70 kilograms (154 pounds) of various occupations typical for men; and for women of 56 kilograms (123 pounds) with various occupations typical for women.

Closely connected with the question of the calories-per-day called for by one's size and occupation, is the question of the control of body weight.

TABLE 2. *Total Daily Energy Requirements of Men and Women of (Conventionally Assumed) Average Weights and with Typical Occupations, from Taylor and MacLeod's Revision (1949) of Rose's Laboratory Handbook for Dietetics, 5th Edition (Macmillan) by permission of the authors and the publisher*

Daily Energy Requirement According to Occupation

	Grade of Work	Calories per Kilogram	Calories per Day[a]
Men			
Tailor	Light exercise	35	2450
Weaver	Light exercise	37	2590
Shoemaker	Moderate exercise	40	2800
Bookbinder	Moderate exercise	40	2800
Carpenter	Moderate exercise	45	3150
Metalworker	Hard work	50	3500
Farm laborer	Hard work	55	3850
Painter	Hard work	55	3850
Excavator	Very severe work	65	4550
Stoneworker	Very severe work	65	4550
Lumberman	Severest work	75	5200
Women			
Machine sewer	Light exercise	35	1960
Bookbinder	Light exercise	38	2128
Farm housewife	Moderate exercise	42	2350
Waitress	Moderate exercise	45	2520
Washerwoman	Hard work	55	3080

[a] Estimated on a body weight of 70 kg. for a man and 56 kg. for a woman.

Food Calories and the Control of Body Weight

While the body's weight may sometimes be significantly influenced by its water balance, in the vast majority of cases overweight means over-fatness.

We have seen that surplus calories of ingested food, whether taken in the form of protein, fat, or carbohydrate, tend to accumulate in the form of body fat. And over-fatness always means that the intake of food calories has been out of proportion to the expenditure of energy *by the person concerned*. Undoubtedly there is more tendency to overweight in some people than in others, and undoubtedly, too, this sometimes extends beyond the question of appetite to endocrine and perhaps other constitutional differences; yet the fact remains that *for the individual* the control of body weight is essentially a matter of a proper balance between what is ingested as food and what is oxidized in the energy metabolism. If one tends to become too fat, the remedy is to eat less or to burn more, or both.

To increase basal metabolism by administration of thyroid, thyroxine, or any artificial drug designed to increase oxidation is too dangerous except under strict medical control.

To increase the energy metabolism by muscular exercise is probably beneficial in a fair proportion of cases but is apt to be an arduous process of weight reduction, especially as exercise usually increases the appetite. Moreover, increased muscular exercise in the obese may endanger the heart. So it is often comforting to remember the principle expounded by M. S. Rose that "the only form of exercise essential to the control of body weight is the exercise of the intelligence."

The scientific attitude does not simply ask, Is this food fattening?, nor even simply, How fattening is it?, but *both* How does it stand as a source of calories? *and* How important is it as a source of protein and of the needed mineral elements and vitamins? If a slogan must be carried in mind, perhaps, "No calories without vitamins," is as good a precept as any, though actually the mineral elements of the diet may be equally important.

Almost always the desirable degree of reduction of calorie intake can be made among the foods that are not important sources of mineral elements and vitamins, and it is among such foods that the "cutting out" or the "cutting down" should be done.

One should not proceed too drastically, nor should one be discouraged or confused by short-time fluctuations of body weight. Not only may the body gain or lose a few pounds of water without apparent reason or effect upon health, but also the fluctuations in the body's glycogen content influence its water content at the same time, each gram of glycogen being usually accompanied by about three grams of water. Thus 400 Calories gained or spent in the form of 100 grams of glycogen may quickly change the body weight about 400 grams, while the gain or loss of this weight of fat would involve about 3600 Calories.

Keeping in mind therefore that sudden fluctuations of a few pounds do not call for any change of plan, and that any weight-reduction plan should aim not at spectacularly rapid results but at steady moderate progress, it is well to deduct about 500 Calories from the daily intake which would presumably keep the body weight constant.

A withdrawal from bodily stores of 500 Calories per day or 3500 Calories per week will normally mean the burning-off of about 380 grams of actual fat. And this will mean a reduction of body weight by about one pound of adipose tissue; for adipose tissue is about four-fifths actual fat and about one-fifth water. Thus the daily deficit of 500 Calories reduces body weight about one pound per week, and this is about as rapid a reduction as one should attempt unless under constant medical advice and observation.

To what extent is the body weight a health problem, and to what extent is it merely a question of style? The evidence seems indubitable that a large proportion of young women do keep themselves thinner than is best for health, happiness, efficiency, and longevity.

One whose body weight is materially below the *standard average* or "ideal" of life insurance companies' experience will (in the absence of medical advice to the contrary) generally be wise to build up his or her weight to this standard. For, extreme thinness is a real hazard, though this fact is often ignored (*a*) because overweight is believed to be both a more frequent and a more dangerous hazard, and (*b*) because thinness is stylish and tends for this reason to become the accepted *mode*. As the late Professor Mary S. Rose emphasized, underweight college women commonly regard themselves as well, and then are surprised to find how much better they feel, and how much less subject to fatigue, when they build up their weight to correspond to the life insurance average for their height and for age 25 or 30 as shown in Table 3. For several years the standard advice has been to bring and keep body weight to that which corresponds to life insurance average for the height *as of age 30*. Now, some but not all authorities are tending to advise *as of age 25,* instead. Hence columns for both these ages are now included in Table 3.

Note that in Table 3 the height includes ordinary shoe-heels and weight includes ordinary indoor clothing. The data of this table are from the tables published by the United States Public Health Service, which include life insurance experience.

For very full data of different studies of relations of weight to height, age, and build, including the development of the concept of "ideal weight" from life insurance experience, the reader is referred to pages 74 to 98 of Taylor and MacLeod's 1949 revision of *Rose's Laboratory Handbook for Dietetics* (Macmillan).

TABLE 3. *Weight for Height as of Ages 25 and 30 (Pounds)*

Height	Women Age 25	Women Age 30	Men Age 25	Men Age 30
4 ft. 8 in.	109	112		
4 ft. 9 in.	111	114		
4 ft. 10 in.	113	116		
4 ft. 11 in.	115	118		
5 ft. 0 in.	117	120	122	126
5 ft. 1 in.	119	122	124	128
5 ft. 2 in.	121	124	126	130
5 ft. 3 in.	124	127	129	133
5 ft. 4 in.	128	131	133	136
5 ft. 5 in.	131	134	137	140
5 ft. 6 in.	135	138	141	144
5 ft. 7 in.	139	142	145	148
5 ft. 8 in.	143	146	149	152
5 ft. 9 in.	147	150	153	156
5 ft. 10 in.	151	154	157	161
5 ft. 11 in.	154	157	162	166
6 ft. 0 in.	158	161	167	172
6 ft. 1 in.			173	178
6 ft. 2 in.			179	184
6 ft. 3 in.			184	190
6 ft. 4 in.			189	196
6 ft. 5 in.			194	201

A moderate amount of body fat is a real asset and not simply as stored fuel. Fat deposits in the abdominal cavity serve as packing and support for the kidneys, and doubtless to some extent for other vital organs as well; while a subcutaneous layer of fat tends to protect muscles from bruises, and the body as a whole from the effects of sudden changes in the temperature of its surroundings.

In cases in which either lack of appetite or a subnormal digestive capacity makes the taking and digesting of sufficient food a real problem, attention should be given to such selection of food and arrangement of meals as to stimulate the appetite and avoid overburdening the digestive apparatus, and care should also be taken that there is sufficient out-door life, and sufficient ventilation indoors, to develop and support a good appetite; that fatigue of any kind or at any time is avoided; that provision is made for complete rest before and after meals; and that the meals contain an abundance of fruits, vegetables, and milk as well as more concentrated foods.

The proper nutrition of an underweight person is only in part the reverse of the proper correction of overweight, because in both cases the calories in the food and the fat in the body while prominent in the problem do not tell the whole story. Such important protective foods as fruit and milk should be fairly prominent in both the fattening and the reducing types of diet. The late Dr. L. H. Peters particularly commended to those on reducing diets liberal servings of salad dressed with cheese and vinegar instead of any dressing made with oil.

The principle embodied in the preceding paragraph,—adjustment of food calories without sacrifice of natural food values,—is of very far-reaching importance, and its practical application is often almost absurdly simple. Thus one may eat a good-sized (thoroughly washed) raw apple with an intake of only about one hundred Calories and with all the mineral elements and vitamin values that such an apple brings; while a baked apple of the same size will probably have at least another hundred Calories of added sugar. So for one who wishes to reduce there is a large advantage in the raw apple. To a still greater extent is the apple "diluted with foreign calories" when it is eaten in the form of apple pie. A raw apple instead of an average piece of apple pie will mean *more* of actual apple (with all of its nutritional virtues) at the same time with a greatly reduced calorie intake. Probably every apple calorie in the pie is diluted with at least three or four foreign calories of sugar, flour, and fat. This principle of avoidance of culinarily-added calories need only be applied to a moderate proportion of the items in a day's food in order to effect a considerable change in the calorie intake while fully maintaining or even increasing the protein, mineral, and vitamin values. The interested student can readily set down in parallel columns two food plans for a day each having the same number of items and variety of flavors and essentially the same amounts of the protective foods of high mineral and vitamin value, but with widely different total calories according as the foods which "bring calories without vitamins" are used in larger or smaller amounts.

The little bulletin by Professor Harriet Barto on *Sane Reducing Diets and How to Plan Them** is excellently concise and scientifically sound. A fuller discussion is included in Rose's *Feeding the Family* (Macmillan).

Do Current Recommended Allowances Encourage Over-eating and Over-weight?

The revision of 1948 lowered the previously recommended Allowances of Calories for sedentary and "moderately active" women, and for sedentary men, by 100 Calories a day, or 4 to 5 per cent below the previous levels. This was in recognition of a widespread view that sedentary adults either probably do not eat as much as the previous Allowances suggested; or, if they do, that they are consuming more food calories than would be best for their health in the long run of a lifetime. At a time when our consciences had been made keenly aware that a very large proportion of our fellow-men do not have enough food for full health, we should not wish to consume more than our own best health requires. It is recognized by all that a Recommended Allowance of food calories should not exceed optimal intake in the sense of the concept that "the proper calorie allowance is that which, over an extended period of time, will maintain a body weight (or rate of growth) at the level most conducive to well-being."

But how are we to know what is this *optimal* food calorie intake level? Significantly, the most fundamental findings upon which to base our answer to this question are not those of the most recent investigations but rather those of an earlier period, in which the methods of greatest precision were being used, and before the less expensive present-day methods had come into use. During that period of most accurate measurement there were recorded some 30-odd "rest experiments" with young to middle-aged men, each of whom lived for an experimental period of one to nine days in the Atwater respiration calorimeter with more accurate measurements of calories involved than those of either the earlier period before these most precise methods had been developed or the later

* Full reference under Suggested Readings below.

(including the present) period in which the much less costly but also less exact methods were coming into general use in studies of food consumption and apparent calorie requirements. The *"rest experiments" in the respiration calorimeter* are of greatest significance to the problem of the calorie needs of human nutrition because these were the cases in which *both* the energy metabolism of the men who served as subjects and the nature and extent of their activities on the experimental days were more exactly known than in other studies either before or since. These experiments averaged 2244 Calories; and about the same number of food consumption studies of men leading *sedentary lives not so completely at rest* averaged 2466 Calories. Hence the 1948 Recommended Allowance of 2400 Calories per day for sedentary men is in good agreement with our best scientific evidence. Natural physiological variability will probably account for many of the *individual* cases of men who appear to be amply nourished at materially lower levels of food consumption; while other such individual cases may be due to *suboptimal physical exercise*. If we nutritionists all thought alike that men of sedentary occupations tend to overweight when living year after year on 2400 Calories a day, we still might legitimately differ as to whether the majority would find greater benefit in eating less or in exercising more. (The present authors make no apology for beginning this section with a question and not furnishing a Yes or No answer. Rather we take the occasion respectfully to suggest that authors of textbooks, perhaps especially in the field of nutrition, should *think and let think.*)

The question with which we began this section is more difficult to answer for women than for men. This is for at least three reasons: The above-mentioned fundamental series of experiments with men spending 1–9 days in the respiration calorimeter has, unfortunately, not been paralleled with corresponding measurements upon women. And the basal metabolism studies of a few minutes' length do not furnish us as conclusive a baseline for the purpose of our present problem. Secondly, largely because of the absence of such a conclusive baseline for long-term consideration of the calorie needs of women, there have inadvertently been included in research papers on food consumption of women a number of data which—whatever their *explanation* may be—are subnormally low for inclusion in averages of supposed normal cases. The fact that such cases have been included as if normal must almost certainly mean that the recent literature underestimates the average calorie consumption of fully normal women. For omission of items or under-estimate of their amounts are doubtless the most frequent and largest errors; and, statistically regarded, these are *cumulative, not compensating, errors.* (Fuller development of this point would be too technical for inclusion here.) Finally, a third source of misunderstanding lies in failure to keep in mind the meanings of the terms *sedentary* and *moderately active* in Recommended Allowances. To avoid not only ambiguity but serious misconception these words in this connection must be thought of in terms of the muscles and not of the mind. Yet even in the writings of nutritionists, busy women working long hours and carrying heavy responsibilities are called at least moderately active whereas in the terms of the Recommended Allowances, they are "sedentary." When understood as intended, the 1948 Recommended Allowances seem well fitted to their purpose.

Energy Needs during Physical Development

For pregnant and lactating women and for children, the Recommended Daily Allowances of food energy are:

Pregnancy (latter half),   2400 Calories per day
Lactation,   3000 " " "
Children under 1 year, 110 Calories per kilo of body wt., per day
"   1–3 years (27 lb.) 1200 Calories per day
"   4–6 years (42 lb.) 1600 " " "
"   7–9 years (58 lb.) 2000 " " "
"   10–12 years (78 lb.) 2500 " " "
Girls 13–15 years (108 lb.) 2600 " " "
"   16–20 years (122 lb.) 2400 " " "
Boys 13–15 years (108 lb.) 3200 " " "
"   16–20 years (141 lb.) 3800 " " "

Investigations of young infants regularly show them to give off at least twice as much energy per unit of weight as their mothers do. This is partly explainable on the ground of size and surface. For, as between a baby and a grown person, the ratio of surface to weight is very different, and, as energy metabolism is more nearly proportional to surface than to weight, the baby's larger surface per pound would of itself mean more calories per pound.

TABLE 4. *Food Allowances for Children of About Average Weight for Their Age* (Based on Gillett's *Food Allowances for Healthy Children* and Rose's *Laboratory Handbook for Dietetics*)

Age, Years	Calories per Day Boys	Calories per Day Girls
1	900–1200	800–1200
2	1100–1300	1000–1250
3	1100–1400	1050–1350
4	1200–1500	1150–1450
5	1300–1600	1200–1500
6	1500–1900	1450–1800
7	1600–2100	1500–1900
8	1700–2300	1600–2200
9	1900–2500	1800–2500
10	2100–2700	1900–2600
11	2100–2800	2000–2800
12	2300–3000	2100–3000
13	2500–3500	2300–3400
14	2600–3800	2400–3000
15	2700–4000	2400–2800
16	2700–4000	2250–2800
17	2800–4000	2250–2800

Secondly, children soon begin to be muscularly active. Their crying and kicking may add from 25 to 100 per cent to the 24-hour calorie requirement. By the time this stage of their development is over, the run-about stage has begun. Most grown people would find their muscles over-worked if they tried to repeat their children's physical activities.

Thirdly, the child's food requirement is further accentuated by the fact that the intake must not only cover the output but provide also for retention by the body of the food substances which become tissue material in the processes of growth.

The Recommended Allowances here given show the extent of extra feeding deemed best for women in pregnancy and lactation; and also the calorie allowances for children of all ages. The assumed average weights of the children and the corresponding Calories are for the mid-points of the respective age ranges. Differences within an age range can readily be allowed-for by simple arithmetical computation when such elaboration is desired. Individual differences between children of like age and weight will of course still remain. And obviously it is even more important with children than adults to make wise choices among the foods which are to furnish the needed calories. Tables 4 and 5 are, therefore, here included as concisely indicating very expert nutritional judgments of normal variations of need for both sexes at different ages; and desirable proportions in which to use foods of different types in meeting the calorie needs.

TABLE 5. *Proportions in Which to Draw the Needed Calories from the Different Types of Food, as Suggested by M. S. Rose (1940)*

Class of Food	\multicolumn{5}{c}{Per Cent of Total Calories in Dietary of Child, Aged:}
	1–2 Years	3–5 Years	6–7 Years	8–9 Years	10–12 Years
I. Food from cereal grains	16	18–20	22	21	20
II. Milk	67.5	45–55	45	40	34
III. Vegetables and fruits	10	16–22	16	18	20
IV. Butter	3	4–8	10	12	14
V. Sugar and other sweets	1	1–3	3	4	6
VI. Eggs, cheese, meat and other flesh foods	2.5	3.5	4	5	8

It should be kept carefully in mind that Table 5 is designed to serve the largest possible proportion of people and therefore concedes as much as practicable to the need for pecuniary economy as well as to custom. For this reason and also because of our steadily advancing knowledge, the ideal dietaries planned today may well use such "protective" foods as fruits and milk even more liberally.

Energy Metabolism in Middle-Aged and Elderly People

Emerson was sixty-three when he wrote with reference to his age, "It is time to take in sail." How shall we translate his poetic expression of physiological experience into terms of the energy metabolism?

First of all it should be emphasized that people differ in their reactions to the passage of years. Some are younger at seventy than others are at sixty, and the difference while largely constitutional is also doubtless due in greater measure than previously believed, or yet generally appreciated, to the internal environment induced and maintained by one's daily choice of food.

But somewhere between the ages of fifty and seventy the energy metabolism may be expected to show significant diminution from the young-adult levels with which most of the preceding text has been concerned. Strictly speaking, the generally accepted normal standards for basal energy metabolism show a slight gradual diminution from the 'teens onward; but this is insignificant compared with the differences in total energy metabolism resulting from differing muscular activity. When, somewhere in middle or advancing age, the effect of diminishing muscular activity is added to that of the slow decline in basal metabolism, the result is a significant decrease in the number of food-calories needed per day. Probably 1500 to 2000 Calories per day, depending upon size and musculature, will meet the energy needs of most people of seventy and over. Quantitative statements, however, can not be made with confidence because the relatively few cases which have been studied accurately and systematically show considerable individual differences, and there probably is and will be somewhat less average difference in activity between men of fifty and of seventy than in the past, as the occupations of middle life are less muscular and the grandfather of today and tomorrow may be expected to retain the activity of early middle age through a longer term of years.

EXERCISES

1. Compute your Calorie requirement per 24-hour day, from your body weight and the number of hours you spend in different activities.
2. Plan a day's dietary to meet your computed Calorie requirement, choosing the foods from among the forty with which you have familiarized yourself in the Exercises of the preceding chapter.
3. How would you change the dietary planned in Exercise 2 to make it a reducing dietary with about 500 Calories less of total energy value?
4. A student 20 years old and 5 ft. 5 in. tall is underweight. Modify the dietary planned in Exercise 2 above so as to build up the body weight of this student. Is the "fattening" diet you have thus planned

appetizing? Is it comfortably digested? Is it reasonably economical in cost?

5. How many Calories of food per day would you allow for a family consisting of a bookkeeper of 45 (weight 155 lbs.); wife of 40 (weight 125 lbs.) who does all of the housework; a girl of 15, a boy of 13, and a boy of 11, all these children of average size for their ages and all attending school?

SUGGESTED READINGS

BARTO, H. 1935 Sane reducing diets and how to plan them. Circular 433 of the Agricultural Experiment Station and Extension Service, University of Illinois, Urbana, Illinois.

BARTO, H., and S. C. MUNGER 1931 Overweight again reduced by system of sane dieting. Illinois Agr. Expt. Sta. Rept. 1931, 281–282; *Expt. Sta. Rec.* 66, 294.

BENEDICT, F. G., W. R. MILES, P. ROTH, and H. M. SMITH 1919 Human vitality and efficiency under prolonged restricted diet. Publication No. 280, Carnegie Institution of Washington.

CANNON, W. B. 1939 *The Wisdom of the Body*, Revised Ed., Chapters X and XII. (Norton.)

CARPENTER, T. M. 1931 The fuel of muscular activity of man. *J. Nutrition* 4, 281–304.

FORBES, W. H. 1944 The effects of hard physical work upon nutritional requirements. *Milbank Mem. Fund Quart.* 23, 89–96; *Nutr. Abs. Rev.* 15, 139.

GREENWOOD, M. L., and B. N. LONSINGER 1944 Food intake of college women: Caloric intake and energy requirement. *J. Am. Dietet. Assoc.* 20, 524–527.

KEYS, A. 1946 Human starvation and its consequences. *J. Am. Dietet. Assoc.* 22, 582–587.

MACLEOD, G., and C. M. TAYLOR 1944 *Rose's Foundations of Nutrition*, 4th Ed. (Macmillan.)

ORR, J. B., and I. LEITCH 1938 The determination of the calorie requirements of man. *Nutr. Abs. Rev.* 7, 509–529.

PEDIATRICS DEPARTMENT OF THE UNIVERSITY OF CHICAGO 1946 Liberal infant feeding. *J. Am. Dietet. Assoc.* 22, 602–604.

PETERS, L. H. 1918 *Diet and Health, with a Key to the Calories*. (Chicago: The Reilly and Lee Co.)

REVIEW 1946 The present knowledge of calories in human nutrition. *Nutrition Rev.* 4, 34–37.

REVIEW 1948 Obesity and atherosclerosis. *Nutrition Rev.* 6, 176–179.

REVIEW 1949 Hunger and human behavior. *Nutrition Rev.* 7, 78–80.

REVIEW   1949b   Nutrition and starvation. *Nutrition Rev.* **7**, 223.
ROSE, M. S.   1940   *Feeding the Family,* 4th Ed. (Macmillan.)
SHERMAN, H. C.   1947   *Food and Health,* New Ed. (Macmillan.)
TALBOT, F. B.   1938   Basal metabolism of undernourished girls. *Am. J. Diseases Children* **56**, 61–66.
TAYLOR, C. M., M. W. LAMB, M. E. ROBERTSON, and G. MACLEOD   1948   The energy expenditure for quiet play and cycling of boys seven to fourteen years of age. *J. Nutrition* **35**, 511–521.
TAYLOR, C. M., O. F. PYE, and A. B. CALDWELL   1948   The energy expenditure of 9- to 11-year-old boys and girls (1) standing drawing and (2) dressing and undressing. *J. Nutrition* **36**, 123–131.
TAYLOR, C. M., O. F. PYE, A. B. CALDWELL, and E. R. SOSTMAN   1949   The energy expenditure of boys and girls 9 to 11 years of age (1) sitting listening, (2) sitting singing, and (3) standing singing. *J. Nutrition* **38**, 1–10.
TRULSON, M., E. D. WALSH, and E. K. CASO   1947   A study of obese patients in a nutrition clinic. *J. Am. Dietet. Assoc.* **23**, 941–946.

VI

HOW TO MEET THE NEED FOR PROTEIN

Uses of Proteins in the Body

A brief glimpse of the nature and significance of protein was met in Chapter II and in the summary (near the end of Chapter III) of the fate of foodstuffs in the body. We saw that protein may (*1*) be used in the building or upkeep of body tissues, or (*2*) may serve as precursors in the formation of certain specific regulatory substances (hormones, enzymes), or (*3*) may in part be used as body fuel—along with carbohydrate and fat.

The prominence of the proteins as components of body tissues, and their importance to life processes as precursors of hormones and enzymes give them a very fundamental place in the science of nutrition. And these facts together with traditional considerations give protein such *prestige* or *status value* as tends to continue the investment of a large share of the food budget in protein notwithstanding the great importance of several of the more recently discovered factors in food values.

Hence the present chapter has a two-fold importance: to amplify and clarify our understanding of the ways in which the proteins (and their amino acids) serve the nutritional needs and processes of the body; and to consider how much protein should be provided in our normal daily dietaries.

Interpretation of the Nutritive Functions of Proteins in Terms of Their Amino Acids

As we have already seen, the large complex protein molecule is hydrolyzed, by digestion, almost completely to the amino acids of which it was essentially composed.

Every typical protein yields on hydrolysis at least several different kinds of amino acids; and no less than twenty-one kinds of amino acid are now recognized as commonly received by the body from its protein food. The familiar names of these are: alanine, arginine, aspartic acid, cystine, glutamic (glutaminic) acid, glycine (glycocoll), histidine, hydroxyglutamic acid, hydroxyproline, isoleucine, leucine, lysine, methionine, norleucine, phenylalanine, proline, serine, threonine, tryptophane, tyrosine, and valine. The chemical names and structural formulae of these amino acids are given in many textbooks of biochemistry including Chapter IV of Sherman's *Chemistry of Food and Nutrition,* 7th Edition.

It is essentially in the form of amino acids that food proteins are absorbed from the intestinal tract and carried to the tissues where they are used. Indeed, Professor W. C. Rose of the University of Illinois has demonstrated that a suitable mixture of amino acids is a nutritionally satisfactory substitute for protein even in the diet of young, growing experimental animals.

From the amino acids which the blood distributes, the organs and tissues build (synthesize) the numerous body proteins upon which many aspects of the life process depend. For, not only are proteins essential components of all protoplasm, and the most abundant constituents of the active tissues: they and their derivatives have other highly significant functions as well. Many of the enzymes and other catalysts which the body makes, it makes either wholly or in part from the digestion-products of the food proteins. Moreover, the hemoglobin in the red blood cells, which transports oxygen from the lungs to the tissues where it is needed, is a protein. And, throughout the body, proteins in solution play an essential part in maintaining neutrality and in controlling the distribution and exchanges of the body water.

In addition to their use for the synthesis of proteins, some of the amino acids go into the formation of less complex substances, such as glutathione (which contains the amino acids glycine, cystine, and glutamic acid); and the hormones epinephrine ("adrenaline") and thyroxine (which are related to the amino acid tyrosine).

Secretin, which was mentioned in Chapter III as the hormone which serves as the "messenger" from the intestine to the pancreas in digestion, has also been found to be an amino-acid derivative. It is classed as a polypeptide, being intermediate in molecular size between such a chemically simple hormone as thyroxine, and, on the other hand, such a typically protein substance as insulin.

The amino acids in excess of those required for the specific functions of the building or upkeep of body proteins or the formation of other nitrogenous substances, are deaminized (lose their amino groups) and the remaining fragments are burned to yield energy or converted into body fat. But, since we know that carbohydrate and fat are efficient fuels to meet the body's energy requirement, this is not to be regarded as a specific function of the dietary protein in the same sense as those functions discussed in the preceding paragraphs. *Upkeep* seems a better word than "repair" to indicate the exchange of material which goes on constantly even in entirely normal (uninjured) tissue. On the other hand, it is partly for reasons of repair that a surgeon may wish the protein content of a diet for his surgical patient to be relatively higher than its fat or carbohydrate content or total calorie value.

Factors Determining the Nutritive Value of Proteins

It has long been recognized that all proteins are not of the same value in nutrition. Thus, in 1872 Voit found that the protein gelatin could not be substituted for meat protein in the diet of dogs without some loss of body protein. Later, Osborne and Mendel, in some of the early work using rats as tools* for nutrition research, compared the nutritive effectiveness of a number of purified proteins (Fig. 16). They found, for example, that when the only protein in the diet of young rats is casein the animals are able to grow normally, while if gliadin, one of the proteins of wheat, is given as the sole food protein the animals, although they maintain their body weight (and stores of protein), grow little or not at all. If, however, zein, *one* of the proteins of corn (maize), is the only protein fed, the animals soon begin to lose weight, and ultimately die. When tryptophane, an amino acid not present in zein (or only

---

* The experimental animal is only a tool or instrument of research when the problems are those of human nutrition; but it may be well to emphasize at this point the fact that the chemistry of the protein metabolism has been studied in considerable detail and found to be in many respects strikingly parallel in human and rat nutrition. Thus the rat, in addition to being a very useful tool, can also function in some degree as a sort of "deputy" for man in the experimental study of proteins in nutrition.

88   ESSENTIALS OF NUTRITION

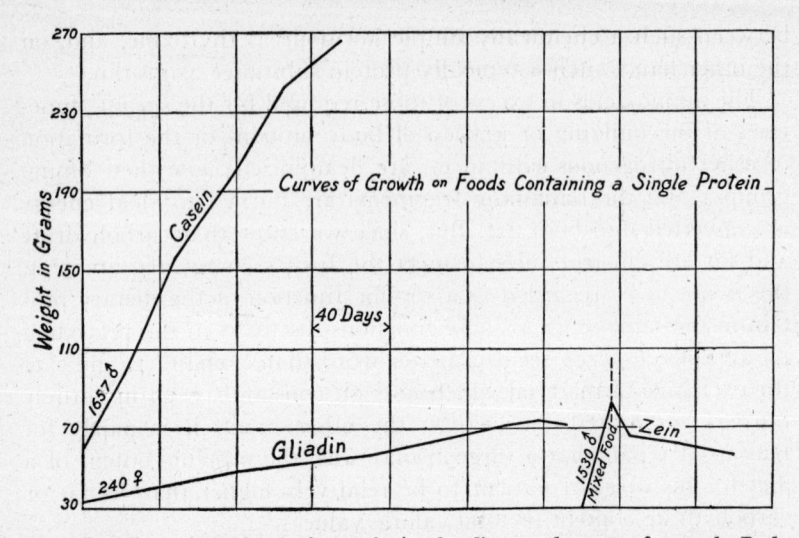

Fig. 16. Effect of the kind of protein in the diet on the rate of growth. Body weight curves of typical rats on diets otherwise similar and adequate but containing in each case only a single protein, casein, gliadin, or zein, fed at the same liberal level, 18 per cent of the food mixture. (From the experiments of Osborne and Mendel.)

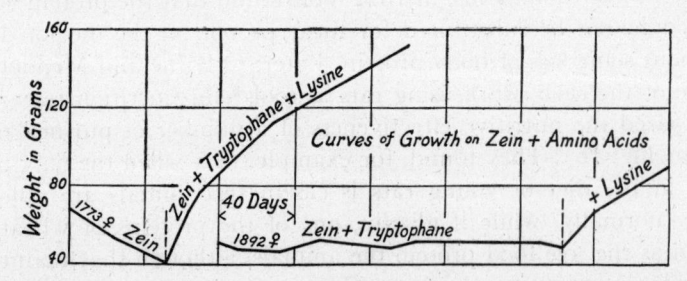

Fig. 17. Effect of adding to a diet containing zein as sole protein the amino acids lysine and tryptophane: showing that a "nutritionally incomplete" protein can support growth when supplemented by the essential amino acids which it lacks. (From the experiments of Osborne and Mendel.)

in traces), but found in casein and in gliadin (and also in maize proteins other than zein), is given in addition to zein, rats may be able to maintain their body weight although they cannot grow. But if lysine, another amino acid which zein lacks, is further given in addition to the protein zein and the amino acid tryptophane, the rats are enabled to gain weight rapidly (see Fig. 17).

Correspondingly, an explanation of the fact that gliadin as sole protein in the diet suffices for maintenance but cannot promote normal growth is suggested by the finding that this protein contains only a very small quantity of the amino acid lysine. Osborne and Mendel observed actually that gliadin fed with supplementary amounts of lysine affords an amino-acid mixture fully satisfactory to meet the needs of a normal rate of gain in body weight.

These and many other instances in which chemical studies of the amino-acid composition of a protein were correlated with nutritional studies of its effectiveness in meeting the body's protein requirement have shown clearly that the nutritive value of a protein depends primarily upon the kinds and relative proportions of the amino acids into which it is resolved (hydrolyzed) by digestion. (There are a few cases in which secondary factors may have some nutritional significance; but they are not of sufficient importance to warrant discussion here.)

Stepwise Gains of Knowledge Through Experimentation

Out of such studies as are illustrated by Figs. 16 and 17 grew also another concept. While body proteins contain about twenty kinds of amino acids, each of which is in this sense essential to the body structure, only certain specific ones of these are *nutritionally essential* (*nutritionally indispensable*) in the sense that they must be supplied by the nutriment before the body can grow (form new protein) at a normal rate, whereas others need not be supplied by the food since they can be derived from other materials ordinarily available within the body. For instance, the amino acids glycine, lysine, and tryptophane are essentially absent from the protein zein. As we have seen (Fig. 17), the feeding experiments with zein as sole dietary protein afford evidence in favor of classifying tryptophane and lysine as nutritionally indispensable, for growth occurs only when *both* of these amino acids are fed in addition to zein. Glycine, on the other hand, appears from this experiment to be nutritionally dispensable, inasmuch as a zein-lysine-tryptophane mixture, which supplies no glycine, can nevertheless satisfy the amino-acid requirements for normal growth.

However, there are not many instances where the nutritional indispensability of an amino acid can be tested so simply as that of the three just discussed. Known cases of *complete absence* of one or two amino acids from an otherwise satisfactory protein are comparatively rare; and, furthermore, methods for the determination of some of the amino acids still fall short of perfection. While it may be possible to show that a given amino acid *is* nutritionally essential without having excluded it altogether from the basal diet, one cannot conclude that a given amino acid *is not* nutritionally essential unless it can be established that normal growth is possible on a diet which is beyond doubt completely devoid of the amino acid in question. Otherwise the possibility remains that the organism does require a dietary supply of the amino acid but that the amounts needed are so small that they can be satisfied by the very low concentration afforded by the basal diet.

It has therefore been necessary to find other means for effectively excluding from the diet the amino acid whose status is under investigation, while supplying to the experimental animal all of the other factors required for normal nutrition. The attainment of this objective, and the resulting classification of the known amino acids as "nutritionally essential" or "nutritionally non-essential" is largely the result of many years devoted to this field of investigation by William C. Rose and his associates at the University of Illinois. These investigators put together mixtures of purified amino acids in the proportions in which they were supposed to occur in some nutritionally "complete" proteins; with the idea that such a mixture when introduced in place of protein into an otherwise suitable diet should permit normal growth, and that one might then proceed to investigate the nutritive importance of individual amino acids by omitting them, one by one, from the mixture and ascertaining the effect of this change upon growth. Casein was chosen as a pattern to be followed in compounding such a mixture of amino acids, but it was soon found that all of the *then* known amino acid components of this protein fed together in the appropriate proportions failed to support good growth, although, under otherwise identical conditions, casein itself gave excellent results. The search for an explanation of this observation led ultimately to the discovery of the amino acid *threonine* which had not previously been identified as a component of proteins. This discovery—in itself of great scientific interest—solved the final difficulty in the way of preparing a synthetic mixture of purified amino acids which can fully meet the nutritional need for protein. Then, by successively excluding one or another amino acid, Rose was able to show that ten amino acids satisfy his definition of "an indispensable dietary component as one which cannot be synthesized by the animal organism, out of the materials *ordinarily available* at a speed commensurate with the demands for *normal* growth." If any one of these ten socalled "nutritionally essential" amino acids is lacking in the amino-acid mixture, normal growth will not occur. But if all ten of these are provided in suitable amounts, the body can form from them the remaining amino acids which enter into the composition of its proteins. The ten amino acids now called "nutritionally essential," in the sense that they must be furnished through the nutriment, are shown in Table 6.

TABLE 6. *Amino Acids Which Are Nutritionally Essential or Indispensable for Growth in the Sense Explained in the Text*

Arginine	Methionine
Histidine	Phenylalanine
Isoleucine	Threonine
Leucine	Tryptophane
Lysine	Valine

More recently, a further discrimination among the amino acids has been made. Rose has proceeded to establish which of the amino acids must be supplied for *adult maintenance*. In this case, it was possible to experiment with human beings, who were fed diets as highly purified as those of the most meticulous animal experiments. Rose found that young male graduate students could maintain their stocks of body protein on diets containing no protein but a mixture of the ten amino acids necessary for normal growth (Table 6). One or another of these amino acids was then removed from the diet and the results noted. Arginine and histidine could be withheld without deleterious effect on the "protein balance"; but when any of the other eight amino acids was lacking, the body began to lose nitrogen (protein) sharply. Thus, isoleucine, leucine, lysine, methionine, phenylalanine, threonine, tryptophane, and valine all are nutritionally essential in the maintenance of nitrogen (protein) equilibrium in normal adult man. Apparently adult man can make arginine and histidine from other essential amino acids at a sufficient rate to meet the needs of normal maintenance. Whether, or under what conditions, the growing child (like young experimental animals) requires arginine or histidine or both, and whether in adults special circumstances such as pregnancy, lactation, or disease, cause demand for certain amino acids not needed for normal maintenance, are not yet known.

That the criterion of indispensability of an amino acid is by definition the inability of the body to form it *fast enough for normal growth* should be kept in mind if confusion and misapprehension are to be avoided. Thus, arginine, which the body can indeed form, but not fast enough for normal growth, is classified as indispensable.

Essential amino acids may be thought of as used in two distinct ways:

(1) *unchanged,* as "building stones" for body proteins, enzymes, etc., for which purpose the particular indispensable amino acid and it alone may be used;

(2) *as precursors,* from which are formed the socalled dispensable amino acids.

It would seem logical to expect that the amounts of the indispensable amino acids which are required will be increased in proportion as the dispensable amino acids of which they are precursors are lacking in the food; and conversely, the need for them should be somewhat diminished if the diet provides liberal amounts of the socalled dispensable acids. Whether or not this merits consideration from a practical point of view will depend upon how specific is the relationship between indispensable and dispensable amino acid. It is shown to be of great importance in the case of the sulfur-containing amino acids, methionine and cystine. According to the usual definition, methionine is characterized as indispensable, cystine as dispensable. Methionine, however, is the only known material ordinarily presented to the body from which cystine may be formed. Thus, of all the usual dietary constituents, methionine alone can fulfill the bodily functions for which methionine itself is required; and only methionine or cystine can supply the cystine needed for body processes. What, then, if a diet supplies a limited amount of methionine—enough, let us say, to meet the growth requirements for methionine *per se* but not sufficient to provide the needed cystine? Whether or not growth can occur under such circumstances will depend directly upon the amount of cystine which the diet supplies. This is illustrated, for example, by Osborne and Mendel's experiments with low-casein diets (Fig. 18); and by the work of Womack and Rose (1941) with purified amino acid mixtures. Additional cystine is said (Sure, 1941) to improve correspondingly the nutritional value of the diet for the support of lactation. Similarly, tyrosine has been shown to "spare" phenylalanine

(Womack and Rose, 1946). In these cases, a socalled nutritionally dispensable amino acid proves to be the very factor which determines the nutritive value of the diet!

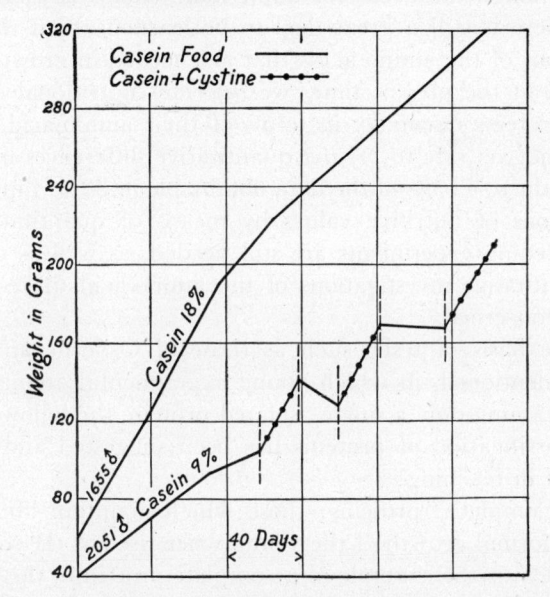

Fig. 18. Effect on growth of reducing the proportion of casein in the diet; and of feeding the amino acid cystine in addition to the lower level. This experiment of Osborne and Mendel illustrates the facts: (1) that a protein which at a liberal level of intake (here 18 per cent) supports normal growth may be unable to do so when fed in reduced proportion (here 9 per cent); and (2) that, as explained in the text, under certain circumstances growth may be promoted by the addition of a so-called nutritionally dispensable amino acid.

How May the Nutritive Value of a Protein Be Assessed?

Except for a few cases presenting abnormalities or particular difficulties in digestion, it is now believed that the nutritive values of the food proteins depend (as has already been intimated) essentially upon the kinds of amino-acid radicles which they contain and the quantitative proportion of each. Of principal interest, obviously, are the socalled nutritionally indispensable amino acids, for which tentative values in a number of proteins and foods are given in Table 29, in Chapter XIX. It should be remembered, however, that methods for the determination of the individual amino acids are still being perfected. Present knowledge is extensive and highly significant; but it is possible that many of the quantitative data are subject to improvement in precision. Furthermore, although the needs for adult maintenance are being established, there is still a great deal to be learned about the relative proportions of the amino acids that are needed in growth.

Hence, at the present time, we *interpret* nutritional differences among proteins essentially in terms of their amino-acid make-up; but it is not yet safe to *predict* quantitative differences in nutritive value on the sole basis of the data obtainable *in vitro*. Empirical determinations of nutritive values by means of quantitatively conducted feeding experiments are still needed, as well as qualitative and quantitative investigations of the amino-acid make-up of the proteins concerned.

On the basis of tests, such as those of Osborne and Mendel already mentioned, in which young experimental animals are fed diets containing only a single, isolated protein, the following qualitative classification of proteins has been suggested and considerably used in teaching:

(1) "Complete" proteins: those which maintain life and provide for normal growth of the young when used as the sole protein food. Casein is the example of a complete protein in the preceding discussion. Other proteins in this group include lactalbumin of milk; ovalbumin and ovovitellin of egg; glycinin of soybean; excelsin of Brazil nut; and edestin, glutenin, and maize glutelin of the cereal grains.

(2) "Partially incomplete" proteins: those which maintain life but do not support normal growth. From the work of Osborne and Mendel already described, it is evident that gliadin is representative of this group.

(3) "Incomplete" proteins: those which, as sole dietary protein, are incapable of supporting either growth or life. Zein clearly belongs to this class, as does also gelatin.

Any such grouping of the proteins, however, should be used with much discrimination, and with great care to insure an understanding of the quantitative aspects of the experimental data, if misconceptions are to be avoided. Edestin is a conspicuous example of a "complete" protein, having served (in experiments by Osborne and Mendel) as the sole protein food of a family of rats for three generations. But when the percentage of edestin in the food mixture was considerably reduced, results like those above described for gliadin were obtained—the diet did not support a normal rate of growth, but this could be secured by adding lysine to the food mixture. Similarly casein when fed in reduced proportion to the total food mixture did not support normal growth; but growth became normal when cystine was added (Fig. 18). Thus "complete" proteins may behave as "partially incomplete" when fed in reduced proportion. It is also to be remembered that varying rates of growth in different species (not to mention other differences) make inadmissible any broad generalizations as to the proportions in which any protein should be fed to species other than that with which its "completeness" or "incompleteness" has been demonstrated.

In 1916, Osborne and Mendel published quantitative measurements of the relative efficiency (for support of growth in young rats) of some of the "complete" proteins. The rate of gain obtained with 8 per cent of lactalbumin required 12 per cent of casein or 15 per cent of edestin; or, as they also state the results, "to produce the same gain in body weight, 50 per cent more casein than lactalbumin was required, and of edestin nearly 90 per cent more."

Lest we attribute undue weight to the differences between *individual* proteins, we should remember that practically all foods except gelatin contain more than one kind of protein. Corn (maize), for example, in addition to the incomplete protein zein contains other proteins, at least one of which yields all the nutritionally essential amino acids. Thus there is less danger of an incomplete assortment of amino acids in even a single natural food than in a single isolated protein. Nevertheless, the mixtures of proteins found in certain articles of food have higher nutritive efficiency than the natural mixtures in certain other foods because they contain the essential amino acids in proportions which approximate more closely the needs of the body. Thus, the various means of estimating relative values agree in indicating that proteins of animal origin are, as a class, superior in nutritive efficiency to most of those derived from plants. Of the animal proteins, those of whole milk and whole eggs share the first place. Next come the animal tissue proteins, among which those of liver and kidney probably have a higher value than those of muscle. Among the nutritionally important plant protein mixtures, those of the cereal grains, though inferior to most animal proteins, have nevertheless been found to possess a higher value than those of white flour. The natural protein mixture of milk is much more efficient than those of the grains, when each food is fed separately as sole source of protein. Yet when grains and milk are fed together in favorable proportions, their proteins so supplement each other in furnishing the nutritionally essential amino acids that the combination may be practically as efficient as the milk proteins alone. This *supplementary relationship* between proteins is of great importance both nutritionally and economically, since it makes possible the full utilization of the low-cost proteins of grains and other vegetable foods, provided only that they are fed in combination with sufficient amounts of those foods which reinforce their content of certain essential amino acids.

In the maintenance of full grown tissues, there need be no special anxiety regarding the adequacy of the amino-acid mixture yielded by the proteins of mixed diets such as are common in this country. But in cases in which new protein must be built up in the body, *e.g.,* growth, pregnancy and lactation, convalescence from a wasting disease, or feeding to build up a chronically undernourished person, the choice of proteins may become a matter of considerable importance. The proteins of milk and eggs are the ones best suited for conversion into body proteins. For this and other reasons it is highly desirable that milk or eggs or both be provided abundantly in the diet of growing children, of pregnant or nursing women, and of all people who require "building up."

A further discussion, which includes an analogy so widely quoted as to be rapidly becoming a classic, will be found on page 16 of Rose's *Feeding the Family,* 4th Edition (1940).

How Much Protein is Needed for Adult Maintenance?

Maintenance requirement is the amount required for nutritional equilibrium in the body.

Whether the body is in protein equilibrium or is gaining or losing protein, is ascertained by means of *nitrogen balance experiments*. These are experiments in which one determines, by means of chemical analyses of food and excreta, the amounts of nitrogen which enter and which leave the body, so that intake may be compared with output in a manner analogous to the balancing of a bookkeeping account.

We may say that the balance has been determined whenever the quantitative relation of intake and output has been ascertained. The body is said to be *in equilibrium* when intake and output are alike. The expression "in balance" is somewhat ambiguous because one has "determined the nitrogen balance" whenever the intake and output have been ascertained and regardless of whether the data show equilibrium or not. Thus we meet the expression "plus balance" or "positive balance" when the data show that the body is gaining,—and "minus" or "negative" balance when the body is losing,—nitrogen or whatever other element may be under similar consideration (as phosphorus, calcium, and iron will be in subsequent chapters). The smallest intake which will support equilibrium, in a series of properly planned experiments, should indicate the body's maintenance requirements in the strict sense of the term.

Using nitrogen as a practicable and sufficiently accurate measure of protein, each gram of nitrogen corresponds to approximately 6.25 grams of protein inasmuch as the mixed proteins of the body and of the food contain on the average 16 per cent of nitrogen. Nitrogen balance experiments, then, can be made to show the amount of protein which the food must furnish to maintain protein equilibrium.

In 1920, the available data which appeared to be applicable to the problem of the normal adult requirement were studied. About one hundred such cases were found, and these gave a mean result of 0.634 gram of protein per kilogram of body weight per day with no significant difference per unit of body weight between the sexes.

Figured to the conventional basis of a body weight of 70 kilograms (154 pounds) this average finding was 44.4 grams of protein per man per day.

This has been somewhat generally used as an approximate measure of maintenance need or requirement in the sense explained above. As an estimate of *actual* need it is somewhat generous in that it contemplates the maintenance of a larger store of protein in the body than such careful students as Chittenden and Folin have deemed to be most desirable. The study of original literature involved in collating the data averaged above, left no doubt that in many if not most cases equilibrium could have been realized at lower levels of intake after the body had given up a relatively small fraction of the protein which it had been carrying; and no one can be sure whether and under what conditions the extra store of protein which most of us carry in our bodies is advantageous or not. Whether one believes in high-protein or low-protein diet is still somewhat a matter of temperament!

All of the generally accepted *dietary standards* for protein lean toward liberality as contrasted with actually demonstrated need.

A common custom has been to add fifty per cent to the above mentioned average of 44.4 grams, thus arriving at a "standard" of 67 grams per 70 kilograms of body weight or, in round numbers, *one gram of food protein per day for each kilogram of body weight.*

This latter (70 grams of protein per 70 kilograms of body weight) is the daily allowance recommended for men by the Food and Nutrition Board of the National Research Council. The allowance for women is a shade more generous, *viz.* 60 grams for a 56-kilogram individual. As will be seen from Table 42 in the Appendix, both these allowances for maintenance provide about 10 per cent of the calories as protein for persons of moderate physical activity.

Maintenance Requirement of Specific Amino Acids

As explained above, Rose has demonstrated that eight amino acids are essential for the maintenance of nitrogen equilibrium in normal adult man. Quantitative determinations of the amounts specifically required of each of these eight amino acids have been, and still are, in progress. In the spring of 1949, Rose, stating that "the results now appear to be sufficiently numerous and definite to warrant positive conclusions," presented the values quoted in Table 7 for the minimum amount of each essential amino acid required for adult maintenance *when the diet furnishes sufficient nitrogen for synthesis of non-essentials.*

Rose suggests twice the minimum value as a "recommended daily intake," and urges that both values be regarded still as "strictly tentative."

It will be noted that the recommended intakes of the essential amino acids total 12.7 grams, in comparison with the National Research Council's recommended intake of 70 grams total protein. Whether this indicates an unnecessary liberality in the latter recommendations or simply that something like four-fifths of the total may be supplied by "non-essential" amino acids, is not yet clear. Studies to establish the minimum total nitrogen required for maintenance when the recommended intakes of the eight essentials are supplied, are awaited with interest; as are also studies of the extent (if any) to which dietary cystine may replace methionine, tyrosine replace phenylalanine, and so on.

TABLE 7. *Minimum and Recommended Intakes of Essential Amino Acids for Normal Maintenance in Man When Diet Furnishes Sufficient Nitrogen for Synthesis of Non-essentials*
("Strictly Tentative Values": W. C. Rose in Federation Proceedings)

Amino Acid	Minimum Daily Requirement	Recommended Daily Intake	Subjects Tested (No.)
	gm.	gm.	
Tryptophane	0.25	0.5	31
Phenylalanine	1.10	2.2	22
Lysine	0.80	1.6	27
Threonine	0.50	1.0	19
Valine	0.80	1.6	23
Methionine	1.10	2.2	13
Leucine	1.10	2.2	8
Isoleucine	0.70	1.4	8

Recommendations for Growth, Pregnancy, and Lactation, as Well as for Maintenance

To express the protein intake in terms of the proportion of the total calories which it supplies is rational as a guide in gauging family and population needs. It has been much used in the teaching of dietetics where the planning of a dietary often begins with the determination of the total food calories to be supplied, and then adds that "about 10 per cent" or "from 10 to 15 per cent" of the calories should be in the form of protein. The allowance of 10 per cent is held to be ample by those who follow Chittenden in his advocacy of "physiological economy in nutrition" or who particularly feel the need of economy as to cost, while an allowance of from 10 to 15 per cent is sufficient to provide for those whose scientific judgments or whose temperaments lean toward relatively high protein intake.

To make the protein allowance a given fraction of the total calories is also rational from the point of view that the relatively high food requirement of children applies about equally to their energy and their protein needs. And furthermore the reduction of total food calories in the dietaries of elderly people may well be paralleled by a proportionate decrease of protein.

In the recommendations of the National Research Council's Food and Nutrition Board, this plan, while not professed, is essentially followed, the allowances for children ranging between 10.5 and 13.3 per cent of the calories as protein.

Muscular work supported by an ample intake of food calories does not necessarily increase the amount of protein metabolized. In other words, the extra calories for the work could be supplied by increased carbohydrate (or carbohydrate and fat) without increase of protein. But usually it appears more practical, and is found more acceptable, to provide for the increased muscular activity by simply increasing the amount of food of the accustomed kind.

Remembering, then, that it is not to be taken as implying that the need for protein varies with muscular activity, we may accept as a good guide for the planning or judgment of family dietaries or population food supply that we look first to the adequacy of the total food calories, and then to see that about ten or ten to fifteen per cent of the calories are in the form of protein.

In pregnancy and lactation, however, the need for protein is increased somewhat independently of the energy need, and probably to a larger extent.

Also there are occasions when one may wish to think of protein requirements directly "in their own right" as in the following recommendations:

In addition to those already cited (70 grams for men and 60 *for maintenance* in women, each irrespective of muscular activity), the National Research Council's Recommended Daily Allowances for protein include the following:

For women in the latter half of pregnancy, 85; and in lactation, 100 grams of protein per day.

For children under one year of age, 3.5 grams per kilogram of body weight per day;

1–3 years, 40 grams per day;
4–6 years, 50 grams;
7–9 years, 60 grams;
10–12 years, 70 grams.

For girls, 13–15 years, 80 grams;
" " 16–20 " , 75 grams;
" boys, 13–15 " , 85 grams;
" " 16–20 " , 100 grams;

These recommended allowances are not to be interpreted too literally and rigidly, but as general guides which imply that more protein may be needed during bodily development than after it has been completed; and that the high point of body-building need will usually be passed at an earlier chronological age in girls than in boys.

To What Extent does Food Selection Influence the Nutritive Efficiency of the Protein Mixture which the Dietary Affords?

The problem of this chapter being how to meet the need for protein, its text may now be concluded with a brief further consideration of the practical effect of differences in food selection.

As already mentioned, the natural mixtures of proteins which staple articles of food contain do not differ nearly so much in amino-acid make-up and resulting nutritive value as do the individual proteins when separated and examined as isolated substances. And a still further evening-up usually results from the presence of different natural foods in a dietary or in a community food supply.

These principles may be illustrated by the following facts regarding the proteins of wheat and of milk:

Osborne and Mendel, isolating from ordinary white flour its most abundant individual protein, gliadin, and feeding this alone, found it of relatively low nutritive efficiency,—"partially incomplete" in the sense explained above.

They also found, however, that other proteins in this same white flour made its protein mixture more efficient in nutrition than the gliadin alone.

Furthermore, they found that the protein mixture of whole wheat is of much higher nutritive value than that of white flour.

They were able to make fairly satisfactory dietaries with whole wheat as the sole source of protein.

And finally, they and others found that the feeding of milk together with whole wheat gives a still higher nutritive efficiency to the protein mixture of the dietary.

TABLE 8. *Protein Contents of Edible Portion of Typical Foods*
(U. S. Dept. Agriculture)

Food	Protein Per Cent	Food	Protein Per Cent
Almonds	18.6	Eggs	12.8
Apples, fresh	0.3	Kale	3.9
Apricots, dried	5.2	Milk	3.5
Bacon, medium fat, uncooked	9.1	Oatmeal	14.2
		Oranges	0.9
Beans, dried	21.4	Oysters (solids and liquor)	6.0
Beef, round, lean	19.5	Peanuts, roasted	26.9
Bread, white	8.5	Potatoes	2.0
" whole wheat	9.3	Rice, white	7.6
Cantaloupe	0.6	Salmon, canned	20.2
Carrots	1.2	Sweetpotatoes	1.8
Cauliflower	2.4	Tomatoes	1.0
Cheese, Cheddar type	25.0	Turnip greens	2.9

It is to be remembered that a given protein may appear "complete" or "partially incomplete" according to the level at which (proportion in which) it is fed. In such case the particular amino acid which first restricts growth is called the "limiting factor." For example: lysine in wheat and its products; methionine (or cystine) in meat and in milk, is under ordinary conditions the limiting factor, respectively. In Chapter XIX we shall meet instances in which the differing limiting factors in the natural protein mixtures of different foods have practical bearings upon the desirable place of each food in the diet. Thus because of their different limiting amino acids, the natural protein mixtures of wheat and soybeans supplement each other, and because of this supplementation the nutritive value of these two foods eaten together is higher than the weighted average of the two taken separately.

So important are the supplementary relationships among proteins in ensuring good nutritive value of the protein mixture of typical well-balanced dietaries, that it does not seem essential here to enter into the discussion of the complicated attempts to set up methods for measuring and expressing the more abstruse of the so-called biological values, concerning the significance of which there is not yet a clear consensus of expert opinion.

As summarized by *Nutrition Reviews* of July 1944, it is "gratifying to learn from several recent reports that corn germ, which constitutes about 7 per cent of the corn kernel, contains 20 per cent of protein of surprisingly high quality." Also, "wheat germ has an amino acid composition similar to corn germ, and is presumably of similar high biologic value."

The Bureau of Human Nutrition and Home Economics has published a leaflet entitled, "Cooking with Soya Flour and Grits," which emphasizes the nutritive value and practicability of soybean products in the American food supply. Its great importance in the Orient has, of course, long been recognized.

In Table 8, typical foods of widely different types are listed in simply alphabetical sequence and their protein content given in percentage of the edible portion of the food, moist or dry according to the condition in which it is usually sold. Analogous tables in other chapters may be arranged in different sequence or expressed on different bases, to give the reader practice in comparing foods from different points of view.

EXERCISES

1. Feed parallel groups of young rats, starting at 3 to 4 weeks of age: (*a*) A mixture of 90 parts white flour, 9 parts butter, and 1 part table salt; (*b*) A mixture of 60 parts white flour, 30 parts milk powder, 9 parts butter, and 1 part of the same table salt. While the introduction of the milk will have enriched the diet in certain mineral elements and vitamins as well, the difference in growth during the first three or four weeks of this experiment may be attributed chiefly to the milk proteins.

(This experiment may then be continued to see what evidences of nutritional deficiency appear later and to interpret them in the light of subsequent chapters.)

2. Feed parallel groups of young rats, starting at 3 to 4 weeks of age: (*a*) Bread moistened with its weight of milk; (*b*) Bread of the same kind moistened with 5-per cent solution of milk sugar and spread with as much butter as corresponds to the milk used in (*a*). If the contrast here found differs from that found in the preceding Exercise, how do you explain the difference?

3. Plan experiments making use, if circumstances permit, of so-called "synthetic" diets (mixtures of artificially purified substances) between which the sole difference shall be: (1) an individual protein, *e.g.*, casein; (2) an individual amino acid, *e.g.*, lysine.

4. If facilities are available, carry out the experiments described in Exercises 1 and 2 and those planned in Exercise 3, continuing them as long as time permits, with daily feeding, watering, and casual inspection of the animals; and at least weekly weighings and careful physical examination.

In addition to the promptly-developing differences in growth, attributable to the protein (amino acid) factors discussed in the foregoing chapter, it is possible that a long-continued comparison would develop other effects which, after your study of the chapters which follow, you might be able to attribute to some mineral or vitamin factor.

SUGGESTED READINGS

BURKE, B. S. 1941 The need for better nutrition during pregnancy and lactation. *J. Am. Dietet. Assoc.* **17**, 102–111.

BURKE, B. S., V. A. BEAL, S. B. KIRKWOOD, and H. C. STUART 1943 The influence of nutrition during pregnancy on the condition of the infant at birth. *J. Nutrition* **26**, 569–582.

ELVEHJEM, C. A. 1948 Tryptophan and niacin relations and their implications to human nutrition. *J. Am. Dietet. Assoc.* **24**, 653–657.

GEIGER, E., and L. E. GEIGER 1948 The role of the time factor in feeding supplementary proteins. *J. Nutrition* **36**, 813–819.

GREENHUT, I. T., R. L. POTTER, and C. A. ELVEHJEM 1947 The phenylalanine and tryptophan content of meats. *Arch. Biochem.* **15**, 450–464; *Nutr. Abs. Rev.* **18**, 49.

GREWE, E. 1945 Use of peanut flour in baking. *Food Research* **10**, 28–41; *Nutr. Abs. Rev.* **15**, 142.

HAWLEY, E. E., J. R. MURLIN, E. S. NASSET, and T. A. SZYMANSKI 1948 Biological values of six partially purified proteins. *J. Nutrition* **36**, 153–169.

HOAGLAND, R., N. R. ELLIS, O. G. HANKINS, and G. G. SNIDER 1948 Supplemental value of certain amino acids for beef protein. *J. Nutrition* **35**, 167–176.

JAFFE, W. G. 1949 Limiting essential amino acids of some legume seeds. *Proc. Soc. Exptl. Biol. Med.* **71**, 398–399.

JONES, D. B. 1944 Nutritive values of soybean and peanut proteins. *Federation Proc.* **3**, 116–120.

JONES, D. B., and J. P. DIVINE 1944 The protein nutritional

value of soybean, peanut, and cottonseed flours and their value as supplements to wheat flour. *J. Nutrition* **28**, 41–49.

Jones, D. B., and K. D. Widness 1946 The comparative growth-promoting value of the proteins of wheat germ, corn germ, and some other protein foods of plant and animal origin. *J. Nutrition* **31**, 675–683.

Keller, E. B., J. R. Rachele, and V. du Vigneaud 1949 Transmethylation with methionine containing deuterium and C^{14} in the methyl group. *J. Biol. Chem.* **177**, 733–738.

Kosterlitz, H. W., and R. M. Campbell 1945 The storage of protein in the adult animal. *Nutr. Abs. Rev.* **15**, 1–14.

Krehl, W. A., L. J. Teply, P. S. Sarma, and C. A. Elvehjem 1945 Growth-retarding effect of maize in nicotinic-acid-low rations and its counteraction by trytophane. *Science* **101**, 489–490.

Kuiken, K. A., C. M. Lyman, S. Dieterich, M. Bradford, and M. Trant 1948 Availability of amino acids in some foods. *J. Nutrition* **36**, 359–368.

Leverton, R. M., and M. R. Gram 1949 Nitrogen excretion of women related to the distribution of animal protein in daily meals. *J. Nutrition* **39**, 57–65.

Lewis, H. B. 1948 Proteins in nutrition. *J. Am. Med. Assoc.* **138**, 207–213.

Maass, A. R., F. C. Larson, and E. S. Gordon 1949 The distribution in normal tissues of radioactive sulfur fed as labeled methionine. *J. Biol. Chem.* **177**, 209–216.

MacLeod, G., and C. M. Taylor 1944 *Rose's Foundations of Nutrition*, 4th Ed. (Macmillan.)

McCollum, E. V., E. Orent-Keiles, and H. G. Day 1939 *The Newer Knowledge of Nutrition*, 5th Ed., Chapters V and VI. (Macmillan.)

Mendel, L. B. 1923 *Nutrition: The Chemistry of Life.* (Yale University Press.)

Mitchell, H. H., and J. R. Beadles 1944 Corn germ: A valuable protein food. *Science* **99**, 129–130.

Nielsen, E. K., and R. C. Corley 1939 Retention of the nitrogen of mixtures of amino acids administered to rats fed diets low in protein. *Am. J. Physiol.* **126**, 223–228.

Ohlson, M. A., W. D. Brewer, D. C. Cedarquist, L. Jackson, E. G Brown, and P. H. Roberts 1948 Protein requirements of women. *J. Am. Dietet. Assoc.* **24**, 744–749.

Osborne, T. B., and L. B. Mendel 1926 The relation of the rate of growth to diet. *J. Biol. Chem.* **69**, 661–673.

Pittman, M. S., H. McKay, B. L. Kunerth, M. B. Patton, N. Edelblute, G. Cox, E. Shepek, and J. Chen 1941 Nitrogen, calcium, and phosphorus intakes of college women. *J. Am. Dietet. Assoc.* **17,** 947–954.

REVIEW 1946 Protein requirements of adults. *Nutrition Rev.* **4,** 264–266.

REVIEW 1949 Availability of amino acids from protein foodstuffs. *Nutrition Rev.* **7,** 99–101.

ROSE, W. C. 1938 The nutritive significance of the amino acids. *Physiol. Rev.* **18,** 109–136.

ROSE, W. C., W. J. HAINES, J. E. JOHNSON, and D. T. WARNER 1943 Further experiments on the role of the amino acids in human nutrition. *J. Biol. Chem.* **148,** 457–458.

ROSE, W. C., M. J. OESTERLING, and M. WOMACK 1949 Comparative growth on diets containing 10 and 19 amino acids, with further observations on the role of glutamic and aspartic acids. *J. Biol. Chem.* **176,** 753–762.

ROSE, W. C., and E. E. RICE 1939 The significance of the amino acids in canine nutrition. *Science* **90,** 186–187.

SCHAEFFER, A. J. 1946 Effect of certain amino acids on healing of experimental wounds. *Proc. Soc. Exptl. Biol. Med.* **61,** 165–166.

SCHWEIGERT, B. S. 1948 Amino acid content of foods. *J. Am. Dietet. Assoc.* **24,** 939–944.

SCHWEIGERT, B. S., and P. B. PEARSON 1948 Further studies on the metabolism of tryptophan and nicotinic acid by the rat and other animals. *J. Biol. Chem.* **172,** 485–493.

STARE, F. J., and D. M. HEGSTED 1944 Nutritive value of wheat-germ, corn-germ, and oat proteins. *Federation Proc.* **3,** 120–123.

SURE, B. 1941 Dietary requirements for fertility and lactation. XXVIII. The lactation-promoting properties of cystine when added to casein diets. *J. Nutrition,* **22,** 491–498.

SURE, B. 1948 The nature of supplementary value of the proteins in milled corn meal and milled wheat flour with dried food yeasts. *J. Nutrition* **36,** 59–63.

VAN SLYKE, D. D. 1942 Physiology of the amino acids. *Science* **95,** 259–263.

WOMACK, M., and W. C. ROSE 1941 The partial replacement of dietary methionine by cystine for purposes of growth. *J. Biol. Chem.* **141,** 375–379.

WOODS, E., W. M. BEESON, and D. W. BOLIN 1943 Field peas as a source of protein for growth. *J. Nutrition* **26,** 327–335.

VII

MINERAL ELEMENTS AND REGULATORY PROCESSES IN NUTRITION

The Mineral Elements

In preceding chapters we have discussed the composition and nutritive functions of foods principally in terms of the organic nutrients: carbohydrates, fats, and proteins. This has involved consideration of the elements carbon, hydrogen, oxygen, and nitrogen, which, as Table 9 shows, are the elements most prominent in the body's structure. In this chapter we shall be concerned with the other chemical elements regularly found in the body which, although most of them are present there in much smaller quantities than the four elements just referred to, are nevertheless essential to its normal functioning.

These other elements are commonly designated as the *mineral elements* or the *inorganic foodstuffs*. But the use of such terms should not be understood to imply that these elements necessarily occur and function exclusively as inorganic or mineral compounds. For example, the most prominent compounds of sulfur in the food and in the body are the amino acids cystine and methionine which have already been considered as constituents of the proteins. Yet although sulfur thus enters, and functions in, the body almost entirely as organic compounds it is, in the normal oxidation processes of the body, ultimately converted into the inorganic compound, sulfuric acid or sulfate ion, and as such becomes an important factor in the mineral metabolism.

Which Mineral Elements are Essential?

It cannot be stated with certainty exactly how many of the mineral elements found in the body are indispensable to its normal structure or functioning; and how many are present merely through accidental introduction from the environment. *All eleven mineral elements* for which figures are given in Table 9 and also *cobalt* and *zinc* are now definitely regarded as essential.

TABLE 9. *Estimated Approximate Elementary Composition of the Adult Human Body*

Element	Percentage
Oxygen	65.
Carbon	18.
Hydrogen	10.
Nitrogen	3.
Calcium	2.2[a]
Phosphorus	1.2[b]
Potassium	0.35
Sulfur	0.25
Chlorine	0.15
Sodium	0.15
Magnesium	0.05
Iron	0.004
Manganese	0.0003
Copper	0.00015
Iodine	0.00004
Cobalt	
Zinc	
Others of more doubtful status	

[a] Estimates vary widely.
[b] Percentage varies with that of calcium.
[c] Quantitative data seem insufficient for numerical expression here.

With regard to the question whether other elements are essential it seems clear that any diet which is adequate in the unquestioned essentials will almost certainly provide the traces at most that may be required of mineral elements whose importance is still unknown. And from this fact it follows that any element needed only in such small amounts that the need of it is still in doubt is unlikely to be an actual limiting factor in nutrition, either in nature or in civilized life; so that from the functional viewpoint of present-day science the elements to which we give attention in nutritional study for practical reasons are also undoubtedly the ones of really major scientific significance.

How do They Function?

The elements concerned in the mineral metabolism may exist in the body and take part in its functions in at least three kinds of ways:

(1) As constituents of the mineral matter of the bones and teeth, giving these structures their strength, rigidity, and relative permanence;

(2) As structural constituents of the soft tissues also, as illustrated by the fact that all the known tissue proteins contain sulfur, several of them as well as some other substances essential to cell structure contain phosphorus, and the outstandingly important hemoglobin of the red blood cells contains iron;

(3) As constituents of substances concerned in regulatory functions, as, for example, the salts held in solution in the body fluids and important in giving these their characteristic influence upon the functional capacities of muscle and nerve, their osmotic pressure, their solvent properties and consequent ability to transport the nutrients and their metabolites, and the property of supplying the material for the acidity or alkalinity of digestive juices while at the same time maintaining approximate neutrality in the blood and body tissues.

Varied as they are, these functions are interrelated at many points; and several of the socalled mineral elements take part in more than one of these three types of function.

Calcium and *phosphorus* function importantly in all three ways, and the preponderance of calcium phosphate in bone and tooth mineral makes them elements which the body needs in relatively large amounts. The next chapter will be devoted to them.

Iron, while occurring in much smaller amounts than calcium and phosphorus, is nevertheless a real problem in nutrition, in the sense that if it is left to chance one does not always get enough, especially under our present-day conditions of living so largely upon artificially refined food. Inasmuch as the iron which enters into nutritional processes goes mainly to form hemoglobin, and *copper* has been found to play an essential rôle in the transformation of iron into hemoglobin, these two elements are discussed together in Chapter IX.

Iodine is an element which *in certain regions* is not sufficiently abundant to be safely left to chance, especially now that people commonly use such highly refined table salt. Here we meet a very special kind of nutritional problem, which seems best treated by itself in Chapter X.

Chlorine, in the form of its salts, the chlorides, plays a very important part in the maintenance of normal conditions in the body. That we do not (and need not) take account of chloride content in our ordinary judgments and studies of food values is due to our practice of adding so much sodium chloride (as common salt) to food in its preservation, in its preparation, and at the table.

The chlorides are among the most important of the body's *electrolytes*. These are substances which in water solution exist as electrically charged particles called *ions*. They function very significantly as regulators of body processes, both collectively, for example, in the control of the osmotic pressure of body fluids and hence of the passage of water into and out of the tissues, and *specifically,* as in their effect on the irritability of muscles and nerves, to be discussed below.

Sodium chloride, being by far the largest constituent of the mineral matter of the blood, assumes special significance in the regulation of water exchanges in the organism. And, as Cannon emphasized repeatedly, these latter are more extensive and more important than may at first thought appear. He points out that "there are a number of circulations of the fluid out of the body and back again, without loss." Thus, for example, it is estimated that from a quart to a quart and one-half of water daily "leaves the body" when it enters the mouth as saliva; another one or two quarts are passed out as gastric juice; and perhaps a similar amount is contained in the bile and the secretions of the pancreas and the intestinal wall. This large volume of water enters the digestive processes; and practically all of it is reabsorbed through the intestinal wall where it performs the equally important function of carrying-in the digested foodstuffs. These and other instances of what Cannon calls "the conservative use of water in our bodies" involve essentially osmotic pressure relationships in which the concentration of sodium chloride plays an important part.

Under our ordinary conditions of everyday living the body is apt to receive and excrete several grams of sodium chloride per day, the amount varying with individual taste as to salting of food at the table and usually ranging considerably higher than is needed for maintenance of approximate equilibrium. In fasting, or on a salt-free diet, chloride output at first reflects to some extent the level of exchange of previous days, but rapidly falls to less than a gram per day. This fact, together with some reasons of a more

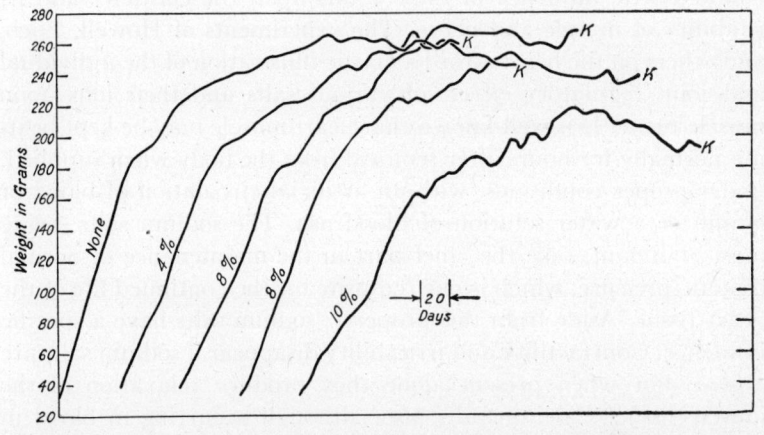

Fig. 19. Growth of male rats on a wheat-and-milk diet with different amounts of added table salt. Up to 4 per cent of salt in the dry food mixture (the curves for those receiving 1 and 2 per cent being here omitted to save space) there was no appreciable effect. At 8 per cent there are somewhat variable indications, and at 10 per cent a distinct indication of unfavorable effect.

medical kind, leads some physiologists and physicians to believe that a more moderate use of salt than the present-day liberal average may be better.

On the other hand, people engaged in occupations which induce profuse sweating may thereby excrete so much salt through the skin as to call (temporarily, at least) for an increased intake in food or drink.

Thus there are scientifically sound possibilities of occasions to safeguard the salt intake: sometimes against too much, and sometimes against too little. But most people at most times may eat their food "salted to taste" without anxiety in either direction; for the healthy body has power to adjust chloride output to chloride intake throughout a wide range (Fig. 19).

Potassium is especially prominent inside the cells of the blood and soft tissues, while sodium predominates in the blood plasma and other inter-cellular fluids. And similarly (although their concentrations are much lower than those of sodium and potassium), magnesium is largely localized within the cells, while calcium is relatively more abundant in the fluids bathing the cells.

However, the body fluids contain some of all four of these elements, and upon the balance between them depends largely the characteristic influence of these fluids upon the elasticity and irritability of muscle and nerve. The experiments of Howell, Loeb, and others on the heart afford a classic illustration of the individual and joint regulatory effects of various salts and their ions upon muscle tissue. It is well known that heart muscle may be kept beating normally for hours after removal from the body when supplied, under proper conditions, with an artificial circulation of blood or lymph or a water solution of blood ash. The sodium salts, being most abundant, take the chief part in the maintenance of normal osmotic pressure, which is one requisite for the continued life of the heart tissue. Aside from this property, sodium salts have a specific influence. Contractility and irritability disappear if sodium salts are absent, but when present alone they produce relaxation of the muscle tissue. Calcium salts also, although occurring in blood in very much smaller quantity, are absolutely necessary to the normal action of the heart muscle; while, if present in concentrations above normal, they cause a condition of tonic contraction, or "calcium rigor"—in sharp contrast to the relaxation induced by sodium salts. Potassium salts, in the small quantities normally present, promote relaxation, through this effect tending to diminish the rate of heart beat; and in higher concentration cause a state of extreme relaxation known as "potassium inhibition."

Thus it is found that the alternate contractions and relaxations which constitute the normal beating of the heart depend upon a balance between calcium salts on the one hand and sodium and potassium salts on the other. Other active tissues of the body doubtless have analogous requirements as to inorganic salts.

In addition to the case just discussed, several other instances of socalled *ionic antagonism* might be cited. For example, *calcium* ion is in some measure antagonistic to *magnesium* ion. Thus, magnesium salts when administered in abnormally large quantities show a soporific and hypnotic action, which effect can be counteracted by the administration of calcium salts. Also the addition of magnesium to an otherwise well-balanced ration tends to cause a loss of calcium from the body. And, conversely, experimental magnesium deficiency results in an abnormal accumulation of calcium in the soft tissues.

Similarly, a high intake of *potassium* salts increases the excretion of *sodium* salts. Since most vegetable foods are relatively rich in potassium, Bunge suggested that this fact may afford an explanation of the craving for common salt which man shares with the herbivorous animals.

Some of the mineral elements have individual and specific functions in addition to their cooperative activities already indicated. For example, the presence of the calcium salts is absolutely essential to the clotting of blood, while magnesium salts enhance the activity of the enzymes known as phosphatases and assist at certain stages in the metabolism of carbohydrates.

The prominence of calcium and phosphorus in bone has already been mentioned. Small amounts of magnesium and sodium appear likewise to be constituents of the skeletal structures.

Manganese, cobalt, and *zinc* are now generally accepted as nutritionally essential elements.

Besides occurring in the amino acids cystine and methionine, *sulfur* is a component of at least two other nutritionally important food substances, thiamine and biotin, which will be considered in later chapters. The sulfur consumed in these and other organic constituents of the diet is practically all converted in the metabolic breakdown processes to sulfuric acid, which must be excreted chiefly as neutral inorganic sulfates and so, as we shall see, presents a major problem in the acid-base economy.

Thus, in the case of sulfur, what entered the body as a neutral element has become a strong "fixed acid" through the normal oxidation process of our metabolism. Even a moderate protein intake results in the formation of around two grams of sulfuric acid (sulfate ion) in the body every day. While the weight of carbonic acid simultaneously produced is many times greater, it leaves the body through the lungs without presenting the same sort of elimination problem as does the end product of the sulfur metabolism. This is discussed further under acid-base balance below.

Organic Acids

Except for the discussion of fatty acids in connection with fats and lipoids, the organic acids which occur in foods, and some of which also occur to an important extent in the body, were only very briefly mentioned in Chapter II. It seems more advantageous to consider them at the present point because of their interrelations with the mineral metabolism, and particularly the part that some of them play in the phenomena of acid-base balance or the maintenance of the body's essential neutrality.

Perhaps we should first define the categories of acids with which the body has to deal from this point of view. Organic chemistry is, in the main, the same as the chemistry of carbon compounds; but we do not ordinarily consider carbonic acid as an organic acid. By *organic acid* (or organic acid radicle) we mean one which contains carbon and which can be burned. But of those which burn readily when heated in air, some do and some do not undergo ready and fairly complete oxidation in the body; and this distinction has an important bearing upon the problem of acid-base balance in foods and nutrition.

The present writers consider it an open question whether study of acid-base balance—as in the small-type section beginning on the next page—belongs strictly to the Essentials of Nutrition, or not. Those who do study it will do well to bear in mind four categories of acids: (1) organic acids readily oxidizable in the body; (2) organic acids not readily oxidizable in the body; (3) carbonic acid, "mineral" but "weak" and readily volatilized through the lungs; (4) fixed mineral acids, presenting a quite different elimination-problem from carbonic acid.

Before proceeding to the phenomena of acid-base balance, some of the organic acids deserve a few words on their own merits as nutrients.

Although the three major organic foodstuffs are practically neutral, certain foods as they are eaten are frankly acid, owing to the presence of substantial amounts of organic acids, such as citric, malic, lactic, and tartaric.

Of these, citric and malic acids are the most widely distributed, one or both of them occurring in appreciable concentration in practically all vegetables, and still more abundantly in fruits. Milk also contains citric acid to the extent of about 1.5 grams per liter.

The body seems able to burn as fuel practically all of the citric acid any diet is likely to contain, forming carbon dioxide and water to be disposed of along with the same products from the metabolism of other organic foodstuffs. Less is known of the fate of malic acid in the human body; but it is believed to be quite readily utilized.

So far as is known, tartaric acid occurs abundantly only in grapes. When these are eaten, the tartrates which they contain appear to be largely broken down by the bacteria in the digestive tract. It is said that only a small fraction, if any, of the tartaric acid is absorbed from the intestines; and that the body tissues have almost no ability to destroy the tartrate which does reach them. Whether, and to what extent, the eating of grapes presents the body with a problem of acid disposal will thus depend upon the degree to which the tartrate radicles are absorbed; and this apparently differs largely among individuals.

Lactic acid is prominent in buttermilk and in sauerkraut and certain other fermented foods.

Acetic acid is found in vinegar, and in pickles and other foods prepared with it.

A substance known as quinic acid is present (along with other organic acids) in plums, prunes, and cranberries. The body cannot carry the breakdown of this substance completely to carbon dioxide and water, but another organic acid, hippuric acid, is the end-product.

Oxalic acid occurs in small amounts in many fruits and vegetables, and to an important extent in spinach, New Zealand spinach, Swiss chard, beet tops, lambsquarters, poke, purslane, and rhubarb. However, the nutritional significance of this organic acid is not primarily one of acid-base effect but attaches rather to its property of combining with dietary calcium to form an insoluble salt which the body cannot absorb and so cannot utilize. The effective loss of food calcium brought about by certain oxalate-rich vegetables will be again considered in the next chapter, as logically influencing our selection of foods.

Acid-Base Balance in the Body

The normal condition of the blood, and, so far as we know, of the tissues generally, is very nearly neutral. Neither a distinctly acid nor a strongly alkaline condition of the blood, or of the system generally, is compatible with health or even with life. The maintenance of the normal condition of approximate neutrality is what one usually has in mind when one speaks of the problem or the phenomena of acid-base balance in the body.

Acidosis is a technical term in medicine, now used in a very special and restricted sense. It designates that condition in which the oxidation of fatty acids in the body, instead of proceeding completely to carbon dioxide and water, halts at an intermediate stage with the formation of acetone, aceto-acetic acid, and beta-hydroxybutyric acid as end-products. Any discussion of this highly special problem of acidosis belongs to medicine and not to the normal nutritional problem or phenomenon of acid-base balance.

Acid-base balance in normal nutrition has to do with the disposal of the acid-forming and base-forming elements in such manner as to maintain a general condition of approximate neutrality within the body. The more precise definition, the limits of variation, and an explanation of the "chemical mechanism" by which the nearly constant condition of approximate neutrality is maintained, are necessarily somewhat technical and involve a more chemical approach than that of the present text.

Carbohydrates and fats when normally oxidized in the body yield carbon dixoide which is eliminated through the lungs by a physiochemical process of marvelous efficiency and great theoretical interest to the chemistry of general physiology; but which from the viewpoint of our present study may be said to be so nearly automatic as not to constitute a responsibility of nutrition in the ordinary sense.

Proteins of course yield carbon dioxide too; but the more distinctive end-products of their metabolism are the nitrogen compounds, from all the amino acids, and the sulfuric acid (sulfate ions) from those which contain sulfur. It is the formation of a considerable amount of such a strong, fixed (non-volatile), acid as sulfuric, from the previously neutral sulfur of food protein, which makes some students of nutrition (including some, but probably not most, physicians) feel that there is an acid-base problem which lies within the distinctly nutritional responsibility of food selection.

In this sense, it is a problem involving both the proteins and the salts or ash constituents of the food.

Some of the proteins contain phosphorus and thus yield phosphoric, as well as sulfuric, acid in metabolism; while many foods contain significant amounts of other organic compounds of phosphorus and also of phosphoric acid radicles (phosphate ions) in the form of mineral or inorganic salts.

Chlorine completes the list of the three *fixed-acid forming* elements which enter in significant amounts into the problem; but here the acid radicle is entirely pre-formed in the food and as it enters the body is usually accompanied by its full equivalent of base.

To balance the (fixed-) "acid-forming" elements (sulfur, phosphorus, and chlorine) the food furnishes significant (though quite variable) amounts of four "base-forming" elements: sodium, potassium, calcium, and magnesium. Also we find that a variable proportion of the nitrogen from protein metabolism leaves the body as ammonium salts of fixed acids (often called "ammonia"), indicating that a part of the "waste" nitrogen from protein metabolism may on occasion help out the base-forming elements in the maintenance of body neutrality. Most of the nitrogen, however, is excreted as the essentially neutral substance, urea.

In normal nutrition the "problem" of acid-base balance is chiefly that of elimination of surplus fixed acid, especially that formed from the oxidation of the sulfur of the food protein. This surplus fixed acid is taken care of chiefly in two ways: (1) by elimination of nitrogen as ammonium salt as just explained; and (2) by the secretion of a more acid urine, which usually means a larger proportion of *acid* phosphate in the urine. In case the surplus of fixed acid is small or transient, a shifting of the proportions between mono- (primary) and di- (secondary) phosphate may suffice; but beyond this, the increased excretion of primary phosphate may involve increased excretion of total phosphate necessarily carrying with it some fixed base and thus tending to deplete the body's *alkaline reserve*.

As a precaution against such depletion, it is sometimes thought worth while to balance the foods in which (fixed) acid-forming elements predominate ("acid-forming foods") by including in the diet corresponding proportions of "base-forming" or "basic" foods (foods "on the alkaline side") which contain more than enough of fixed base-forming elements to neutralize the fixed acid formed by the metabolism of these foods.

Meats and fish, eggs, and grain products are acid-forming foods in the sense here explained. Their acid-forming character can not be adequately demonstrated by burning in air and testing the ash, because the surplus sulfuric acid is driven off by such heating in air.

Table 10 shows the relative acid-forming properties of some such foods per 100 grams and per 100 Calories.

Table salt and all foods which are practically without protein or natural ash constituents may be regarded as neutral in metabolism.

Base-forming elements predominate slightly in milk and to a more pronounced degree in most fruits and vegetables, of which some typical illustrations are given in Table 11. Foods such as the citrus fruits are *acid as eaten but base-forming or "on the alkaline side" in metabolism* because their organic acid radicles (whether present

TABLE 10. *A Few of the Foods in Which Acid-forming Elements Predominate*

Food (Edible Portion)	Approximate Potential Acidity (cc. Normal Acid) Per 100 Grams	Per 100 Calories
Beef, clear lean	12	10
round steak	11	7
Eggs	11	7
Oysters	15	30
Oatmeal	12	3
Rice	9	2
Wheat, entire	12	3
Wheat flour	9	2
White bread, made with water	6	2

TABLE 11. *A Few of the Foods in Which Base-forming Elements Predominate*

Food (Edible Portion)	Approximate Potential Reserve Alkalinity (cc. Normal Alkali) Per 100 Grams	Per 100 Calories
Apple	3	6
Banana	8	8
Cantaloupe	7	18
Carrot	14	30
Orange (or juice)	5	10
Pear	4	5
Potato	9	10
Tomato (or juice)	5	24
Watermelon	4	12

as free acid or as acid salt) are largely or completely burned in the normal oxidation processes of the body.

At present it should be frankly recognized that there are differences of opinion as to the significance of the acid-base balance of foods among those who are such able and thoughtful students of the subject as to entitle their views to respect. Some hold the regulatory "mechanism" of the normal body to be so efficient that the balance of acid-forming and base-forming elements in the food is of no consequence to nutrition and health. Others, agreeing that the blood maintains its neutrality with great efficiency, still think that the body is better off when it is not forced to excrete a markedly acid urine. We may doubtless accept the evidence of experience that many people have been benefited by giving a higher place to fruits and succulent vegetables in their daily dietaries; but how the credit for the benefit is to be distributed between base-forming elements and vitamins is as yet an open question. In our opinion more of the newest knowledge of nutrition is needed before anyone can confidently attempt a conclusive weighing of the evidence.

EXERCISES

1. Put about 10 grams of grapefruit juice in a platinum or silica dish. Show that the juice is acid. Evaporate it to dryness and burn it to ash. Show that the ash is alkaline.

2. Explain why the typical "acid-forming" foods do *not* yield a correspondingly acid ash when burned in the air. What acid, produced in significant amounts in metabolism, is a "fixed acid" in the body, but is volatilized when heated in an open dish?

3. With the facilities available to you, can you show that the urine is rendered less acid by eating oranges or grapefruit, more acid by eating lean meat or eggs?

SUGGESTED READINGS

ALLEN, F. M. 1949 Hypertension and nutrition. *Nutrition Rev.* 7, 257–261.

BEST, C. H., and W. S. HARTROFT 1949 Nutrition, renal lesions, and hypertension. *Federation Proc.* 8, 610–617.

BILLS, C. E., F. G. MCDONALD, W. NIEDERMEIER, and M. C. SCHWARTZ 1949 Sodium and potassium in foods and waters: Determination by the flame photometer. *J. Am. Dietet. Assoc.* 25, 304–314.

CANNON, W. B. 1939 *The Wisdom of the Body,* Revised Ed. (Norton.)

CRANDALL, L. A. 1939 *An Introduction to Human Physiology,* 2nd Ed., Chapters V-VIII. (Saunders.)

DANIELS, A. L., and M. K. HUTTON 1925 Mineral deficiencies of milk as shown by growth and fertility of white rats. *J. Biol. Chem.* 63, 143–156.

FENN, W. O. 1949 Potassium. *Sci. Amer.* 181, 16–21.

HARTMANN, B. G., and F. HILLIG 1934 Acid constituents of food products. Special reference to citric, malic, and tartaric acids. *J. Assoc. Official Agr. Chemists* 17, 522–531.

KOHMAN, E. F. 1939 Oxalic acid in foods and its behavior and fate in the diet. *J. Nutrition* **18**, 233–246.

LANFORD, C. S. 1942 Studies of liberal citrus intakes. I. *J. Nutrition* **23**, 409–416.

MAYNARD, L. A., and S. E. SMITH 1947 Mineral metabolism. *Ann. Rev. Biochem.* **16**, 273–290.

MCCLURE, F. J. 1949 Mineral metabolism (fluorine and other trace elements). *Ann. Rev. Biochem.* **18**, 335–354.

MCCOLLUM, E. V., E. ORENT-KEILES, and H. DAY 1939 *Newer Knowledge of Nutrition*, 5th Ed., Chapters VII, VIII and XI. (Macmillan.)

MONIER-WILLIAMS, G. W. 1949 *Trace Elements in Foods.* (John Wiley & Sons, Inc.)

NEWBURGH, L. H., and A. REIMER 1947 The rationale and administration of low-sodium diets. *J. Am. Dietet. Assoc.* **23**, 1047–1051.

REVIEW 1946 Present knowledge of the minerals in nutrition. I, II. *Nutrition Rev.* **4**, 195–198, 227–231.

REVIEW 1949 Magnesium deficiency. *Nutrition Rev.* **7**, 198–200.

ROINE, P., A. N. BOOTH, C. A. ELVEHJEM, and E. B. HART 1949 Importance of potassium and magnesium in nutrition of the guineapig. *Proc. Soc. Exptl. Biol. Med.* **71**, 90–91.

SENDROY, J. (Jr.) 1945 Mineral metabolism. *Ann. Rev. Biochem.* **14**, 407–430.

SHERMAN, C. C., L. B. MENDEL, A. H. SMITH, and M. C. TOOTHILL 1936 The citric acid formed in animal metabolism. *J. Biol. Chem.* **113**, 247–263.

SHERMAN, C. C., L. B. MENDEL, A. H. SMITH, and M. C. TOOTHILL 1936b The metabolism of orally administered citric acid. *J. Biol. Chem.* **113**, 265–271.

SHOHL, A. T. 1939 *Mineral Metabolism.* (Reinhold Pub. Corp.)

TOSCANI, V., and V. BUNIAK 1947 Sodium and potassium content of meats. *Food Research* **12**, 328–331.

UNDERWOOD, E. J. 1940 The significance of the "trace elements" in nutrition. *Nutr. Abs. Rev.* **9**, 515–534.

VALLEE, B. L., and J. G. GIBSON, 2nd 1948 The zinc content of normal human whole blood, plasma, leucocytes, and erythrocytes. *J. Biol. Chem.* **176**, 445–457.

VIII

PHOSPHORUS AND CALCIUM

Occurrence and Functions of Phosphorus

Phosphorus occurs in the body as a constituent of many of its materials, and functions in many nutritional processes. A glance at its occurrence in nature is of interest as introducing us to "the phosphorus problem" of nutrition and of food supply.

The late Dr. F. W. Clarke, long the chief chemist of the United States Geological Survey, estimated that phosphorus constitutes 0.11 per cent of the crust of the earth; but it is rather unevenly distributed, and largely locked up in the form of phosphate rocks some of which are very resistant to weathering and so yield their phosphates but slowly to the soil. Hence phosphorus is one of the elements in which soils are most often poor, relative to the needs of the plants which grow upon them. For about eighty years the attitude of science had been that the phosphate fertilization of the soil may be expected to result in larger crops, rather than crops containing significantly higher percentages of phosphorus.

Within the past forty years, however, it has been found, first in South Africa and thereafter in several other parts of the world, that phosphorus-poor soils may produce phosphorus-poor forage with resulting tendency to shortage of phosphorus in the nutrition of cattle obliged to subsist on such pastures.

The general tendency in plants is toward a relative concentration of calcium in the leaves and of phosphorus in the seeds. Hence pasture-plants become poorer in phosphorus in the late summer and autumn when the seeds have fallen to the ground. And in general, there is relatively more danger of shortage of phosphorus in the leaf diet of grazing cattle; and of calcium deficiency in the dietaries of people who eat relatively little of leaf foods and relatively large amounts of seeds and their milling- and bakery-products. However, it would not be scientifically justifiable to ignore the phosphorus problem of human nutrition. (At the "rickets age" phosphorus may be the limiting factor in the body's development.)

Phosphorus is an essential constituent of every known tissue and cell in the body. Although probably nearly 90 per cent of the total phosphorus of the adult body is in the skeletal system, yet the amount and the wide distribution of the phosphorus compounds of the soft tissues including the body fluids, give them a position in the active metabolism of the body fairly analogous to that of the proteins, although the total amounts involved are not so large.

Amount of Phosphorus Required

With phosphorus functioning in so many ways in the body, considerable interest attaches to the question of the amount which the body must receive daily from the food in order to meet the needs of replacement of the phosphorus spent in connection with these functions.

From the data of about one hundred studies, each of some days' duration, in which the quantitative balance of intake and output of phosphorus was determined in a manner analogous to the nitrogen-balance experiments described in Chapter VI, an average of 0.88 gram of phosphorus per man per day was found to be required for the maintenance of healthy adults in nutritional equilibrium. For much the same reasons as with protein, it is customary to add fifty per cent when setting a "dietary standard."

The National Research Council's explanation of the absence of a column of figures for phosphorus in its table of Recommended Allowances is as follows: "Available evidence indicates that the phosphorus allowances should be at least equal to those for calcium in the diets of children and of women during the latter part of pregnancy and during lactation. In the case of other adults the phosphorus allowances should be approximately 1.5 times those for calcium. In general it is safe to assume that if the calcium and protein needs are met through common foods, the phosphorus requirement also will be covered, because the common foods richest in calcium and protein are also the best sources of phosphorus." (National Research Council, Reprint and Circular Series, No. 129, Recommended Dietary Allowances, p. 17.)

Calcium Requirements: (a) for Minimal Adequacy; (b) for Best Lifetime Results

We have seen in the latter part of Chapter VI how balance-experiments with graded intakes are used in studies of protein requirements; and have indicated briefly above that analogous studies of the phosphorus balance serve to indicate phosphorus requirements. In a similar way, calcium-balance experiments may serve for the finding of minimal-adequate calcium needs. But in the case of calcium it is especially important to distinguish between the merely minimal-adequate intakes and those which yield *best* results in the long run of a lifetime.

Up to 1920 there had been published about one hundred calcium balance experiments with healthy human adults, in which (in the light of the knowledge of that time) it was thought that the output approximated the "rock bottom" level of actual need for normal minimal-adequate maintenance. The mean (arithmetical average) of the findings thus brought together in 1920 was 0.45 gram as an estimate of the lowest possible maintenance level for the average normal man. And, obviously, in a normal adult population, about one-half of the people would have their needs covered by such an average figure, and about one-half would not. For a tentative allowance intended to meet the needs of practically all normal cases, it was (in 1920) suggested that the "dietary standard" be set fifty percent higher than the above "rock bottom" average, *i.e.*, at 0.68 gram per day for adult maintenance. This served as a tentative "standard" for about twenty years.

By 1941 accumulated evidence from many researches—outstandingly those at the University of Illinois—had shown that the 1920 compilation tended to low results in using simple output as an indication of need in experiments showing negative balances. When only the experiments more closely approaching equilibrium were used and negative balances were more fully corrected, the estimated average need was raised from 0.45 to 0.7 gram. Without statistical analysis of the data it was thought that adding one seventh to the last-mentioned average would suffice; and the National Research Council set its Recommended Allowance for normal adult maintenance at 0.8 gram of calcium per day in its tables of 1941 to 1945. Further research, however, showed that individual variation is a larger factor in calcium requirement than had been supposed. These and other research findings called clearly for an increase of the 0.8 gram allowance; and showed that, statistically considered, an allowance of 1.0 gram of calcium a day is called for if it is to cover the maintenance needs of all but about one in one hundred of the normal adult population. Much new evidence obtained by a method of charting plus and minus balances observed in people on their accustomed dietaries also pointed plainly to the desirability of 1.0 gram as a recommended allowance.

Thus it was in the light of a large amount of consistent and comprehensive evidence that the National Research Council in 1948 increased its Recommended Allowances for adult maintenance to 1.0 gram of calcium a day.

As the original calcium allowances had provided generously for children and for pregnant and lactating women, these latter were not changed when the maintenance allowance was increased. Thus the calcium allowance for the people as a whole was increased by only about one tenth.

From the viewpoint of the food budget this one tenth more of food calcium can readily be provided by shifting a little of the present (or previous) expenditure for some other food or foods to the increased purchase of the foods which are the outstanding sources of calcium in our accustomed dietaries, *i.e.,* to milk, with its products other than butter, and to green leaf vegetables, other than those of the Goosefoot Family (Chenopodiaceae). Home gardening can provide the increased supply of greens for many families. *Milk and green vegetables together* also constitute such an important source of protein, iron, and vitamins in addition to their calcium, that increased purchase of them can be offset in the budget by diminished consumption of almost any of its items with a net gain to the nutritive value of the dietary as a whole.

Significance of Long-term Liberality of Food Calcium

As explained in Chapters V and VI, respectively, the continued consumption of any considerably larger amount of total food (counted in Calories) than is needed for optimal growth or the maintenance of the best body weight, tends to an undesirable accumulation of surplus body fat; while a corresponding surplus consumption of protein has only a doubtfully measurable effect either upon the protein content of the body or upon its health and longevity.

Surplus calcium has a different significance from either surplus calories or surplus protein, in that long-term studies show that stepwise increases of calcium intake above the minimal-adequate level tend to higher levels of positive health and an increase in the length of normal life. This finding rests, first, upon a large amount of direct human experience, in which, however, the investigator obviously cannot so control the food and the drinking-water as to make calcium the sole variable throughout whole natural life cycles; and, second, experiments with laboratory animals whose food habits and nutritional processes are sufficiently similar to the human and which can be, and have been, kept under complete quantitative and qualitative control throughout entire life cycles and successive generations.

In typical long-term experiments of this kind, rats of the Columbia chemical laboratory colony were fed its Diet No. 16 with and without graded additions of food calcium, the basal diet containing 0.19 per cent of calcium in the air-dry food mixture. The fact that this basal diet was adequate to all the nutritional needs of the rats (in the ordinary understanding of the word adequate) is amply shown by the fact that families are still (1950) thriving in the 72nd generation on this diet. Yet this level of calcium intake, *while adequate, was less than optimal.* For strictly parallel "lots" or experimental families, differing only in that their food contained more calcium, made *better* records. Thus with 0.35 per cent calcium as compared with 0.19 per cent, there was a more efficient use of the food consumed (whether calculated on the basis of its energy value or of its protein content) with moderately increased rate of growth and adult size; and distinctly earlier maturity, higher adult vitality, and increased duration of the "prime of life" or "useful" life—the period between the attainment of maturity and the onset of senility. The rats on the diet of higher calcium content also lived longer even if the comparison is made without including infant mortality. In other words the higher calcium intake increased not only the average length of life but also the *adult life expectation.*

When the diet, otherwise unchanged, was still further increased in its calcium content, the gains in wellbeing just described were again increased in measurable degree. Thus successive increases in dietary calcium induced successive gains in positive health up to intake levels relatively much higher than what we have considered safe standards in the past.

In the particular series of experiments of which we are here speaking, the increased length of adult lives on diet with 0.35 per cent calcium over those with 0.19 per cent, was clearly statistically significant with the males, but less so with the females; perhaps because the females receiving 0.35 per cent calcium had borne and suckled more young, and brought them to higher average weight at a standard weaning time, than had those with 0.19 per cent calcium. When, then, the females on the higher of these two calcium intake levels lived only slightly longer than those on the lower level, the question arose whether this was because females are less able than males to invest extra calcium in extra length of life, or because at the calcium intake levels of these particular experiments, these females had invested their extra calcium in more and superior offspring instead. That the latter is the correct answer has been shown by further experimentation in two quite different ways: *First,* in females kept unmated and thus having no offspring in which to invest it, the extra calcium conferred at least as much improvement in longevity as it did in the corresponding males. *Second,* it was shown in another series of experiments that with still larger allowances of dietary calcium the females were enabled *both* to rear more and sturdier offspring and to enjoy longer lives themselves.

These and many other experiments indicate that at least two to three times the minimal-adequate intake of calcium is needed for *best* long-term results. Animal experimentation cannot be expected to give us (by itself) exact quantitative knowledge of human requirements, but these comprehensive and searching animal experiments do guide our judgment and justifiably confirm our confidence in leaning to liberality of calcium allowances for people of both sexes and all ages. This gives greatly accentuated interest and significance to the problems of the influence of nutrition upon the chemical composition and internal environment of the normal body.

Analyses of large numbers of the offspring of parallel families of laboratory animals (rats) on diets containing on the one hand a little over the minimal-adequate calcium content and on the other hand from three to four times as much, have shown that this liberal increase over a level of intake already adequate for normal health and development results in a higher percentage of calcium in the body at a given age or size. The difference becomes measurable very early in life, is greatest during the period of most rapid growth, and is still significantly measurable in the adult. (For full accounts see Campbell, Pearson and Sherman (1943), Lanford, Campbell and Sherman (1941), Lanford and Sherman (1938), and Sherman (1947) in the Suggested Readings at the end of this chapter.) All the evidence indicates that this more rapid calcification of the skeletal system is advantageous to the nutritional well-being and positive health both at the time and throughout the subsequent life of the individual whose development has been thus expedited by a liberal calcium content in the family food supply.

As previously noted, 99 per cent or more of the calcium retained by the body takes the form of the relatively resistant bone and tooth minerals of the skeletal system. The question therefore arises

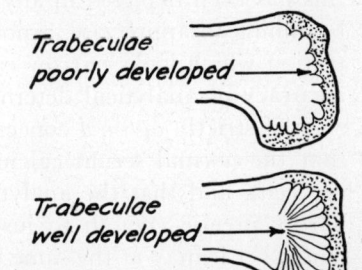

Fig. 20. Diagrammatic representation of the bone trabeculae as affected by the calcium content of the food.

whether an increased amount of such sparingly soluble calcium salt in the body's hard structures will significantly influence the concentration of calcium in the soft tissues and body fluids. Here it is of great interest that different investigators, using different species, have consistently found that increased retention or storage of calcium in the body involves increased development of the bone *trabeculae*. These are delicate crystals of calcium salts which grow from the inner surfaces of the ends of the bones, forming, when abundant, a mesh-work of readily available calcium-containing material in the normal bone cavities, especially near their ends. As the walls of the bones are at their ends so porous and vascular as to constitute an important part of the path of the circulating blood, the nutritionally-induced differences of trabecular development, as illustrated in Fig. 20, result in large differences in the surface area of calcium-containing material with which the blood comes in contact in the course of its circulation. Thus the larger the store of body calcium and the development of the bone trabeculae the more steadily is the *full* normal concentration of calcium in the blood, lymph, and soft tissues maintained. This is probably of great importance (though perhaps not yet fully appreciated) because so many vicissitudes in our life processes result in small losses of calcium which temporarily lower the concentration of calcium in the blood, the full maintenance or quick restoration of which plays, as we have already seen, so essential a part in the body's self-regulatory processes. Hence, even though the body's calcium reserve is laid up in a form of such slight solubility, the more abundant the reserve the greater the calcium-saturating surface with which the circulating blood has contact and the quicker the restoration of a normal blood calcium level whenever this has been depleted in any way. Moreover, as we are only now beginning to appreciate, a normal range of blood calcium concentration which looks narrow enough from the viewpoint of current accuracy of analytical determination may still be wider than the zone of strictly *optimal* concentration. For instance, it may be said that the normal serum calcium concentration is 0.009 to 0.0115 per cent, and that the analytical determinations now current are hardly precise enough to justify attempting a more refined estimate; yet it may at the same time be true that the individual having such rich development of bone trabeculae as to ensure an almost constant maintenance of something near the maximum of these values may have an advantage over the individual whose blood calcium even though within the normal range is more often in the lower levels of this zone. Thus differences in a body's reserves of even such an insoluble asset as the calcium in the bones may very really and significantly influence the internal environment in the sense of the quantitative chemistry of the fluids and soft tissues of the body which directly and immediately environ its life processes.

Calcium and Phosphorus in Growth and Development

Flexibility of the body at birth is an obviously advantageous property and is well fixed in our species as well as in several others. But flexible bones must mean skeletal structures in a less calcified condition than in the normal adult. Thus we are all born calcium-poor; and normal growth and development call for a marked increase not only in the amount but also in the percentage of calcium in the body. The same is true, in less degree, of phosphorus.

The quantitative relations have been determined most fully and accurately in the case of the rat, where representative individuals of different ages can be taken in large numbers from well controlled colonies, and the entire body subjected to chemical analysis. Here it was found that the growth and development of the body to normal adult status involved a 75-fold increase of body weight over that at birth; an increase of 150-fold in the amount of phosphorus, and of 340-fold in the amount of calcium, which was contained in the body at birth.

The quantitative relationships are less extreme in the case of the human being which is born with something like one-twentieth of its adult weight and with bones correspondingly more calcified than those of the new-born rat.

The stage of skeletal development which the rat shows at birth is that of before-birth in a normal baby, and the new-born baby's skeleton is perhaps comparable in its stage of development to that of a rat about two weeks old. Still, the normal development of the baby involves not only a great deal of growth, but also and at the same time a great deal of hardening, of its bones.

Thus during growth and bodily development there is a relatively much accentuated need for calcium as compared with the needs for tissue building materials of other kinds.

The inevitable fact of being born calcium-poor is to be regarded as advantageous to the event of birth itself, but as a nutritional handicap thereafter. To enable the growing body to overcome this handicap without undue delay, to build a good skeletal framework and a sound set of teeth notwithstanding the fact that it started life under the handicap of a low calcium content, requires a food supply richer in calcium than many people find easy to realize.

Thus there is a very real "calcium problem" in human nutrition; and not only in infancy but throughout the period of rapid growth and development. Todd and his associates in their anatomical studies found a large proportion of skeletons subnormally calcified; Jeans and Stearns find that children differ markedly in the efficiency with which they utilize food calcium; and Leitch, holding with Todd and with Jeans that the optimally developed skeleton is considerably more highly calcified than has hitherto been realized, estimates that standards for calcium intakes and retentions should be higher than in the past.

Even among investigators who have given special attention to the calcium retentions of growing children, there are still differences of interpretation. One regards the finding of a relatively high retention as evidence of good practice in feeding; another, as evidence that calcification had previously been abnormally retarded. We have endeavored to exclude cases of the latter kind from the averages which appear on the last line of Table 12; but some critics may still regard these estimates as representing a higher level of retention than can be sustained throughout the first nine years of life.

The Recommended Daily Allowances of the National Research Council provide 1.0 gram of calcium for children of all ages up to and including 12 years, with from 1.0 to 1.4 grams between the ages of 13 and 20 years.

Mitchell, Outhouse and their coworkers at the University of Illinois, under conditions tending to minimal estimates of normal utilization, find that growing children retain an average of 20 per cent of the calcium they receive in their food. This, with the Recommended Allowance of 1.0 gram of food calcium a day, would mean the retention of 73 grams of calcium per year. Allowing for 20 grams of calcium in the body at birth, and for average growth in body weight, this would result in the body containing about 1.95 per cent of calcium at the age of 4; and a little over 2 per cent at the age of 9 years. Whether the body thus early equipped with a good framework will thereafter continue to maintain its higher percentage of calcium is still an open question.

As mentioned above, relatively more calcification occurs before birth in the child than in the rat. What the rat mother does in supplying her offspring is done predominantly during the suckling period, whereas the human offspring makes heavy demands upon its mother for calcium not only in lactation but in the latter part of pregnancy also. The calcium requirement of human embryonic development must obviously be met through the mother, and is a matter of concern to her as well as to the baby. The National Research Council has therefore consistently recommended a liberal calcium allowance for pregnancy; and also during lactation so long as the baby is getting most of his nourishment by breast-feeding. The Council also recommends the same maintenance allowance of calcium for women as for men (notwithstanding the difference in average size) in order "to provide for bodily storage in anticipation of reproduction and lactation."

TABLE 12. *Different Estimates of Normal Retention of Calcium During Growth and Development of the Human Body: Retentions in Milligrams per Day*

Age:	1st Year	2nd Year	3rd Year	4th Year	5–9 Years	10–15 Years	16–22 Years
Shohl's average "from the literature" (adapted)	163	110	90	68	136	190	65
Macy's average (adapted) probably mainly of more recent data	189	276	276	180	220	260	32
An average of recent data compiled by the present writers	220	235	286	246	238	192	?

Calcium Content of the Body in Relation to Age, Growth, and Food

Fundamental to a complete interpretation of the bearing of animal experimentation upon the problem of the desirable levels of calcium intake in human nutrition are the comprehensive quantitative studies made by Dr. F. L. MacLeod upon rats of widely differing ages and nutritional histories (Sherman and MacLeod, 1925). Later Lanford studied more intensively the influence of the calcium content of the food as sole experimental variable in relation to the calcium content of the body of the rat from 28 to 180 days of age with the results shown concisely in Table 13 and in Figure 21. (For detailed data and fuller discussion see Lanford and Sherman, 1938, in Suggested Readings at the end of this chapter.) The findings as plotted in Figure 21 show that while body weight and *amount* of body calcium increased smoothly on the diets of both calcium levels, the curves for *percentages* of body calcium are different. That for males on the low-calcium diet shows a slight, and that for females a more pronounced, *dip* during about the period of adolescence.

TABLE 13. *Calcium Content of the Body as Influenced by Age and by Food*

Ca in Food %	Age Days	Body Weight Grams	Calcium in Body Grams	Percent
Male Rats				
0.20	28	39	0.279	0.715
0.20	60	102	0.692	0.677
0.20	90	173	1.262	0.726
0.20	180	260	2.651	1.023
0.64	28	40	0.385	0.956
0.64	60	117	1.128	0.971
0.64	90	172	1.765	1.026
0.64	180	282	3.137	1.113
Female Rats				
0.20	28	40	0.300	0.748
0.20	60	95	0.641	0.676
0.20	90	134	1.109	0.830
0.20	180	167	1.999	1.196
0.64	28	41	0.384	0.949
0.64	60	106	1.113	1.049
0.64	90	150	1.748	1.165
0.64	180	190	2.472	1.305

This dip in the curve does not mean a negative calcium balance. These animals were increasing their amounts of body calcium but less rapidly than their body weights were increasing, so that their percentages of body calcium were decreased for a time during which they were *calcium-poor in this sense* notwithstanding the fact that their calcium balances were positive throughout. Further studies of this phenomenon (which doubtless has its analogue in the experience of human families which live for long times on low-calcium diets) have been, and are being, made in the Columbia chemical laboratories. Addition of protein, as such or as meat, tends to increased rate of growth and earliness of puberty in females which, however, more often than their controls break down in early reproduction or lactation and thus increase the deathrate of adolescent and young adult females. This may be conceived as due (1) to an over-stimulation of growth and sexual maturity by the protein enrichment of the calcium-poor basal diet, or (2) to a protein/calcium imbalance, or (3) to a combination of these. Current experiments are indicating that the hazard is forestalled when the diet is sufficiently enriched in calcium at the same time as in protein. While such animal experimentation can not be expected to furnish a precise direction as to optimal levels of intake for human nutrition, it does guide our judgment as to how the emphasis may best be laid. This new evidence makes it wise to be liberal in dietary

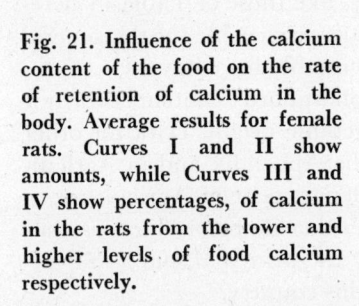

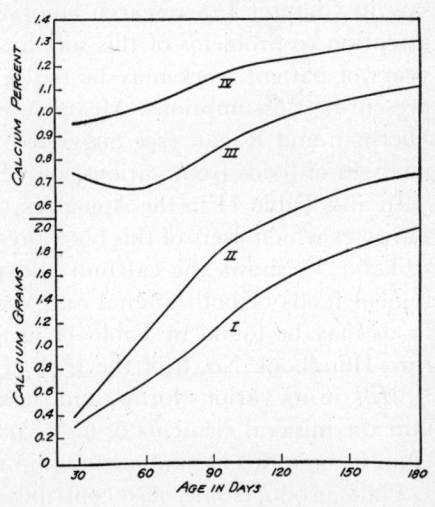

Fig. 21. Influence of the calcium content of the food on the rate of retention of calcium in the body. Average results for female rats. Curves I and II show amounts, while Curves III and IV show percentages, of calcium in the rats from the lower and higher levels of food calcium respectively.

allowances of calcium, and especially it indicates that dietaries which are generous in protein should be of liberal calcium content also.

The National Research Council's Recommended Daily Dietary Allowances of Calcium as Revised in 1948 are as follows:

For women in the latter half of pregnancy, 1.5 grams; and in lactation, 2.0 grams;
For other women and for men, 1.0 gram;
For children under 10 years of age, 1.0 gram;
" " 10–12 years of age, 1.2 grams;
" girls 13–15 years, 1.3 grams;
" " 16–20 " 1.0 gram;
" boys 13–15 " 1.4 grams;
" " 16–20 " 1.4 grams.
For fuller explanation see Appendix D.

Selection of Foods to Provide Calcium and Phosphorus

The calcium and phosphorus of the food have come, of course, ultimately from the soil (and the "ground waters" contained in it). Of late, there has been a tendency in some quarters to emphasize, perhaps unduly, the effect of soil and fertilizer upon the percentages of mineral elements in the resulting crops. Some striking assertions on this point are much in need of fuller investigation; and, as we saw in Chapter I, a research laboratory which will devote special attention to problems of this sort has now been established. Many years of patient work may be required to prove or disprove some present-day assumptions. Meanwhile, as more fully explained by Sherman and Ragan (see Suggested Readings below), averages of analyses of foods from various sources, like those of Table 14 herewith and Table 41 in the Appendix, are serviceable for the general purposes which users of this book presumably have in view.

Table 14 shows the calcium and phosphorus contents of a few typical foods of both animal and vegetable origin. Data for other foods may be found in Table 41 in the Appendix and in Agriculture Handbook No. 8 of the U. S. Department of Agriculture.

Milk in its various forms, and such other dairy products as contain the mineral elements of milk, are the principal sources of calcium in such diets as are common in this country.

Plant products may also contribute important amounts.

Both the calcium and the phosphorus contents of the *edible roots* are usually between 0.03 and 0.05 per cent. The starchy potato tuber contains a similar amount of phosphorus, but distinctly less calcium.

In general, the *bulbs, stems,* and *twigs* are similar in calcium and phosphorus content to the roots, while *leaves* are richer in calcium, and *flowers* and *seeds* are richer in phosphorus. Analyses of the edible twigs, the flowerbuds, and the leaves of the same samples of broccoli resulted as shown in Table 14.

Green leaves, in the diets of people who appreciate them, rank second only to milk and its products as source of calcium. Those of the loose-leaf varieties of cabbage and lettuce, contain much more calcium than the relatively colorless inner leaves of the headed varieties, though the phosphorus contents are about the same. Spinach and other leaf foods of "the goosefoot family" (Chenopodiaceae, including beet greens, chard, lambsquarters, and spinach) have been found to contain relatively large amounts of oxalic acid which interfere with the utilization of calcium. The Compositae (including dandelion, endive, escarole, and lettuce) and the Cruciferae (including broccoli, Brussels sprouts, cabbage, collards,

TABLE 14. *Calcium and Phosphorus Contents of Typical Foods: Averages of Data Available in 1949*

Food	Calcium Percentage	Phosphorus Percentage
Foods of Animal Origin		
Beef, lean muscle	0.011	0.203
Eggs	0.054	0.210
Milk	0.118	0.093
Cheese, Cheddar type	0.873	0.610
cottage	0.082	0.263
Grain Products		
Oatmeal	0.054	0.365
Wheat, entire	0.038	0.385
White flour	0.019	0.093
White bread	0.05[a]	0.10[b]
Fruits and Vegetables		
Apples	0.006	0.010
Broccoli, flowerbud	0.089	0.111
leaves	0.318	0.067
twigs	0.073	0.038
Oranges	0.033	0.023
Potatoes	0.011	0.056

[a] The calcium content of bread varies from about 0.02 to about 0.08 per cent according to the amounts of milk solids and "yeast food" used.

[b] Phosphorus also varies with ingredients used in breadmaking, but not so much as does the calcium content. This is partly because milk contains somewhat more calcium than phosphorus, and partly because "yeast foods" are chiefly calcium salts other than phosphates.

kale, kohlrabi, mustard greens, turnip greens, and watercress) contain only insignificant amounts of oxalic acid and are correspondingly better sources of calcium.* These statements are based on determinations of oxalic acid in many specimens and by several investigators, while the direct experimentation upon calcium utili-

* For oxalic acid contents of about 80 foods, see Taylor and MacLeod, page 274 of the Fifth Edition of *Rose's Laboratory Handbook for Dietetics* (Macmillan).

zation has been chiefly with (1) spinach, (2) loose-leaf lettuce, and (3) kale and Chinese cabbage, as respectively representing the three botanical families whose leaves are most used as human food.

Upon bringing together the evidence of several investigations it is seen to be established by well-controlled experiments that the calcium of cabbage, collards, kale, leeks, lettuce, rutabaga leaves, tendergreen, and turnip tops, like that of milk, is well utilized in nutrition; while that of spinach, beet greens, and New Zealand spinach is utilized very poorly if at all.

Foods may also have favorable influence upon calcium assimilation in other ways as well as through the calcium that they directly supply. Thus it has been shown both by calcium balance experiments with children and by experiments with rats whose calcium retention was measured by actual analyses of their bodies, that orange juice added to the dietary may increase calcium retention to a distinctly larger extent than the whole amount of calcium which the orange juice itself contains. (See the papers by Chaney and Blunt (1925) and by Lanford (1939) in the list of Suggested Readings below.)

Mindel, Esselen, and Fellers (1939) find that apples and cranberries have a similar favorable effect upon calcium retention.

Other Nutritionally Available Sources of Calcium

By making use of the suggestions of the preceding section, most readers of this book can so adjust their food budgets as to increase their dietary intakes of calcium and some other important nutrients with little if any increase in total expenditure for food. In areas where this is less easy, and in families or institutions in which it is desired to increase the calcium intake with no readjustment whatever in dietary pattern, there may be interest in nutritionally available sources of calcium other than (and additional to) natural foods.

Such a supplementary source of calcium we already have in natural drinking waters, but these vary rather widely in their calcium contents.

A more substantial calcium supplement can be made almost automatic, as McCollum pointed out several years ago, by mixing calcium carbonate or phosphate (or a mixture of them) into the household supply of table and cooking salt.

As already successfully done in Great Britain, calcium could be made a regular part of flour and bread enrichment.

Bones of meat animals (including birds and fish) constitute a rich source of calcium which can be brought into human nutrition in any (or more than one) of an interesting variety of ways. The simplest way is merely to masticate as much as one can of whatever bones accompany the meat, fish, and poultry to the table. Thus a Serbian professor startled his colleagues of an American faculty club by un-selfconsciously eating the bones which came in his chicken pie, according to what travelers tell us is the general custom of Eastern Europe and the Middle East. The very long stewing of meat-on-its-bone with water and corn, observed by LaFarge among the Indians of the American Southwest, doubtless brings a significant share of the bone calcium into human nutrition. The Oriental custom of preserving and cooking meat-on-the-bone with vinegar brings into human (physiological) consumption a still larger proportion of the bone calcium. The fact that even dry grinding makes the calcium of bones about as available as food calcium generally has been established by the laboratory research of Drake, Jackson, Tisdall, Johnstone, and Hurst (1949). Ashes of leafy plants have been used as a supplementary source of dietary calcium. Alfalfa-ash suggests itself in this connection and could readily be had in large quantities at little cost if there were a demand for it.

Calcium-enriched meat has been favorably noticed by the *Journal of the American Medical Association*.

Needless to say, salts and other compounds of calcium are obtainable through chemical supply houses or as pharmaceutical preparations.

In parts of the Orient the chewing of native leaves and nuts prepared with lime is reported as bringing considerable amounts of calcium into human nutrition. Even without the admixture of lime, many leaves are already fairly rich sources of calcium.

While we have only fragmentary knowledge of such incidental sources of calcium, it seems more probable that many people living on supposed calcium-poor diets get significant amounts of supplementary calcium from sources which we do not know, than that our investigations have seriously overestimated the amount of calcium which should be recommended as an allowance for the support of optimal nutritional status. People can live on smaller amounts than those of the Recommended Allowances, but probably are not then so well off in the long run of a life-time.

EXERCISES: for student, or for instructor, or for both as a group project

1. Calculate the amounts of phosphorus and of calcium in the dietaries planned under Exercises 2 and 3 of Chapter V.

2. Would either more phosphorus or more calcium be desirable in either of these dietaries?

3. Tabulate the calcium content (*a*) per 100 grams, (*b*) per 100 Calories, for each of the forty foods of Exercise 2 of Chapter IV.

4. If you wish to increase the calcium content of one of the dietaries you have planned, can it better be done by changing the proportions of foods it already contains, or by substituting for one or more of these foods others which you could now select from among the forty foods of the preceding Exercise?

5. Would you substitute weight for weight or calorie for calorie, and why?

SUGGESTED READINGS

ARMSTRONG, W. D., and C. P. BARNUM   1948   Concurrent use of radio-isotopes of calcium and phosphorus in the study of the metabolism of calcified tissues. *J. Biol. Chem.* **172**, 199–204.

CAMPBELL, H. L., O. A. BESSEY, and H. C. SHERMAN   1935   Adult rats of low calcium content. *J. Biol. Chem.* **110**, 703–706.

CAMPBELL, H. L., C. S. PEARSON, and H. C. SHERMAN   1943   Effect of increasing calcium content of diet upon the rate of growth and length of life of unmated females. *J. Nutrition* **26**, 323–325.

CANNON, W. B.   1939   *The Wisdom of the Body,* Revised Ed., Chapter IX. (Norton.)

CHANEY, M. S., and K. BLUNT   1925   (Effect of orange juice on calcium retention in children.) *J. Biol. Chem.* **66**, 829–845.

CHEN, C.-Y., and L.-K. YI   1948   The utilization of calcium in steamed bone meal. *Nutrition Research Bull.* **7**, 7–10; *Chem. Abs.* **43**, 3893.

DRAKE, T. G. H., S. H. JACKSON, F. F. TISDALL, W. M. JOHNSTONE, and L. M. HURST   1949   The biological availability of the calcium in bone. *J. Nutrition* **37**, 369–376.

FINCKE, M. L.   1941   The utilization of the calcium of cauliflower and broccoli. *J. Nutrition* **22**, 477–482.

HOH, P. W., J. C. WILLIAMS, and C. S. PEASE   1934   Possible sources of calcium and phosphorus in the Chinese diet. *J. Nutrition* **7**, 535–546.

HUNSCHER, H. A.   1930   Metabolism of women during the reproductive cycle. II. Calcium and phosphorus utilization in two successive lactation periods. *J. Biol. Chem.* **86**, 37–57.

LANFORD, C. S.   1939   The effect of orange juice on calcium assimilation. *J. Biol. Chem.* **130**, 87–95.

LANFORD, C. S., H. L. CAMPBELL, and H. C. SHERMAN   1941   Influence of different nutritional conditions upon the level of attainment in the normal increase of calcium in the growing body. *J. Biol. Chem.* **137**, 627–634.

LANFORD, C. S., and H. C. SHERMAN   1938   Further studies of the calcium content of the body as influenced by that of the food. *J. Biol. Chem.* **126**, 381–387.

LEVERTON, R. M., and H. N. RHODES   1949   Nitrogen, calcium, phosphorus, and basal energy metabolism of obese college women during weight reduction. *J. Am. Dietet. Assoc.* **25**, 1012–1016.

MACLEOD, G., and C. M. TAYLOR   1944   *Rose's Foundations of Nutrition*, 4th Ed. (Macmillan.)

MACY, I. G.   1942   *Nutrition and Chemical Growth in Childhood*. Vols. I and II. (Charles C. Thomas.)

MALLON, M. G., and F. P. UREY   1941   The calcium content of Southern California head lettuce and its distribution in the outer and inner leaves. *J. Home Econ.* **33**, 182–186.

MAXWELL, J. P.   1934   Osteomalacia and diet. *Nutr. Abs. Rev.* **4**, 1–8.

MCLEAN, D. S., G. K. LEWIS, E. JANSEN, M. HATHAWAY, H. BREITER, and J. O. HOLMES   1946   Further studies on the calcium requirement of preschool children. *J. Nutrition* **31**, 127–140.

MINDELL, A., W. B. ESSELEN, JR., and C. R. FELLERS   1939   The effect of apples and cranberries on calcium retention. *Am. J. Digestive Diseases and Nutrition* **6**, 116–119.

MITCHELL, H. H., and J. M. SMITH   1945   The effect of cocoa on the utilization of dietary calcium. *J. Am. Med. Assoc.* **129**, 871–873; *Nutr. Abs. Rev.* **15**, 721.

PITTMAN, M. S., H. MCKAY, B. L. KUNERTH, M. B. PATTON, N. EDELBLUTE, G. COX, E. SHEPEK, and J. CHEN   1941   Nitrogen, calcium, and phosphorus intakes of college women. *J. Am. Dietet. Assoc.* **17**, 947–954.

REVIEW   1947   Variations in human calcium requirement. *Nutrition Rev.* **5**, 122–124.

SEMMONS, E. M., and E. W. MCHENRY   1945   The calcium content of samples of commercial bread. *Canad. Med. Assoc. J.* **52**, 265–267; *Nutr. Abs. Rev.* **15**, 45.

SHERMAN, H. C.   1947   *Food and Health*, 2nd Ed., Chapters X and XI. (Macmillan.)

Sherman, H. C., and F. L. MacLeod   1925   The calcium content of the body in relation to age, growth, and food. *J. Biol. Chem.* **64,** 429–459.

Sherman, H. C., and M. S. Ragan   1942   Quantitative distribution of phosphorus and calcium in certain fruits and vegetables. *J. Nutrition* **23,** 283–292.

Shields, J. B., B. W. Fairbanks, G. H. Berryman, and H. H. Mitchell   1941   The utilization of calcium in carrots, lettuce, and string beans in comparison with the calcium of milk. *J. Nutrition* **20,** 263–278.

Speirs, M.   1939   The utilization of the calcium of various greens. *J. Nutrition* **11,** 275–278.

Steggerda, F. R., and H. H. Mitchell   1941   Further experiments on the calcium requirements of adult man and the utilization of the calcium of milk. *J. Nutrition* **21,** 577–588.

Van Duyne, F. O., C. S. Lanford, E. W. Toepfer, and H. C. Sherman   1941   Life-time experiments upon the problem of optimal calcium intake. *J. Nutrition* **21,** 221–224.

Williams, J. C.   1936   Calcium in meat cooked with acid. *Food Research,* **1,** 537–549.

Wittwer, S. H., W. A. Albrecht, and R. A. Schroeder   1947   Vegetable crops in relation to soil fertility. V. Calcium content of green leaf vegetables. *Food Research* **12,** 405–413.

IX

IRON AND THE NUTRITION OF THE BLOOD

Small as is the amount of iron in the body, its functions are very vital, as may be seen from the following five kinds of iron compounds. (1) The chromatin substance of the nucleus of every cell is an iron-protein compound. So is (2) the hemoglobin which constitutes the outstanding material of the red blood cell and has the important responsibility of carrying oxygen and assisting in the maintenance of neutrality within the body. Closely related are (3) myoglobin, or muscle hemoglobin; and (4) the cytochromes and cytochrome oxidase of active body tissues which are said (Schultze, 1947) to "mediate about 90 percent of the energy transfer associated with the aerobic phases of tissue respiration." And also (5) there are other highly important body enzymes, such as catalases, which contain iron as an essential element.

Beside these active forms, the normally nourished body has a variable amount of stored iron, largely in the form of *ferritin*—a brown non-diffusible substance from which the iron can be released as needed for hemoglobin formation.

There is a considerable concentration of the body's iron in its blood, for while the blood usually constitutes about 7 percent of the body weight it contains probably 55 to 60 percent of the body iron. Hence any considerable shortage of iron in the body results before long in some kind or degree of anemia. Iron constitutes one-third of one percent of the hemoglobin molecule, and hemoglobin is the main solid constituent of the red blood cell.

Thus the study of iron in nutrition is intimately interwoven with the problems of hemoglobin formation and regeneration, the building of the red cells of the blood, and the cure and prevention of anemia. Here, as throughout this book, we are interested in the relations of food and nutrition to health, but we are leaving medical problems to the physician.

While an iron-poor body tends to be anemic, it is important to keep clearly and constantly in mind that shortage of iron is not the only cause of anemia. And even an anemia curable by iron does not necessarily owe its origin to a shortage of iron in the food. The building and upkeep of the blood is a complex process: it requires iron as an essential element; but it requires also other things, and right conditions.

Copper, while not entering into the constitution of the hemoglobin molecule, exercises an essential influence upon the formation of hemoglobin. Thus there is the possibility that hemoglobin formation or regeneration may be retarded by shortage of copper, though under ordinary present-day conditions of life there is strong probability that the accidental intakes of copper will usually be ample for the body's needs.*

Deficiency of *cobalt* has also been found in some regions but is not (yet, at least) believed to be a significant factor in human nutrition.

Life-cycle of red blood cell.—The red cells (erythrocytes) of the blood are conceived as being formed in the bone marrow, circulating in the blood for an average life-time of about 4 months, and finally undergoing fragmentation, probably in the spleen, liver, and kidneys. The wearing-out of the individual red cell or corpuscle involves the breakdown of the *stroma* or containing-structure, and also of hemoglobin molecules. The main non-protein parts into which hemoglobin is broken down are: (1) the pigment, bilirubin, which is then carried to the liver and excreted in the bile, and (2) iron compounds which may be used again in the formation of new hemoglobin. It was the interest in this re-using of the iron which gave rise to the term hemoglobin regeneration. This term gained such currency that we now sometimes meet it in scientific literature in connections which seem to indicate that the writers have used it without discrimination as to whether a real regeneration or a new formation of hemoglobin is actually involved.

---

* Anemias due to copper deficiency are recognized in the cattle, sheep, and other ruminants of certain districts, and also in an occasional human infant (Moore, 1947).

Anemia

The term *anemia* usually indicates a condition in which the blood is deficient (below normal) in hemoglobin, or in red corpuscles, or in both. Classifications of anemia vary. Haden classifies the chief causes of anemia as follows:

I. Increased blood loss
   (a) Mechanical loss, hemorrhage (discussed below).
   (b) Increased destruction of blood in the body, as in certain familial abnormalities, in some infections, and under the influence of some toxic substances.

II. Depressed blood formation
   (a) Depressed bone marrow function, as in nephritis, tumors of the bone marrow, some infections, and the toxic effects of some deleterious substances.
   (b) Deficiency of specific substances
      (1) Hypochromic anemia type in which the lack is of some substance or substances required for hemoglobin formation.
      (2) Pernicious anemia type, having to do with depressed formation of the body or stroma of the red cell rather than its hemoglobin.

The anemias may also be characterized in terms of the blood picture which they present. One measurement so used is the *color index*, which is the quotient resulting from the division of hemoglobin-in-percentage-of-the-normal by number-of-red-cells-in-percentage-of-the-normal. If there is greater proportional reduction of hemoglobin than of red blood cells the blood is said to have a low color index, and the anemia is characterized as *hypochromic*. In the reverse condition where the number of cells has decreased more than has the hemoglobin, the color index is said to be high, and the type of anemia, *hyperchromic*.

The fact that a shortage of iron in the food results, if long continued, in anemia, does not necessarily mean that the majority of cases of anemia are to be attributed to shortage of dietary iron. On the contrary, of the five chief types of anemia recognized in Haden's classification, only one type can be regarded as due to iron deficiency in the food. Perhaps only a minority of the cases of anemia encountered can be explained on the simple ground that the food was poor in iron or protein or both. And the fact that administration of iron is helpful does not prove that the anemia occurred because of iron-poor food. For, when iron is given therapeutically, the dosage is usually so many times greater than the iron content of a good average diet that the iron therapy has more of a pharmacodynamic than of a normal nutritional aspect. In other words, the prevalence of anemia is more a medical problem than a simple problem of food supply.

Nutrition in the broader sense is of course involved in all such processes as hemoglobin formation and regeneration and in the building of the stroma of the corpuscles, so that in this sense recovery from anemia is largely a nutritional problem whether or not the anemia occurred because of any nutritional deficiency of the food.

Correspondingly we find that experimental studies of anemic conditions have added to our knowledge of nutrition, and have even been utilized as a means of evaluating an aspect of the nutritive value of foods.

Three distinct types of anemia (hemorrhagic, pernicious, and iron-deficiency) have thus figured somewhat prominently in the literature of nutrition and should be very carefully distinguished; for undiscriminating statements regarding nutritional anemia and its cure by foods may be very misleading.

Hemorrhagic anemia.—The word hemorrhage tends to suggest a sudden large loss of blood, but it is to be remembered that there may be unseen gradual losses of blood, as, for example, through the wall of the alimentary tract, which if persistent become significant.

A large loss of blood at one time obviously first reduces the volume in circulation. The volume, however, is rapidly restored by the transfer into the blood stream of fluid from the tissues, with corresponding dilution of the blood both as regards the concentration of red cells and of their hemoglobin. Then, in the regeneration of blood after hemorrhage, new red cells are formed more rapidly than is hemoglobin, so that the red cell count becomes normal earlier than does the concentration of hemoglobin and the depth of red color. In this state the blood is said to have a *low color index*. This condition of low color index (greater paucity of hemoglobin than of erythrocytes) is quite similar whether it results from a single large loss of blood or from the chronic loss of small amounts.

In the rebuilding of the blood to normal after anemia has resulted from hemorrhage, the problem usually seems, therefore, to center in the question of inducing restoration of the hemoglobin; but to take it as *simply* a hemoglobin problem may be misleading. For hemorrhage depletes the blood of all its characteristic constituents, and while the body usually restores the others more rapidly, thus leaving hemoglobin as the limiting factor in the regeneration, the extent to which this is true may depend very largely upon the body-stores of the individual as determined by the previous nutritional history, and perhaps still more largely upon the nature of the dietary during the period in which the rebuilding of the blood is being observed. Whipple, who has experimented very extensively and systematically with hemorrhagic anemia in dogs, early recognized the importance of both these latter factors. To control individual variations, he keeps his animals under continuous laboratory-sanitarium care and observation between, as well as during, the experimental periods, and to prevent unknown influences entering through the food, Whipple has long used a basal diet which he worked out and standardized for this purpose. This feature is of great value in giving precision and validity to his comparisons of different "experimental variables" tested as additions to the standard basal dietary. The reader, however, in interpreting this and other work, should keep constantly in mind the fact that if some other basal diet had been just as carefully devised and systematically employed it might have given the findings a somewhat different aspect throughout.

Hemorrhagic anemia, iron-deficiency anemia, and pernicious anemia are all in a sense nutritional; but if it be asked how any given foods compare as to value in nutritional anemia, the answer must depend upon the type of anemia in question. The value of any food-supplement in the Whipple type of hemorrhagic anemia is its value as a source of what is most needed to make good the difference between what has been removed from the body by hemorrhage and what the basal experimental diet supplies; while in the second type of anemia the value will depend more specifically upon iron (or iron and copper); and in the pernicious anemia type the nutritional need is not for iron or copper, and may or may not overlap the need of the hemorrhagic type but certainly is not identical with it. For, as already briefly mentioned, hemoglobin is usually the limiting factor in the rebuilding of blood after hemorrhage, while the building of the red cell stroma is usually the limiting factor in pernicious anemia; and the specific substance seems now to have been identified as vitamin B_{12}.

Pernicious anemia type.—The type of anemia which was designated as pernicious at a time when it seemed peculiarly resistant, both to therapy and to scientific understanding, has now been largely conquered. Or perhaps we should rather say that it has been largely solved as a scientific problem and the means for the therapeutic conquest of individual cases as they arise are now available and widely understood. The blood picture in pernicious anemia is mainly that of deficient formation of red cells, these being usually subnormal in number, often irregularly shaped, and variable in size, but with many very large cells, hence a greater than normal average size (hence the term macrocytic anemias).

Moreover, the sufferer from pernicious anemia characteristically shows deficient gastric secretion.

Through the researches of Castle and others, an explanation of the specific need in pernicious anemia was suggested in terms of *two factors*, the *intrinsic* and the *extrinsic*. According to this view, the extrinsic factor is furnished by the food (in Castle's experiments by beef), and the intrinsic factor is furnished by a normal gastric juice. These two factors react to form the *anti-pernicious anemia substance*. The primary cause of a typical case of pernicious anemia is (according to this view) an abnormality of the gastric juice which renders it inadequate as a source of the intrinsic factor, and the remedy consists either in re-establishing the normal functioning of the stomach as a secretory organ or in supplying the anti-pernicious anemia substance in some artificial way. Liver and liver extracts have been largely used for this latter purpose.

Certain other kinds of anemia in which the blood picture resembles that of pernicious anemia (macrocytic anemias) were thought to be caused by a dietary deficiency of extrinsic factor, still others by poor absorption of this factor from the intestinal tract, and yet others by a combination of circumstances.

Recently certain vitamin factors have been discovered to stimulate blood formation in anemias of this sort, but their relationships to one another and to the classic Castle concept of macrocytic anemias are not yet (1950) altogether clear. First, folic acid (pteroylglutamic acid), a "B-vitamin" identified as to molecular structure in 1946, was shown to cause prompt and dramatic improvement of the blood picture in pernicious anemia and other anemias of this type. For some macrocytic anemias, folic acid appears to be fully effective; but it does not cure the nervous symptoms ("combined system disease") which are in some cases a part of true pernicious anemia. Then, in 1948, a red crystalline product, which has been called vitamin B_{12}, was separated from liver and found to produce rapid blood restoration and cure of nervous and other symptoms when injected into patients with pernicious anemia. For full effectiveness when taken by mouth, however, simultaneous administration of normal gastric juice appears necessary in the pernicious anemia patients. At the time this is written, the Harvard group inclines to the view that the action of the intrinsic factor is to facilitate absorption of the dietary vitamin B_{12} (which they regard as the extrinsic factor) rather than actually to react with it, as postulated in the original Castle theory.

Thus both folic acid and vitamin B_{12} seem to be essentially concerned in normal red blood cell formation (erythropoiesis); but how and to what extent they are interrelated in this function is not yet clear. Furthermore, there are indications that still other unidentified factors may also play a part. From the practical viewpoint of pernicious anemia as it is seen in the clinic, however, "it seems established that vitamin B_{12} is a completely effective therapeutic agent" (*Current Research,* August 1949).

Iron-deficiency anemia.—The anemia familiarly produced in the laboratory by keeping young animals an abnormally long time on a diet of milk alone, has been shown to be due to a deficiency of iron, or copper, or both. If this condition were encountered clinically it would be classified as a *hypochromic* anemia, because it shows a low color index, *i.e.,* a greater deficiency in hemoglobin than in erythrocyte count. And if the low color index was not secondary to hemorrhage, food-deficiency, or some infective or other toxic condition, the case would be classified as one of *idiopathic hypochromic anemia.*

The usual clinical type of hypochromic anemia is more frequent in women than in children or men, and it responds to iron therapy.

But the doses of iron used to effect a cure are usually so many-fold greater than the amounts contained in any ordinary dietary that the success of the iron therapy can not logically be interpreted as indicating that the anemia was due to simple shortage of food-iron. It is thought that the menstrual hemorrhage may perhaps play the dominant part in the origin of these hypochromic anemias of women; and as they appear in some women on the same sort of diet on which other women maintain a normal condition of the blood, the term idiopathic may therefore appropriately carry the suggestion that the woman who is less fortunate in this respect may be the victim of an idiosyncrasy in hemoglobin-economy, either losing more than other women or being slower in rebuilding what has been lost. To the extent that this view is adopted, the question then naturally arises whether "standards" for the iron contents of women's dietaries should be set so high as to provide (if possible) for the idiopathic losses of the few as well as the normal nutritional needs of the many. To attempt to give all dietaries a degree of richness in iron which is far beyond the needs of most people may unduly complicate the planning of diets and the general food supply problem. The policy of leaving idiosyncratic needs (idiopathies) to be treated as individual medical problems is certainly safer in the case of iron than of most other nutritional factors because an iron-poor condition of the body declares itself more promptly and unmistakably than perhaps any other nutritional subnormality and is apt (we may hope) to be noted and to receive medical attention before it becomes a significant hazard to health or efficiency.

Other nutritional anemias.—Sebrell (1949) has listed, in addition to the above, other nutritional anemias due to shortages of other factors including amino acids, pyridoxine, pantothenic acid, niacin, vitamin C, and riboflavin. Some of these factors will appear more fully in later chapters.

Iron Requirements in Normal Nutrition

Here as in our other quantitative studies of nutritional needs we shall probably do best to start by asking how much need be metabolized by the healthy adult.

The reported studies bearing on the problem of minimum requirements for adult maintenance are less numerous in the case of iron than those on nitrogen, calcium, and phosphorus already considered. Furthermore, the experimental determinations of iron in foods and excreta are especially liable to error through contamination of the samples with iron from the ordinary dust of laboratory air or from the utensils in or with which they are handled. For this reason, and because special problems of interpretation arise in the case of iron, a considerable measure of critical weighing and selection of the data must at the present time enter into any estimate of minimum need. However, without attempting to draw an average of all available figures, it may be pointed out that several recent studies (in which the pitfalls of iron-balance determinations seem to have been largely avoided) agree in indicating something in the neighborhood of 6 milligrams of food iron daily as the usual need for normal adult maintenance.

There are also indications that the amount of iron which any given individual must ingest in order to balance the iron losses from the body depends in part on the quality of the diet in other respects than its iron content. For example, in a study by Leverton and Marsh (1942) one group of young women who were receiving an average of 7.21 milligrams of iron and what the authors considered an otherwise superior diet were able to store 1.55 milligrams of iron, while another group with almost the same iron intake (7.09 milligrams) but whose diets were less favorable in other regards showed an average *net loss* of 1.30 milligrams of body iron daily.

Earlier studies had shown also that on nutritionally well-balanced diets the body seems able to maintain equilibrium of iron with a lower intake than is required when, for instance, the diet is either deficient in calcium, or contains an excessive addition of a calcium salt. Similarly the adequacy of intake of calcium, where this was the sole variable, was shown by Mendel, Smith, and Orten to have an important influence on the use of iron by animals in a different kind of experiment. And in British experiments with sheep on quite ordinary low-calcium food supplies (representative of the diets of many people) Sir John Boyd Orr found that, as the sheep continued to lose calcium from their bodies, they also grew anemic.

The problem of the maintenance requirement of iron by adults is further complicated by the question, How shall the "maintenance" allowance provide for the menstrual blood-loss and its replacement in women? Estimates of the amount of iron leaving the body in the menses vary too greatly for satisfactory discussion. A part, no doubt, of this disconcertingly large variation in the reported data is due to physiological variations among "ostensibly healthy" women. But undoubtedly another cause of divergence lies in experimental errors. As already indicated, many articles in our everyday environment, as well as the invisible dust of most laboratories, contain amounts of iron which are large compared with the amounts involved in nutrition. Hence, analytical data are subject to large or small plus errors in the case of iron. But, whether one accepts the lower reported figures, which correspond to an average loss throughout the entire month of 0.1 milligram daily, or the much higher ones, which suggest an average daily loss of fully one milligram of iron, current dietary recommendations provide what seems to be a liberal margin of safety to cover such losses.

The National Research Council Committee on Food and Nutrition recommends a daily allowance for normal adult maintenance of 12 milligrams of food iron for men and women alike. For pregnancy and for lactation the recommendation is raised to 15 milligrams. Some physicians, including Strauss of the Harvard Medical School, recommend the regular inclusion of supplementary iron salt in the dietaries of pregnant women. It may prove wise to extend this provision to such other women also as may appear to their physicians to have (for any known, or even unknown, reason) a requirement for more iron than a "good average" dietary will regularly supply, for an attempt at great enrichment of the iron content of the diet through food selection may distort the dietary or the food budget by the inclusion of an undue proportion either of fibrous or of expensive food materials. Perhaps it can be considered that this is now taken care of by the general use of iron-enriched flour, bread, and breakfast cereals.

Moore (1947) points out, with reference to the practice of blood donation (which has become so widespread in the past decade) that each pint of blood so withdrawn represents a loss of 200 to 250 milligrams of iron; so that, four or more such donations by one person in a year may make it difficult to compensate, for this loss of iron, through food alone. He therefore recommends that blood donors take supplementary iron, but not in such quantities as are considered "full therapeutic doses."

Iron in the Nutrition of Children

The normal child is born with a considerable store of reserve iron in the body. Undoubtedly this endowment at birth is of value to the baby's prospect of survival, of healthy development, and of having a healthy and vigorous progeny in its turn.

Or, in a different way of speaking, "Nature finds it more efficient and safer" to transfer this iron to the baby through the mother's placenta than through her mammary glands in lactation. For, while milk contains iron, and in favorable conditions the milk iron is well utilized, still there are certain digestive hazards which are avoided or minimized by the advantage which the newborn baby enjoys of having enough iron already stored in his body to meet the iron requirements of his normal development for perhaps six months if he absorbed no iron from his food, or perhaps a year when he absorbs a normal proportion of the rather small amount of iron which milk contains.

Both the reserve iron stored in the body before birth and the food iron absorbed by the baby are largely used in the building of hemoglobin. Even so, if the baby grows rapidly his body size may, and in the majority of cases does, increase somewhat faster than the total body hemoglobin, with the result that the child goes through a period of what is oddly called "physiological anemia." More clearly stated, such a child is in a normal (physiological) phase of his development and need not (should not) be considered anemic even if his hemoglobin percentage is lower than at other ages, or perhaps than in more slowly growing children of the same age.

The recommendations of the National Research Council Committee on Food and Nutrition (reproduced in full in Table 42 in the Appendix) provide for growing children daily intakes of iron ranging upward with increasing age from 6 milligrams during the first year to 15 milligrams during adolescence. Viewed in the light of such experimental evidence as we have on actual requirement, these allowances appear generous.

Iron and Copper in Foods

Little weight can be attached to such statements regarding the iron content of foods as were based upon the data obtainable from the ordinary tables of ash analyses of the past, as these were usually obtained by methods which are likely to over-estimate greatly the amount of iron. More recently, other methods of estimating iron have come into use which are liable to relatively large laboratory errors in both directions. Table 15 shows the approximate amounts of iron now believed to be present in the average edible portion of typical food materials expressed (1) in milligrams per 100 grams of edible material, (2) in milligrams per 100 grams of protein, and (3) in milligrams per 3000 Calories.

Iron contents of many other foods will be found in the Appendix.

Estimates of the amounts of iron contained in many American family food supplies have been made. The majority of these were found to furnish about 15 to 20 milligrams of iron per man or "consumption unit" per day. Apparently, therefore, the typical American dietary contained a much better surplus of iron than of calcium, even before the enrichment program which now safeguards the iron still further. Yet the following notes on the iron contents of different types of food are still of interest.

Meats constitute a prominent source of iron in American dietaries. In ordinary muscle meats the iron exists chiefly as hemoglobin, belonging in part to the muscle cells and in part to retained blood. Since fatty tissue contains much less iron, the iron content of fat meat is much lower than that of lean, and in order to establish a useful general estimate of the amount of iron in meat it seems best to refer the iron to the protein content rather than to the gross weight of the meat. The results will still be influenced by the extent to which the blood has been either accidentally or intentionally removed from the muscle.

For fresh lean beef (containing the usual proportion of blood) the results collected by Sherman averaged 0.00375 per cent iron, but Forbes and Swift (1926) reported considerably lower results, 0.0024 to 0.0025 per cent. Hence, in computing the data for Table 15, a value intermediate between the averages of the two sets of findings has been used.

Some years ago, chiefly as a means of avoiding the serious discrepancies which might otherwise arise from the great variability of meat in fatness, it was suggested that a rough estimate of the amount of iron furnished by the meat of a dietary might be made by assuming that with every 100 grams of protein the meat would furnish about 0.015 gram (15 milligrams) of iron. This estimate

Forbes and Swift consider to be "a little high for beef and veal, and much too high for lamb and pork, while it does not apply at all

TABLE 15. *Iron in Edible Portion of Typical Foods*

Food	Iron/100 G. Fresh Substance	Iron/100 G. Protein	Iron/3000 Calories
	milligrams	*milligrams*	*milligrams*
Beef, clear lean	3.0[a]	13	80[a]
Beefsteak, medium fat	2.7[a]	13	38[a]
Eggs	2.7	21	51
Egg yolk	7.2	44	61
Oatmeal	4.5	32	35
Rice, white	0.7	11	8
Beans, dried	6.9	33	60
Carrots	0.8	67	53
Kale	2.2	56	132
Potatoes	0.7	35	25
Apples	0.3	100	14
Bananas	0.6	50	18
Oranges	0.4	44	24
Prunes, dried	3.9	170	39

[a] Figures for meats can be only rough approximations because of variations in fatness, as well as differences between different cuts. Forbes and Swift report that organs contain more iron than muscle meats, while pork and lamb contain much less than beef.

closely in relation to heart, brain, liver, spleen, kidney, and blood." All of these latter are such minor products in comparison with ordinary muscle meats that even if completely utilized as human food their effect would be to raise but slightly the percentage of iron in the meat supply as a whole. Hence it appears from the work of Forbes and Swift that the custom of assuming in dietary calculations that meats furnish about 15 milligrams of iron per 100 grams of protein has somewhat overestimated the value of beef and veal, and much overestimated that of lamb and pork, as sources of iron; but that the use of this factor becomes more nearly correct as products such as liver, spleen, and kidney are being more largely utilized as human food. It should, however, always be kept in mind that any such single factor can serve merely for the discussion of meats as a whole and not for the comparison of one meat with another.

The copper content of beefsteak was found by Lindow, Elvehjem, and Peterson to be about one part in 1,000,000; and other beef products showed very similar figures, except liver, which contained, weight for weight, about twenty times as much copper as muscle tissue.

Eggs.—The edible portion of hens' eggs has shown as the average of several analyses approximately 0.003 per cent of iron. Whether the iron content of eggs can be increased materially by giving to poultry food rich in iron, is a disputed question. It seems probable that both the relatively high iron content of the egg and its copper content of about two parts per million are properties rather definitely fixed by nature. In experiments at the University of Wisconsin the iron and copper contents of eggs remained practically unchanged when the diet of the hen was enriched with added iron, or copper, or both. There would seem to be no room for doubt regarding the assimilation and utilization of the iron compounds of eggs, since they serve for the production of all the iron-containing substances of the blood and tissues of the newborn chick, there being no introduction of iron from without during incubation. Iron-balance experiments with young women have shown that the iron of egg is also highly efficient in human nutrition. As already noted, Dr. Mary S. Rose, after special experimental investigation, considered eggs in all respects equal to liver in normal nutrition.

Milk.—Analyses of samples of cows' milk of widely different origin have given results varying both with the milk and with the analyst. We here use the figure of the government table of composition of food. The iron of milk is readily absorbed and assimilated. Moreover, metabolism experiments indicate that the iron of milk is likely to be utilized to especially good advantage, perhaps on account of its association with a liberal (but not excessive) proportion of calcium, and with other materials of high body building value.

According to work at the University of Wisconsin, milk contains only 0.000015 per cent of copper, and neither the iron nor the copper content of milk is much influenced by the feeding of iron or copper salts, or both, in addition to the normal ration of the cow. Thus milk is apparently rather well stabilized by nature in the matter of its calcium, phosphorus, iron, and copper contents. The fact that the Wisconsin workers find a higher copper content in calves' liver than in beef liver may perhaps be taken as an indication that the body of the young mammal is thus provided with a reserve store of copper as well as of iron at birth.

Grain products.—Iron occurs in considerable quantity in the cereal grains, but the greater part of it is in the germ and outer layers, and so is rejected in the making of the "finer" mill products, though now largely restored in "enriched" flour and bread. To test the value of the iron in the outer layers of the grain, Bunge a generation ago carried out the following experiment:

A litter of eight rats was divided into two groups of four each. One group was fed upon bread from fine flour, the other upon bread made from flour including the bran. At the end of the fifth, sixth, eighth, and ninth weeks, respectively, one rat of each group was killed, and the gain in weight, the total amount of hemoglobin, and the percentage of hemoglobin in the entire body were determined.

Here the bran-fed rats not only made a much greater general growth, but developed both a greater amount and a higher percentage of hemoglobin. There can be no doubt that the iron and other ash constituents of the outer layers of the wheat were well utilized in these cases.

More recent work of M. S. Rose and her collaborators also shows clearly the good utilization of the iron of whole wheat in hemoglobin formation as tested with rats; and the high efficiency of the iron of whole wheat in human nutrition as measured in balance experiments with young women.

So far as iron is concerned, however, "enrichment" aims to restore an equivalent for what was lost in the milling of white flour.

Fruits and fresh vegetables are often regarded as of low nutritive value because of their high water content and low proportions of protein and fat; but largely for this very reason they may be especially important as sources of food iron, because they can be added to the diet without replacing other foods, and without making the total calorie consumption excessive. Present transportation facilities and methods of preserving tend to equalize the cost and increase the available variety of fruits and vegetables throughout the year. It was found, in an experimental dietary study made in New York City, that a liberal use of vegetables, whole wheat bread, and the cheaper sorts of fruits resulted in a gain of 30 per cent in the iron content of the diet, while the protein, fuel value, and cost remained practically the same as in the ordinary mixed diet obtained under the same market conditions. Gillett and Rice also found that the general advance of nutrition consciousness and dietary intelligence had similarly improved the typical family food supplies of the New York City poor between 1914–15 and 1928–29. This was found by the use of the data for iron in foods which were available some years ago. Peterson and his coworkers suggested that fruits and vegetables generally may have even higher iron values than hitherto appreciated. This led to a large number of new determinations of iron in fruits and vegetables by Stiebeling, who also computed new general averages for fruits and vegetables which took account of Peterson's and other data as well as her own. All these (and, of course, also more recent) data have been utilized in obtaining the averages used in this book.

Current Applications and Interpretations

Stiebeling and Phipard found in the dietaries of a group of 26 East North Central families that fruits and vegetables furnished 34 per cent of the total food iron; meats, including poultry and fish, 29 per cent; grain products, 19 per cent; eggs, 10 per cent; milk and its products, 7 per cent; and miscellaneous items, 1 per cent.

Whether and to what extent the iron of one group of foods has a higher, and that of another group of foods a lower, availability or utilizability in normal nutrition, are, in our opinion, questions which cannot yet be answered definitely.

Furthermore, we would emphasize that the foregoing dietary allowances for food iron do not need general upward revision because of recent and current findings indicative of low "availability" or "utilization" of the iron of everyday foods, because it is upon iron-balance experiments with just such everyday foods that dietary standards have been based.

The figures for iron contents of foods given in Table 15 and in the Appendix of this book are those of the U. S. Department of Agriculture's Agriculture Handbook No. 8.

These averages are in a fair proportion of cases, including most of the more important food sources of iron, the results of analyses of samples so numerous and from so many sources, that *as general averages* they probably will be relatively little changed by the future accumulation of further data. Current work is being largely directed to the study of the causes and extent of variations from the general average. It remains true, however, that figures for iron are subject to relatively larger probable error than are the corresponding data for calcium and phosphorus. This is partly because the actual percentages of iron in food are so small that the unavoidable errors of the laboratory work of preparing and analyzing the food samples tend to become a large fraction of the finding. Probably, too, the methods for quantitative determination of iron are more "treacherous" than those for protein, or phosphorus, or calcium; in the sense that the "personal equation" tends to be relatively larger and more variable in the determinations of iron. For these reasons it is difficult to judge whether or not a given type of food is relatively more variable by nature in its iron than in its protein, phosphorus, or calcium content.

But if our knowledge of iron requirements in nutrition and iron contents of foods still seems less precise than we would wish, reassurance is afforded by the general "enrichment" of flour and bread with iron, and by the important fact that any tendency toward an iron-poor condition of body is apt to be recognized and corrected promptly.

EXERCISES

1. Calculate the iron contents of the dietaries previously planned, and compare with your judgment of the requirements of the people to be fed.
2. What substitutions, preferably from among the forty foods previously tabulated, would enrich one of these dietaries in its iron content without any disadvantageous change in its general character or in its cost?
3. Would it be more practicable to make the proposed substitution weight for weight, or Calorie for Calorie?
4. Would it be feasible to provide as much iron as an average medicinal dosage per day through food selection without distorting the dietary or making it unduly costly?
5. Is there, in the light of present-day knowledge, any sound objection to making nutritional use of iron salts, under medical guidance, so as to be freer in planning the best use of the food money?
6. To what extent are your answers influenced by the current "enrichment" of flour and bread, and the "restoration" of breakfast cereals? And why?

SUGGESTED READINGS

Ascham, L. 1935 Study of iron metabolism with preschool children. *J. Nutrition* 10, 337–342.

Bethell, F. H., C. C. Sturgis, R. W. Rundles, and M. C. Meyers 1945 Blood: A review of the recent literature. *Arch. Int. Med.* 76, 239–254, 358–396; 77, 80–119.

Callender, S. T., E. O. Powell, and L. J. Witts 1945 The life-span of the red cell in man. *J. Pathol. Bacteriol.* 57, 129–139; *Nutr. Abs. Rev.* 15, 131.

Coons, C. M. 1932 Iron retention by women during pregnancy. *J. Biol. Chem.* 97, 215–226.

Daniels, A. L., and O. E. Wright 1934 Iron and copper retentions in young children. *J. Nutrition* 8, 125–138.

Elvehjem, C. A., and E. B. Hart 1932 The necessity of copper as a supplement to iron for hemoglobin formation in the pig. *J. Biol. Chem.* 95, 363–370.

Elvehjem, C. A., W. H. Peterson, and D. R. Mendenhall 1933 Hemoglobin content of the blood of infants. *Am. J. Diseases Children* 46, 105–112.

Elvehjem, C. A., and W. C. Sherman 1932 The action of copper in iron metabolism. *J. Biol. Chem.* 98, 309–319.

Frost, D. V., V. R. Potter, C. A. Elvehjem, and E. B. Hart 1940 Iron and copper versus liver in treatment of hemorrhagic anemia in dogs on milk diets. *J. Nutrition* 19, 207–211.

Granick, S. 1946 Ferritin: its properties and significance for iron metabolism. *Chem. Rev.* 38, 379–403.

Haden, R. L. 1935 Classification and differential diagnosis of the anemias. *J. Am. Med. Assoc.* 104, 706–709.

Hahn, P. F. 1937 The metabolism of iron. *Medicine* 16, 249–266.

Hahn, P. F., W. F. Bale, E. O. Lawrence, and G. H. Whipple 1938 Radioactive iron and its metabolism in anemia. *J. Am. Med. Assoc.* 111, 2285–2286.

Hahn, P. F., and G. H. Whipple 1939 Hemoglobin production in anemia limited by low protein intake. Influence of iron intake, protein supplements, and fasting. *J. Exptl. Med.* 69, 315–326.

Hart, E. B., H. Steenbock, J. Waddell, and C. A. Elvehjem 1928 Copper as a supplement to iron for hemoglobin building in the rat. *J. Biol. Chem.* 77, 797–812.

Helmer, O. M., and C. P. Emerson, Jr. 1934 The iron content of the whole blood of normal individuals. *J. Biol. Chem.* 104, 157–161.

JOHNSTON, F. A.   1943   A new theory of iron metabolism. *J. Am. Dietet. Assoc.* **19**, 839–840; *Chem. Abs.* **38**, 2709.

KAUCHER, M., E. Z. MOYER, A. P. HARRISON, R. U. THOMAS, M. M. RUTLEDGE, W. LAMECK, and E. F. BEACH   1948   Nutritional status of children. VII. Hemoglobin. *J. Am. Dietet. Assoc.* **24**, 496–502.

LEICHSENRING, J. M., and I. H. FLOR   1932   Iron requirement of the pre-school child. *J. Nutrition* **5**, 141–146.

LEVERTON, R. M.   1941   Iron metabolism in human subjects on daily intakes of less than 5 milligrams. *J. Nutrition* **21**, 617–631.

LEVERTON, R. M., and A. G. MARSH   1942   The iron metabolism and requirement of young women. *J. Nutrition* **23**, 229–238.

LEVERTON, R. M., and L. J. ROBERTS   1937   Iron metabolism of normal young women during consecutive menstrual cycles. *J. Nutrition* **13**, 65–95.

MACKAY, H. M., and L. GOODFELLOW   1931   Nutritional anemia in infancy with special reference to iron deficiency. Med. Research Council Special Report Series, No. 157; *Bull. Hyg.* **6**, 826; *Chem. Abs.* **26**, 3010.

MADDEN, S. C., and G. H. WHIPPLE   1940   Plasma proteins: their source, production, and utilization. *Physiol. Rev.* **20**, 194–217.

MCCARTHY, E. F., and D. D. VAN SLYKE   1939   Diurnal variations of hemoglobin in the blood of normal men. *J. Biol. Chem.* **128**, 567–572.

MITCHELL, H. S., and M. VAUGHN   1927   The relation of inorganic iron to nutritional anemia. *J. Biol. Chem.* **75**, 123–137.

MOORE, C. V.   1947   Iron metabolism and hypochromic anemia. Pages 117–143 of *Nutritional Anemia*. (The Robert Gould Research Foundation, Cincinnati, Ohio.)

MOORE, C. V.   1948   Nutrition and hematology. *Nutrition Rev.* **6**, 193–195.

MYERS, V. C., and H. M. EDDY   1939   The hemoglobin content of human blood. *J. Lab. Clin. Med.* **24**, 502–511.

ORTEN, A. U., and J. M. ORTEN   1943   The role of dietary protein in hemoglobin formation. *J. Nutrition* **26**, 21–31.

PYE, O. F., and G. MACLEOD   1946   The utilization of iron from different foods by normal young rats. *J. Nutrition* **32**, 677–687.

REVIEW   1947   Storage iron. *Nutrition Rev.* **5**, 85–86.

REVIEW   1948   Vitamin B_{12} and pernicious anemia. *Nutrition Rev.* **6**, 245–247; 291–293.

REVIEW   1949   Castle's extrinsic factor and vitamin B_{12}. *Nutrition Rev.* **7**, 146–147.

ROSE, M. S., and E. McC. VAHLTEICH   1932   Factors in food influencing hemoglobin regeneration. I. Whole wheat flour, white flour, prepared bran, and oatmeal. *J. Biol. Chem.* **96,** 593–608.

Rose, M. S., E. M. Vahlteich, and G. MacLeod   1934   Factors in food influencing hemoglobin regeneration. III. Eggs in comparison with whole wheat, prepared bran, oatmeal, beef liver, and beef muscle. *J. Biol. Chem.* **104,** 217–229.

Schlaphoff, D., and F. A. Johnston   1949   The iron requirement of six adolescent girls. *J. Nutrition* **39,** 67–82.

Schultze, M. O.   1947   Some biochemical aspects of metabolism of iron and copper. Pages 99–115 of *Nutritional Anemia.* (The Robert Gould Research Foundation, Cincinnati, Ohio.)

Sebrell, W. H.   1949   Anemias caused primarily by malnutrition. *Federation Proc.* **8,** 568–578.

Sheets, O., and M. Barrentine   1944   Hemoglobin concentration and erythrocyte counts of the blood of college men and women. *J. Am. Dietet. Assoc.* **20,** 521–523.

Smith, M. C., and L. Otis   1937   Hemoglobin regeneration in anemic rats in relation to iron intake. *J. Nutrition* **13,** 573–582.

Strauss, M. B.   1933   Anemia of infancy from maternal iron deficiency in pregnancy. *J. Clin. Invest.* **12,** 345–353; *Chem. Abs.* **27,** 2982.

Vahlteich, E. McC., E. H. Funnell, G. MacLeod, and M. S. Rose   1935   Egg yolk and bran as sources of iron in the human dietary. *J. Am. Dietet. Assoc.* **11,** 331–334.

Vaughan, J. M.   1934   *The Anemias.* (Oxford University Press.)

Waddell, J., H. Steenbock, and E. B. Hart   1929   The specificity of copper as a supplement to iron in the cure of nutritional anemia. *J. Biol. Chem.* **84,** 115–130.

Whipple, G. H.   1935   Hemoglobin regeneration as influenced by diet and other factors: Nobel prize lecture. *J. Am. Med. Assoc.* **104,** 791–793.

Wintrobe, M. M.   1933   Blood of normal men and women. Erythrocyte counts, hemoglobin, and volume of packed red cells of 229 individuals. *Bull. Johns Hopkins Hospital* **53,** 118–130.

Wintrobe, M. M.   1947   Physiological implication of the anemic state. Pages 4–44 of *Nutritional Anemia.* (The Robert Gould Research Foundation, Cincinnati, Ohio.)

Wintrobe, M. M., and R. T. Beebe   1933   Idiopathic hypochromic anemia. *Medicine* **12,** 187–243.

X

IODINE

The Endocrine Glands and Especially the Thyroid

It has now become a concept familiar to almost everyone that the physical and mental development of an individual as well as the course and rate of his metabolic processes are controlled to a large extent by a group of organs known as the *endocrine glands* or the *glands of internal secretion.* Each of these elaborates one or more of the physiologically active, specific chemical substances, known as *hormones,* which it distributes through the blood stream to the entire body, exerting in this way a "chemical control" over even the most remote parts. When, for some reason, there is either a deficiency or an overabundance of the secretion of one of the endocrine glands, physical or metabolic abnormalities may become evident. Most of these conditions lie outside of the sphere of this book (the student interested in these aspects is referred for a non-technical discussion to Hoskins' *Endocrinology,* Revised Edition); but one such manifestation, the disturbance of the thyroid gland known as simple goiter, has now been shown to be predominantly of nutritional origin and amenable to control by nutritional measures.

The *thyroid gland* is situated near the base of the neck and consists of two lobes, one to each side of the trachea ("wind-pipe"), connected by an *isthmus* lying across the front of the trachea. It is this structure which becomes swollen to give the familiar picture of goiter.

Goiter has been known from time immemorial: references to it are found in many of the oldest writings, and the works of the old masters attest its prevalence in their times. An Englishman who paid an extended visit to Switzerland and the adjacent parts of France and Italy in the eighteenth century, and whose letters written thence were afterward published, told of the great prevalence of goiter in certain localities. In the part of Savoy where he stayed it was so nearly universal that anyone without goiter was said to be not a true Savoyard. Growth of the goiter was regularly expected to accompany the growth and development of the child. Thus a middle-aged man whose little granddaughter's goiter was the size of a chestnut piously hoped to live to see it as large as a pear.

Even a generation ago there were regions in this country and abroad where some measure of thyroid enlargement was discernible in a large majority of the adolescent children; and today, although recognition of its nutritional origin has made it possible to prevent almost completely the onset of the disorder, advanced goiters are a fairly common sight, at least among middle-aged and elderly persons for whom this knowledge came too late.

Establishment of the Relationship of Iodine to Goiter

It is said that for many centuries burnt sponge was a more or less popular folk remedy for goiter. Medical men, following the suggestion made by Coindet in 1820, found that painting the goiter with tincture of iodine was also frequently efficacious. As the existence of the element iodine had been discovered in burnt seaweed, Coindet postulated that iodine present in the sponge was responsible for the effectiveness of the old treatment. However, the *rationale* of both of these curative measures was fully appreciated only when Baumann, in 1895, actually found iodine in the thyroid gland. This led the way on the one hand to investigations on the natural distribution of iodine and its relation to the incidence of goiter, and on the other hand to Kendall's discovery and separation in pure form of *thyroxine,* an iodine-containing amino-acid derivative secreted by the thyroid gland (Fig. 22).

There are certain regions of the earth where—until modern preventive methods were introduced—goiter occurred so persistently and so extensively as to be called *endemic*. Notable among these districts were the Himalayan Mountain region of South Central Asia; the Alps, Pyrenees, and Carpathian Mountain regions of Europe; the Andean plateau and southeastern Brazil in South America; and the St. Lawrence and Great Lakes basin, extending through northern Ohio, Michigan, Minnesota, the Dakotas, and adjacent Canadian provinces; and the Pacific Northwest including Oregon, Washington, and British Columbia, in North America.

Examination of the soil, the drinking water, and the vegetation in these regions showed them to be relatively poor in iodine as compared with regions where goiter is not prevalent. The iodine content of the waters and foods of any district seems to depend largely upon the chemical nature of the rocks and the amounts of soluble iodide which these yield in their natural weathering. In general, the leached soils deposited from the last glacial period are said to be poor in iodine. Such soils account for the low iodine content of the crops in certain regions of this continent. Furthermore, since

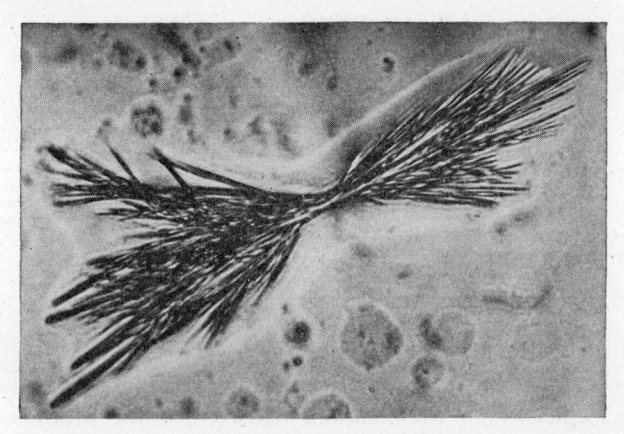

Fig. 22. Crystals of thyroxine. (Courtesy of Dr. E. C. Kendall.)

seawater, and therefore the spray which evaporates in the air at the seashore, is relatively rich in iodine, regions near the ocean and not separated from it by high mountains receive iodide from seaspray dust carried inland by the winds. No doubt the relative influence of rocks and sea upon the iodine content of the soil and of the drinking water varies considerably in different regions. That the resulting differences may be very great is illustrated by the finding of McClendon and his coworkers that drinking waters from different parts of the United States ranged in their content of iodine from 0.01 to 73.30 parts per 1,000,000,000—seven thousand times as much in the maximum case as in the nine minimum cases.

McClendon also showed that differences in the relative frequency of goiter among men drafted from various parts of the country for service in the First World War were strikingly associated with differences in the amounts of iodine found in the drinking waters in the regions from which the recruits were drawn, goiter being very much more common in sections where the water supplied relatively little iodine.

Similarly it was found that foods produced in the regions characterized as goitrous contain in general distinctly less iodine than the same foods from the so-called non-goitrous districts. A few instances are cited in Table 16.

TABLE 16. *Iodine Contents of Foods from Goitrous and Non-Goitrous Regions*

Kind of Food	From Goitrous Regions	From Non-Goitrous Regions
	Iodine: parts per billion of dry matter	
Wheat	1–6	4–9
Oats	10	23–175
Carrots	2	170
Potatoes	85	226
Milk	265–322	572

It is still difficult to judge how far the reports of differences in iodine contents of foods have been exaggerated by analytical errors. The example which McClendon has selected for prominence in his 1939 monograph shows 111 parts per billion of iodine in the cabbage grown in eastern Minnesota where the goiter rate is 1.72 per cent, and 174 parts per billion of iodine in that grown in the western part of the same state where the goiter rate is 0.85 per cent. Here there was presumably a maximum of scientific control, and a minimum of analytical error.

Observations such as those which have been cited, associating a low intake of iodine in food and drink by a section of the population with a high tendency to goiter, strongly suggested that the former circumstance might be the predominant factor in the causation of the latter. Further evidence of the relationship was afforded when McClendon and Williams in 1923 produced goiter experimentally in rats by a diet low in iodine, fed under conditions of laboratory control.

Apparently, the increase in size of the gland is the result of an effort on the part of the thyroid to compensate for a shortage of iodine from which to synthesize its hormone(s) (thyroglobulin and/or thyroxine), by increasing the number of secreting cells and the volume of fluid secreted.

Simple Goiter Prevented by Adequate Iodine Intake

The now classical experiment of Marine and Kimball demonstrated that *simple goiter,* in most if not all cases, is a *deficiency disease* resulting from inadequate dietary intake of the *nutritionally essential* mineral element *iodine* and preventable by a sufficient supply of this food factor. These investigators administered iodine systematically to as many as volunteered of the school children of Akron, Ohio, of the ages at which goiter most commonly appears. The iodine was given as sodium iodide in small doses twice weekly over a period of a month and the treatment repeated twice yearly. The success of this preventive measure was striking. Of more than 2000 children treated, only 5 developed goiter; while, of a similar number not treated but of the same age and living in the same locality, about 500 showed thyroid enlargement during the same time. In other words, about 99 per cent of the goiters which would otherwise have developed were prevented by the simple administration of sodium iodide.

While the characterization of goiter as the most easily preventable of all diseases is a justifiable aid to memory, it should also be remembered that not all goiters are attributable to shortage of iodine. McCarrison some years ago described a goitrous village in India of which the best explanation appeared to be the infection of the thyroid by contaminated drinking water; and in a more recent Canadian report,* abstracted in the *Journal of the American Medical Association,* infected water rather than shortage of iodine was thought to be the chief cause of the goiters found locally in Saskatoon. That local epidemics and sporadic cases of goiters due to infection may occasionally be encountered should be frankly recognized; but should not blur the established fact that in typical regions of endemic goiter the incidence of this disease has been enormously reduced by simply supplying iodide in drinking water or in table salt. The reduction of incidence in school children by 85 per cent in three Swiss cantons and still more in the Ohio city

* Binning, C.   1939   *Canadian Public Health J.* **30**, 393–399.

already referred to may presumably be taken as fairly representative of the efficacy of these methods of iodide supply.

Thus it is probably a fair generalization that nearly 99 per cent of the simple goiters of goitrous regions are attributable to iodine deficiency and are preventable by the regular use of iodide in drinking waters or (more simply) iodized salt in the households of all the people.

In large cities, or over large areas, where the use of iodized salt has been advocated by health officers but without means of making it universal, subsequent surveys have shown greatly reduced goiter-incidence in the families using iodized salt as compared with next-door neighbors who did not.

Incidentally, it has been observed by medical schools in Great Lakes cities, that even stray dogs living largely on garbage get therefrom the benefit of the use of iodized salt in so many households that it is now quite difficult to find a stray dog with a goiter, whereas formerly the stray dogs of these cities were commonly goitrous.

Thus, according to a widely quoted statement of Dr. David Marine, goiter is "the simplest, the easiest, and the cheapest of all known diseases to prevent."

The Body's Need for Iodine

Evidently, the body has a rather definite nutritive requirement for iodine which must be met if the thyroid gland, one of the most important regulators of body processes, is to function normally. When the supply of iodine is only moderately deficient, the thyroid gland may become enlarged to form a goiter and yet be able to provide the thyroid hormone in normal or nearly normal quantities, so that the individual continues to enjoy fairly good health. But in severe iodine deprivation, despite the compensatory enlargement and increased activity of the gland, a deficit of the thyroid hormone exists and may cause the profound disturbances in physical and mental well-being and development known as *myxedema*. The edema from which this disease takes its name is well illustrated in the accompanying Fig. 23. Another characteristic feature of this condition is a markedly lowered rate of energy metabolism, the chemical processes of the body upon which growth and function depend being stepped down, sometimes to half the normal rate.

Correspondingly, the victim is exceedingly sensitive to the cold; suffers from flabbiness and weakness of the muscles, tiring easily on slight exertion; and his mental processes become progressively more sluggish. These symptoms are relieved often with dramatic promptness when thyroxine is administered.

Iodine deficiency in childhood may markedly stunt the growth in height. Here also the cure due to thyroxine and the change in general appearance are frequently striking, as in the case of the girl shown in Fig. 24.

Fig. 23. Photographs of a young woman before and after the cure of myxedema by thyroxine. Besides the disappearance of the edema, note the increased mental alertness evident in the second photograph. (Courtesy of Dr. E. C. Kendall.)

Qualitatively, the requirement for iodine might be stated as a sufficient amount of iodine to meet the daily losses from the body and maintain within the body such store as is needed to provide for the manufacture in the thyroid gland and the distribution throughout the body of sufficient amounts of thyroid hormone to support a normal rate of physiological activity, without the gland becoming abnormally enlarged.

It is estimated that the body of a full-grown healthy man contains in all about 25 milligrams of iodine; or, roughly, about 1 part of iodine in 2,800,000 parts of body substance. About three-fifths of

168 ESSENTIALS OF NUTRITION

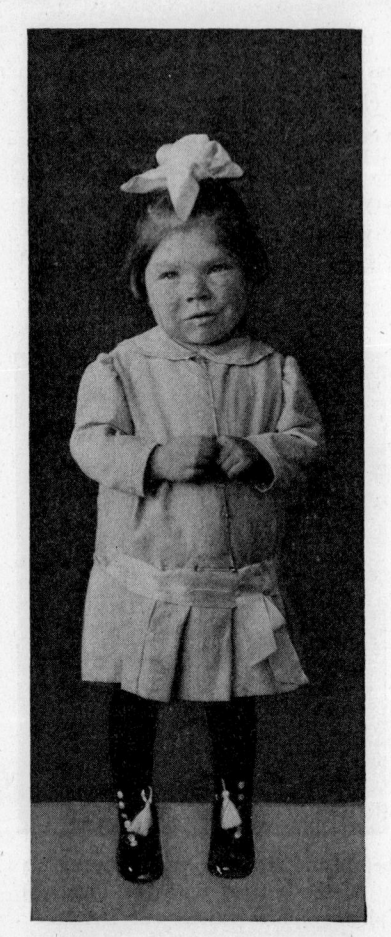

Fig. 24. Restoration of growth in a girl upon treatment with thyroxine. The two photographs were taken in the same dress at an interval of six months. This child was the first one to be treated with thyroxine. (Courtesy of Dr. E. C. Kendall.)

this is found in the thyroid gland. The body iodine occurs in part as inorganic iodide and in part in organic combination as thyroxine, thyroglobulin, di-iodotyrosine, and possible other forms. How much iodine must be taken-in daily to maintain this store of iodine in the body, is not precisely known. According to the National Research Council the requirement is probably about 0.002 mg. to 0.004 mg. daily for each kilogram of body weight, or a total of 0.15 to 0.30

mg. daily for an adult. "This need is met by the regular use of iodized salt; its use is especially important in *adolescence* and *pregnancy*."

If the iodine need of pregnancy is not met by the mother's intake, the tragic condition of myxedema in the baby may result.

When amounts of iodine in excess of the minimal requirement are furnished by the food and drink, an easily mobilized reserve store of iodine is built up in the body. This capacity for storing iodine undoubtedly explains how, in the experiments of Marine and Kimball, the protective effect of a period of intensive iodide dosage extended through five succeeding months when no further supplementary iodide was given.

How May the Needed Iodine be Supplied?

With the exception of seafoods, which are consistently rich sources of iodine, most foods are too variable in their iodine content to be depended upon to meet the dietary need for this element. It is true that many foods grown in the so-called non-goitrous regions are rich enough in iodine that their use might supply the whole or a significant part of the nutritive requirement. But in these regions generally the drinking water also shows a relatively high iodine content, often much more than enough to satisfy body demands. Whereas in the goitrous regions, where the drinking water is comparatively poor in iodine and there is consequently greater need to supply this element from other sources, the native plant products may contain only a fraction of the iodine present in the same plants grown in non-goitrous sections!

(It should be emphasized strongly that iodine is an exception— or, at any rate, an extreme case—among the mineral elements with regard to the relatively large variations in the concentration in which it may occur naturally in the same type of plant.)

Thus, while in normal regions the drinking water and natural food products provide the iodine required for the proper functioning of the body, reliance cannot be placed on either of these sources in districts where goiter is known to be prevalent. To prevent this disorder and promote normal nutrition in such regions, it was necessary to find a means of insuring a supplementary intake of iodine by every individual in the community. With this aim, a small amount (one part in 5000 to 200,000) of sodium or potassium iodide is now being incorporated in the table salt marketed in those sections of the country where goiter was formerly common.

The efficacy of this "iodized salt" as a goiter preventive has now been well established by experience. For the individual in whom the disease already exists, however, the problem of treatment lies in the realm of medicine rather than of nutrition. Indeed, there are certain goitrous conditions in which increased iodine intake may be actually injurious. However, there appear to be no good grounds for any fear that normal individuals may receive too much iodine for optimal health. And the iodide added to table salt should be regarded, not as a drug, but as restoring the table salt to something more like its natural composition. Sea salt and natural salt obtained from salt wells contain iodine.

EXERCISES

1. Obtain from the United States Public Health Service the most recent available evidence as to the prevalence of goiter in different regions. Is the region in which you live relatively goitrous or relatively free from goiter?

2. Can you explain the prevalence or rarity of goiter in your region by reference to (*a*) relation to the sea, (*b*) relation to the geological formation, (*c*) food habits of the people, (*d*) use of iodized salt?

SUGGESTED READINGS

ANDREWS, R. L., and G. W. STACE   1945   Losses of iodine from iodized salt. *Analyst* **70**, 88–89; *Nutr. Abs. Rev.* **15**, 39.

BOGERT, L. J.   1949   *Nutrition and Physical Fitness,* 5th Ed. (W. B. Saunders Co.)

CRANDALL, L. A.   1942   *An Introduction to Human Physiology,* 3rd Ed. (W. B. Saunders.)

HOSKINS, R. G.   1950   *Endocrinology,* Revised Ed. (W. W. Norton.)

KARP, A., and DEW. STETTEN, JR.   1949   The effect of thyroid activity on certain anabolic processes studied with the aid of deuterium. *J. Biol. Chem.* **179**, 819–830.

KIMBALL, O. P.   1931   The prevention of goiter in Detroit and Cleveland. *J. Am. Med. Assoc.* **97**, 1877–1879.

KIMBALL, O. P.   1949   Endemic goiter—a food deficiency disease. *J. Am. Dietet. Assoc.* **25**, 112–115.

MACLEOD, G., and C. M. TAYLOR   1944   *Rose's Foundations of Nutrition,* 4th Ed. (Macmillan.)

MANN, W., C. P. LEBLOND, and S. L. WARREN   1942   Iodine metabolism of the thyroid gland. *J. Biol. Chem.* **142**, 905–912.

MARINE, D.   1928   Iodine in the prevention and treatment of goiter. Chapter VI of *Chemistry in Medicine*. (Chemical Foundation.)

MARINE, D.   1935   The pathogenesis and prevention of simple or endemic goiter. *J. Am. Med. Assoc.* **104**, 2334–2341.

MCCLENDON, J. F.   1927   The distribution of iodine with special reference to goiter. *Physiol. Rev.* **7**, 189–253.

MCCLENDON, J. F.   1939   *Iodine and the Incidence of Goiter.* (University of Minnesota Press; Oxford University Press.)

MCCOLLUM, E. V., et. al.   1939   *The Newer Knowledge of Nutrition*, 5th Ed., Chapter X. (Macmillan.)

NATIONAL RESEARCH COUNCIL   1948   Recommended Daily Dietary Allowances. Reprint and Circular Series, No. 129.

PERLMAN, I., et al.   1941   Radioactive iodine as an indicator of the metabolism of iodine. I, II. *J. Biol. Chem.* **139**, 433–447, 449–456; *Chem. Abs.* **35**, 4437.

SEBRELL, W. H.   1949   Iodine—a food essential. *Public Health Reports* **64**, 1075–1087; *Nutrition Rev.* **8**, 129–132.

XI

ASCORBIC ACID (VITAMIN C)

The Former Prevalence of Scurvy and the Discovery and Identification of the Antiscorbutic Substance

So little did fresh fruits and vegetables figure in the food supply of Northern and Central Europe a few centuries ago, that when Catherine of Aragon came to England it was necessary for the household of Henry VIII to send abroad to get the materials for a salad. And during the period (and in the regions) in which these foods were so scarce for so much of the year, scurvy was so prevalent that medical writers seriously discussed the suggestion that all diseases be regarded as outgrowths of scurvy.

European medical literature, however, has so short a history that we do not know for how long scurvy had been such a scourge: it is known to have afflicted the Crusaders in the thirteenth century, and near the end of the fifteenth century when Vasco de Gama made his historic voyage around the Cape of Good Hope, he reported the death by scurvy of 100 men out of his crew of 160.

The formal medical name for scurvy is *scorbutus;* and things capable of preventing scurvy are often called *antiscorbutics*. Gradually it was learned that this antiscorbutic property is manifested by many "fresh" parts of plants.

In 1535, when Cartier was obliged to winter in Canada on his second voyage to Newfoundland, scurvy killed a quarter of his men. Nearly all the others were severely ill with it, but on advice of the natives a remedy was found in decoctions of the twigs and needles of evergreen trees. Recent investigations of Russian government bureaus interested in the settlement of northern Siberia indicate that leaves and twigs of both pines and spruces may be thus utilized as antiscorbutics. Tolstoy tells in *War and Peace* of the long-standing habit of the Russian peasants to scour the country in early spring, hunting for and devouring practically everything green and freshly growing.

Returning to the history of the exploration and settlement of America, we find that, in provisioning for regions which did not afford fresh fruits, thought turned first to wine as a substitute and then to beer as a substitute for wine. And crude, freshly fermenting beer was more or less generally recognized as antiscorbutic. Dr. John Nichols of Washington writes us (personal letter of 1938) of early New England records which show that shipmasters who brought colonists were careful to make sure that there be someone on board who could look after the malting of barley and the brewing and care of the beer. John Alden, whose name has been immortalized in literary romance, was, Dr. Nichols finds, first enlisted primarily as a cooper to have charge of the brewing equipment and the beer barrels. The malting process is, of course, merely a carefully regulated sprouting of the barley grain, which, like other seeds, is not antiscorbutic in the "resting" state but develops the antiscorbutic property as it sprouts. The simultaneous enzyme activity, changing starch to maltose, provides material for the fermentation. Thus a freshly fermenting infusion of (unroasted) malt has the antiscorbutic property of sprouting seeds; but *present-day* beer is so highly clarified that all antiscorbutic (and practically all other vitamin) value is usually lost.

Lind of the British navy described in his *Treatise on Scurvy* (1757) the treatment of an outbreak of scurvy on shipboard in 1747 under conditions which gave his experience much of the definiteness of a laboratory experiment. He took 12 patients (of the crew of the *Salisbury*) who appeared to be equally scorbutic and treated two by each of six regimes then more or less currently recommended. The two who received the limited amount of oranges and lemons available made dramatic recoveries.

In 1841 the American physician Budd advanced from the concept of an antiscorbutic property possessed by certain foods to the explicit postulate of a definite individual substance (chemical "element" in the terminology of his day), which he predicted would be identified "in a not too distant future." And in 1931-32, King, then of the University of Pittsburgh, first effected the chemical identification of the antiscorbutic substance (Fig. 25). His identification was quickly confirmed, and within a short time the substance had been synthesized by more than one method.

During the ninety years between Budd's prediction and its fulfillment by King, much was learned through clinical, field, and laboratory observations.

Government regulations required the carrying of citrus fruit juice by British ships, and its regular issue to all members of the crew on long voyages. This was found to be effective. It also came to be generally recognized that as potato culture had become more common in Europe scurvy had become less common, and correspondingly that the failure of the potato crop in any considerable region meant scurvy in that region the following winter or spring. Thus the failure of the potato crop in Ireland in 1846 was followed both by famine and by a crushing epidemic of scurvy.

Fig. 25. Crystals of ascorbic acid (vitamin C). (Courtesy of Dr. C. G. King.)

In 1906, Hopkins of Cambridge University definitely included scurvy among the diseases due to nutritional deficiency, and in 1907 the Norwegian investigators, Holst and Frölich, published the first of their researches in this field. The clinical work of Hess and the laboratory work of Mendel and his students followed quickly; and these scientific advances enabled army and navy medical men both largely to prevent scurvy and also to systematize the recording and interpretation of the necessarily fragmentary observations made during the First World War. Later, when increased numbers of scientific workers were able to return to the fundamental problems of the nutrition laboratories, there was a period in which pioneering laboratory work upon several substances of demonstrated nutritional importance was simultaneously very active before the chemical nature of any of these substances could yet be known.

As a temporary expedient to reduce the confusion in the rapidly growing literature, the term *vitamine* which Funk had coined was combined with McCollum's terms *fat-soluble A* and *water-soluble B* to form the new terms *vitamin A* and *vitamin B;* and Drummond, in proposing this system, added the antiscorbutic substance as *vitamin C*.

If the alphabetical sequence of the designations had followed the chronological sequence of what we now regard as clearly postulated nutritional concepts, the ABC order of these three substances would be reversed; for the antiscorbutic substance was explicitly postulated as a chemical individual many years earlier than was the antineuritic substance (vitamin B); and the existence of the latter was apparently known earlier than was that of the fat-soluble substance which came to be called vitamin A.

King and his collaborators worked systematically for years to concentrate and isolate vitamin C as a chemical individual, testing and measuring their progress at each step by quantitative determination of the antiscorbutic potencies of their products. In the early spring of 1932, they had thus completed the physical isolation and chemical identification of the substance investigated as vitamin C. It then became possible to devise methods for its rapid determination, with fair accuracy even in small amounts of material; and thenceforward its investigation has proceeded rapidly.

With vitamin C chemically identified and found to be a relatively simple substance, there yet was difficulty in finding a name of convenient length and satisfactorily indicative of its chemical nature. Hence usage has increasingly adopted the name *ascorbic acid* as being distinctive and as perpetuating the historical association of the substance with scurvy, through the study of which its existence was first postulated and finally proven.

The Nutritional Significance of Vitamin C

In vitro, and presumably in the life processes of plants, the outstanding property of ascorbic acid is that of entering readily into oxidation-reduction reactions. *In human nutrition,* at least equal significance attaches to its function in the formation and maintenance of the intercellular cement substances of the tissues. While most biological teaching tends strongly to emphasize what goes on within the cells, it is just as fundamentally scientific to realize that many of these intracellular activities can proceed normally only on condition that the intercellular cement substance holds the cells in proper relation to each other and to the body fluids which bathe and nourish them.

Wolbach offers, as a result of his pathological research, an impressive array of ways in which body function may be impaired through the effects of shortage of vitamin C upon the integrity of the intercellular material in different bodily organs and tissues:

(1) Hemorrhages, which may occur anywhere in the body, and which are a prominent feature of the classical picture of scurvy. Sometimes the hemorrhages are tiny *petechiae* visible in or through the skin, sometimes crescent-shaped areas at the bases of the teeth, sometimes invisible hemorrhages in the joints, making them stiff and sore. At autopsy, hemorrhages are often found also in the wall of the digestive tract and at the rib junctions.

(2) Structural changes in the gums and teeth, the latter having been considered by some investigators to be the most delicate structurally observable indications of shortage of vitamin C.

(3) Changes in the growing ends of bones, sometimes causing confusion between rickets and scurvy in children.

(4) Defective calcification due to degeneration or lack of proper development of the bone matrix.

(5) Displacement of bones due to weakness of the supporting cartilage.

(6) Anemia due to interference with the functioning of the blood-forming cells in the bone marrow, as well as to the loss of blood by hemorrhage.

(7) Damage to heart muscles, sometimes shown by enlargement of the heart.

(8) Degeneration of muscle structure generally.

(9) Injury to the sex organs.

With shortage of vitamin C constituting the underlying nutritional fault which may show itself in such different ways as these, it is to be expected that constitutional differences among individuals may determine the way in which any one person will suffer from this same sub-optimal feature of food supply.

Hence, even though the symptoms may be somewhat confusingly varied, we may still have a clear impression that vitamin C is a nutritional factor of very far-reaching importance.

It must not be thought that nowadays scurvy exists only in remote places or in the minds of alarmists. No less sane a scientist than Professor Hopkins of Cambridge University reported not many years ago an experience which came to his attention in a large school in England. During the winter term at this school the standards of work and play fell to an unsatisfactory level; the boys became listless and irritable, and various minor complaints were reported. Attempts to explain the condition were for some time unsuccessful. At last the suggestion was made that the diet be investigated by some one with modern knowledge of nutrition. The food conditions had traditionally been considered quite satisfactory. It was found, however, that the diet contained nothing in the way of uncooked foods and practically no green vegetables. A small fruit shop nearby, where the boys had formerly purchased fresh fruit with their pocket money, had been closed for some time. Upon restoring a liberal amount of fresh fruit to the diet the whole trouble disappeared. These school boys had evidently been suffering from incipient scurvy, due to the low intake of vitamin C during the period in which they did not have fruit.

Shortage of vitamin C may begin to be injurious considerably before the classical signs of scurvy appear, and for the reasons indicated above the earliest effects may show considerable individual variation. Hence clear-cut evidence and consensus of opinion as to the incidence of pre-scurvy or early or incipient effects of suboptimal intakes of vitamin C are lacking. There is, however, strong evidence that suboptimal concentrations ("levels") of vitamin C in ostensibly healthy people are more frequent than hitherto realized. Medical surveys of nutritional status, using the delicate methods recently developed, have revealed, in different parts of Canada and the United States, relatively large proportions of people (especially in the low income groups) who are living at relatively low ascorbic acid levels which, even if they do not show gross symptoms of scurvy, undoubtedly mean something less than optimal resistance. For King and his coworkers have shown with guineapigs* that relative shortage of vitamin C lowers resistance to bacterial toxins and that this lowering of resistance is demonstrable before ordinary signs of scurvy appear. King has also pointed out that the full benefit of vitamin C to healing wounds requires about ten times as high a daily allowance of this vitamin

---

* Guineapig is preferably written as a single word to mark it as an arbitrary term in as much as these animals are not closely related to ordinary pigs.

as is needed to prevent scurvy. Thus if optimal level includes the concept of keeping the body in best condition to meet emergencies, the lowest intakes sometimes accepted as minimal-adequate would need to be multiplied at least by five and perhaps by ten to reach the optimum.

Quantitative Metabolism and Requirement in Man

Of the vitamin C which the body receives, a part disappears in the tissues and is evidently consumed in performing its nutritional function; a part leaves the body unchanged, chiefly in the urine; and a part is held by the tissues and fluids of the body.

Extensive studies indicate that normal human blood contains, as an average, between 1.0 and 1.5 milligrams of vitamin C per 100 grams; and the solid tissues that are characterized by high metabolic activity normally have higher concentrations of this vitamin.

It is especially noteworthy that the amount of vitamin C contained in the body, the rate at which it is destroyed, and the rate at which it escapes through the kidneys, are all subject to relatively large variation even under such conditions as are frequently encountered in daily life (Fig. 26). We cannot doubt that these differences in "level of vitamin C nutrition" are significant in relation to health and efficiency, and that the problem of human requirement for vitamin C should be considered not simply in terms of prevention of scurvy, but rather as a problem of ensuring the maintenance of such concentrations of vitamin C in the blood and body tissues as are conducive to the highest attainable health under all the vicissitudes likely to be met in the course of our lives. And there are indications that with advancing age the body may need more vitamin C than in the prime of life; or that liberal intake of this vitamin may help to moderate the aging process.

Other things being equal the lower the intake of vitamin C the smaller the amount which appears in the urine; and simultaneously with low intake and low output, low concentrations of vitamin C in blood have repeatedly been found and are doubtless regularly to be expected (Fig. 26). Such quantitative studies as have yet been made with spinal fluid indicate that its level of vitamin C content tends to rise and fall with the level in the blood; and it is reasonable to suppose that this is also true of the body tissues generally, though some of them may fluctuate in lesser degree than others.

ASCORBIC ACID (VITAMIN C)

[Figure 26: Bar chart showing Vitamin C content (Mgs. %) from 0 to 2.5 for individuals on ADEQUATE DIET BEGINNING OF TEST (R.R., E.P.W., B.I., E.S.W., R.M., L.W.) and INADEQUATE DIET BEGINNING OF TEST (A.M., R.S., F.S., J.S.). Cross-hatched bars = Initial value; solid bars = After receiving one pint orange juice daily for one week.]

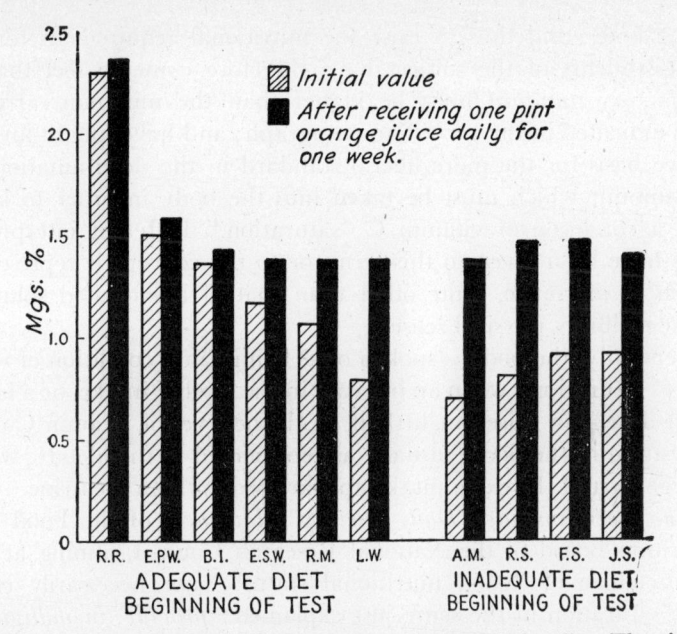

Fig. 26. Vitamin C content of the blood as influenced by diet. The six individuals to the left had all been receiving an apparently adequate diet prior to the beginning of the test. Note, however, the considerable individual differences among them with regard to the initial concentration of vitamin C in the blood (cross-hatched bar), one showing a value distinctly higher, another a value lower than the "usual normal range." The four individuals to the right who were known to have had an inadequate intake of vitamin C prior to the test all showed "subnormal" levels of vitamin C in the blood. After generous amounts of vitamin C in the form of orange juice had been given for a week to both groups, the blood level of vitamin C (solid bar) was found to be about 1.5 mg. per 100 cc. in all cases except the one individual who showed exceptionally high value throughout. Note that values already normal were slightly increased by the liberal intake. (From Farmer and Abt in "The Vitamins" by permission of the American Medical Association, publishers, and by courtesy of the Milbank Memorial Fund.)

An intake of 25 to 30 milligrams of ascorbic acid per normal adult per day, or 1 milligram per 100 Calories of food in family dietaries, appears to be sufficient to prevent scurvy or any other manifest symptom of vitamin C deficiency; and may therefore be taken as a standard of *minimal* adequacy.

But many common infections, injuries, and strains or stresses now seem rather clearly to increase the rate of destruction of vitamin C in the body, and thus to raise the nutritional requirement for it. Most students of the subject have therefore come to feel that a *satisfactory standard* must be higher than the minimum arrived at as indicated in the preceding paragraph; and have sought an objective basis for the more liberal standard in the determination of the amount which must be taken into the body in order to keep it in a condition of vitamin C "saturation." Different interpretations have been given to this term, or to the concept it represents, which is, of course, quite other than that of a saturated solution in the ordinary physical sense.

Generally, the body is spoken of as being "in a condition of vitamin C saturation" when an increase in the level of intake, or a large extra dose, can raise but little if at all the level of vitamin C concentration in the body (usually as represented in the blood), while a large part of the extra intake appears promptly in the urine.

The Recommended Daily Dietary Allowances of the Food and Nutrition Board of the National Research Council, aiming at the maintenance of "good nutritional status" (not necessarily complete saturation in the sense just explained) *provide, in milligrams of ascorbic acid:* for men, 75; for women, 70, rising to 100 in the latter half of pregnancy and 150 during lactation; for children under 1 year of age, 30; 1–3 years, 35, 4–6 years, 50; 7–9 years, 60; and 10-20 years, 75-100 mgms. For the further details of the recommendations for the last-named period the full table in the Appendix may be consulted.

Here, as elsewhere, the artificial concentrates should be considered as drugs to be used only when prescribed by a physician; while the non-medical student of nutrition who desires to increase his intake of some dietary factor should do so by shifting the proportions in which he consumes everyday foods. One who desires 100 milligrams of vitamin C may advantageously take it in the form of seven ounces of average orange juice; or may readily figure an equivalent in the form of some other food or foods from the data of Table 18 below or of Table 41 in the Appendix.

There is no danger that any selection of foods one might make would involve any risk of injury from surplus of this vitamin.

There is, on the other hand, some difference of expert opinion as to how important it is to provide such liberal intakes as to keep the vitamin C level in the body high at all times. From a starting point of excellent nutritional status and all-round health, one may go a long time on a low vitamin C level before visible signs of scurvy appear. In a well-controlled case in which a healthy young man went on a diet good in other respects but lacking in vitamin C, the level of this vitamin in the blood plasma fell to zero in 42 days, and that of the white blood cells in 122 days; while visible symptoms of scurvy appeared in 5 to 6 months. Experimental wounds made after the man had been 3 months on this diet healed well; but those made after 6 months of such deprivation of vitamin C were slow in healing. (For fuller discussion, if desired, see Lund and Crandon (1941) in Suggested Readings below.)

No doubt many people go through life "passably healthy" and doing ordinary work with bodily levels of vitamin C chronically much below physiological saturation. Thus the Milbank Memorial Fund studies of nutritional condition in New York City high school students showed plasma ascorbic acid levels below 0.6 mg. per 100 ml. in 48 per cent of 1059 boys and in 46 per cent of 1088 girls. These low levels were considered "indicative of insufficient intake" by these research workers, and when the research was extended to include quantitative inquiry into the kinds and amounts of foods consumed, it was concluded that vitamin C came next after vitamin A and calcium in the frequency with which the dietary fell below the current standards. The full account is given in the paper by Wiehl (1942) listed among Suggested Readings below.

Promptness of response becomes significant if one wishes to keep the blood level high at all times. In the work of Todhunter, Robbins, and McIntosh (1942) five college women showed close similarity to each other and also for the same person studied at different times, in the rate of increase of plasma ascorbic acid after swallowing 50 milligrams of the vitamin either in crystalline form or by the eating of fruit. The blood plasma level began to rise within 30 to 60 minutes, and returned to the fasting level in 3 to 4 hours. The maximum was reached within 1¼ hours after taking the vitamin in crystalline form or as orange juice or orange sections; 2 hours after eating strawberries; and 2½ hours after eating cauliflower. The same investigators also found that the original fasting level may be expected to influence the extent to which ascorbic acid will be increased, but not the time at which the peak of the rise is reached. Starting from about the same fasting level, however, the amount taken at a sitting determines the extent of the rise and the time the plasma level will remain above the starting point.

It is true that the white blood cells may hold a higher level while that of the plasma falls, but there may be some significance for the body as a whole in the plasma's ups and downs. From this viewpoint it appears advantageous to have vitamin C liberally represented not only in the day's intake but in nearly every meal, with perhaps also some fruit or a glass of fruit juice at bed-time.

Since studies of nutritional status of populations in New York City, in Tennessee, and in North Carolina have revealed a rather high incidence of shortages of this vitamin, as had previous analogous surveys in Maine and in Canada, and since the data of food consumption studies of Stiebeling and coworkers also warn us that many families still live on dietaries of undesirably low vitamin C value, there is a general trend toward acceptance of the relatively liberal Recommended Allowances and correspondingly a growing emphasis upon the vitamin C values of foods.

Expression of Vitamin C Values

In this book we shall follow the growing practice of expressing vitamin C values directly in terms of the substance itself. Above we have expressed nutritional needs in terms of milligrams per day; and below will be found data for vitamin C (ascorbic acid) contents of foods in milligrams per 100 grams of food.

Data still met in terms of International Units are readily translated into milligrams, for, by current definition, 20 International Units = 1 milligram of vitamin C.

At this point it may also be well to explain the expression "mg. per cent" which, while open to criticism as not being explicit, is largely used for convenience as meaning milligrams per 100 grams, cubic centimeters, or milliliters, for cases in which the concentration is so low that its numerical expression would be the same whether referred to one or another of these bases.

Conservation of Vitamin C in the Preparation and Preservation of Foods

From the earliest scientific conception of scurvy as due to the lack of an antiscorbutic substance, it was recognized that in general fresh foods have more and preserved foods have less of this factor. As the concept became clearer, the statement came to take the form that not only are some foods, such as citrus fruits, relatively rich in this factor while others such as bread, butter, meat, and sugar are poor or lacking in it; but also that it is an unstable factor so that cooking and preservation are apt to diminish whatever antiscorbutic value the food originally possesses.

Now that all of the more familiar vitamins are known as distinct chemical individuals *not* closely related in their chemical and physical properties, we see that it is unscientific to try to make broad and simple generalizations or comparisons, for the behaviors of the vitamins will arrange them in different sequences according to the particular chemical or physical condition whose influence is being considered. Yet for most practical purposes we may still regard vitamin C as the most easily destroyed of the known vitamins.

Because many familiar fruits and vegetables such as apples, cabbage, and potatoes may lose a considerable proportion of their vitamin C value in ordinary cooking, it has become customary to emphasize raw food in this connection, and to regard this vitamin as thermolabile,—liable to be destroyed upon heating. Strictly speaking, it is not so much destroyed by heat itself as by a process of oxidation which is accelerated by increase of temperature. The rate of destruction is lower when air is excluded by steam or by vacuum; and it is higher when acidity has been reduced or alkalinity increased by the addition of soda to the food. The destruction of vitamin C is also catalyzed by the presence of even very small amounts of copper. In addition to all these environmental influences (and perhaps others, as yet less clearly defined) there are properties within the natural foods themselves which affect the conservation or deterioration of their vitamin C values. In general the more acid foods hold their vitamin C value better; but if cabbage juice is brought to the same acidity as tomato juice it still will lose more of its vitamin C on heating, because of the natural, inherently higher, oxidation potential of the juice of the cabbage.

The destruction of vitamin C upon heating in solution, as in the juices of typical foods, is a process which proceeds at a rate which can be measured experimentally and which has been studied quantitatively with reference to the influence of temperature, time of heating, the acidity or alkalinity of the solution, and other factors.

In the case of tomato juice of natural acidity it was found that boiling for one hour destroyed practically 50 per cent, and boiling for 4 hours destroyed practically 68 per cent of the antiscorbutic vitamin. At lower temperatures there was less destruction in a given time. Figure 27 shows the time curves of the heat destruction of the vitamin at 60°, 80°, and 100° C. It will be noted that, throughout the entire range of times and temperatures covered by these experiments, the destruction was always greater the higher the temperature whatever the time of heating selected for the comparison; and also that at whatever temperature the material was heated the destruction of the vitamin also continued to become greater the longer the heating was continued.

Thus both time and temperature are important factors in the heat destruction of vitamin C and neither the time nor the temperature can be treated with indifference in any heating operation in which it is desired to conserve as much as possible of the antiscorbutic property of the food. Both time and temperature of heating must be held to the lowest practicable minimum if vitamin C is to be conserved to the best advantage.

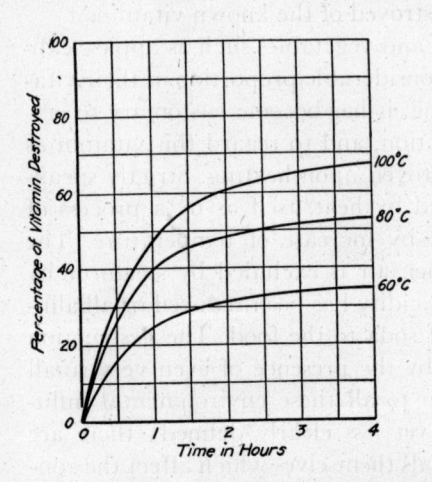

Fig. 27. Curves representing the rates of destruction, at different temperatures, of the vitamin C of tomato juice at its natural acidity.

The best conservation of the antiscorbutic value of the food also demands that one avoid adding any soda or other alkali to the food, or the water used in its cooking.

Not only is vitamin C more readily destroyed in an alkaline than in an acid solution; any decrease of acidity, even though the material may still remain acid, means that a greater percentage of the vitamin will be destroyed under the same conditions of time and temperature. Thus tomato juice, which lost 50 per cent of its vitamin C in one hour at 100° C. at natural acidity, lost 58 per cent under the same heat treatment when it had been about half neutralized, and 61 to 65 per cent when it had been made very faintly alkaline.

Alkalinity, even in slight degree, appears to be distinctly deleterious to vitamin C even at ice-box temperature, for when the solution last mentioned was stored in an icebox for from one to five days it was found to have lost much the largest part of the vitamin C which had survived the hour of heating. In this case, however, the material was not protected from contact with air during storage.

It is quite clear that one should not speak of the vitamin as being "destroyed at" a certain temperature; but rather as being *more rapidly* destroyed the higher the temperature. The question is not so much *whether,* but rather *in what degree* (or at what rate), the vitamin is destroyed "at boiling," "at steam-table temperature," etc. If, for instance, the material shown in Fig. 27, after losing 20 per cent of its vitamin C at 100° C. (boiling temperature) was thereafter kept hot for serving by placing it on a steam-table at 60° C. the destruction would continue at, of course, a lower rate.

The American Medical Association's Council on Foods issued in July 1939 a report on "Allowable claims for the vitamin and mineral content of canned fruits and vegetables intended for infant feeding" which includes a Decision that sufficient experimental evidence has accumulated to warrant the view that vitamin A and riboflavin are little affected by good modern canning procedures, but that thiamine and vitamin C are more or less adversely affected, "the degree of destruction depending on the characteristics of the food itself, the time and temperature of processing, and possibly other factors." In the future, therefore, they propose to recognize claims for thiamine and vitamin C values of such canned foods only when "supported by acceptable evidence of the potency of the finished product."*

One should, therefore, not attempt to answer broad, undiscriminating questions as to whether or to what extent a given vitamin is destroyed by a given cooking or canning process; for the rate of such destruction differs too widely among different foods, and is also influenced by too many environmental conditions.

It may safely be said, however, that *among* the conditions which are favorable to conservation of vitamin C are: to minimize time

* *J. Am. Med. Assoc.* 113, 215 (July 15, 1939).

of exposure, temperature, and contact with air or dissolved oxygen, and to add no soda.

As vitamin C is readily soluble in water, the rejection of cooking water, or of the fluid contents of the can, may involve a loss no less serious than that of the actual destruction which takes place in the cooking and canning processes. In some careful experiments the loss in cooking has been found to have been even much more largely due to the dissolving away of the vitamin than to its actual destruction. Thus, Wellington and Tressler* found that in the boiling of shredded cabbage less than one-sixth of the original vitamin C was destroyed, while about two-thirds of it was lost from the vegetable in the sense that it passed into the cooking water. When larger pieces of cabbage were boiled, the amount extracted was less. The utilization of "pot liquors" in making soups and stews has doubtless helped to protect many poor families from scurvy.

TABLE 17. *Approximate Losses of Vitamin C in Cooking Foods. Examples Selected from the Data of Taylor and MacLeod:* Rose's Laboratory Handbook for Dietetics (Macmillan.)

	Percentage Loss
Apples,	
baked	80
stewed	40
Asparagus, fresh, boiled	30
Broccoli, all methods	40
Cabbage, all methods	45
Carrots, boiled	45
Cauliflower, all methods	35
Onions, all methods	30
Peas, all methods	40
Potatoes, all methods	25
Sweetpotatoes, all methods	40
Tomatoes, all methods	25
Turnip greens, all methods	45

It is noteworthy that broccoli, cabbage, cauliflower, and turnip greens, while among the foods showing largest cooking loss, are yet excellent sources of vitamin C after cooking because their ini-

* Wellington, M., and D. K. Tressler 1938 Influence of method of cooking on vitamin C content of cabbage. *Food Research* 3, 311–316.

tial content of this vitamin is so high. Kale is also an excellent source if not too drastically overcooked.

In accord with the growing practice of discussing retentions rather than losses, Moore, Atkins, Wiederhold, and MacDowell (1945) report that after 3 days at refrigerator temperature (40°F.) both covered and uncovered orange juices showed retentions of 98 per cent of their original vitamin C; and that grapefruit juice also showed 98 per cent or better retention.

Quantitative Distribution of Vitamin C in Foods

There is much of both scientific interest and practical value in a consideration of the different types of food as sources of vitamin C now that we are beginning to appreciate the great importance of this constituent of our food to our nutritional wellbeing and resultant health and efficiency.

In a study by Stiebeling* of presumably typical American dietaries it was found that citrus fruits and tomatoes, while representing less than five per cent of the expenditure for food and furnishing less than two per cent of the total protein, furnished over 37 per cent of the total vitamin C. Potatoes and sweetpotatoes are not nearly so rich, but their large place in the food supply makes them important sources contributing about 23 per cent of the total vitamin C. Green and yellow vegetables show a contribution of nearly 13; all other fruits and vegetables about 20; milk and its products 5 to 6; meats and fish, breadstuffs and cereals, together less than 2 per cent of the vitamin C; and sweets, fats, and eggs only negligible amounts, if any.

Assuming, as we doubtless may, that the data thus studied by Stiebeling are fairly representative it will be seen that we derive probably nine-tenths of our vitamin C from fruits and vegetables, and most of the remainder from milk. Doubtless the flesh foods could be made to furnish a larger proportion if we ate them, as the Eskimos do, in larger amounts, with less intervention of storage and cooking between slaughter and consumption, and with a reversal of our usual practice of taking the muscle meats for ourselves and giving the glandular organs to the dogs. Another and perhaps more important consideration in clearing up what some regard as

* Stiebeling, H. K.   1936   Report Serial No. R 409, Bureau of Labor Statistics, U.S. Department of Labor.

an inconsistency between our view of vitamin C and some of the reports upon food habits of carnivorous peoples is that the latter have sources of vitamin C which are apt to escape the attention of explorers and even anthropologists. The natives of Kamchatka were anthropologically described as living exclusively on meats and fish; but a later more meticulous investigation revealed the fact that they also eat berries, bark, and leaves. Evidently so did those Canadian Indians who were supposed to be carnivorous until occasion arose for them to teach Cartier's men the importance of evergreen twigs and leaves as antiscorbutic food.

There probably are no strictly carnivorous peoples; for it is much more probable that explorers who think they have found such have failed to observe or to appreciate the significance of the eating of berries and the chewing of bark, roots, and twigs. Of course it may also be true that people descended from untold generations of Arctic ancestors may have intensified, as a characteristic of survival value under their conditions, the property of being able to get along with less vitamin C than we require.

To return to the consideration of the different types of foods as sources of the vitamin C of our normal dietaries, it is noteworthy that the breadstuffs and cereals which furnish such a large proportion of our food-calories and protein are such insignificant sources of vitamin C in the forms in which we ordinarily eat them. These seeds, however, and also the mature legumes, form vitamin C when they germinate, so that, in lack of other adequate sources, cereal or legume seeds may be germinated and eaten with their young sprouts. Evidently there is here some process of change which the sprouting seed performs efficiently; and which our bodies perform very inefficiently if at all. In the plant cycle too, it would seem to be in some sense a reversible process; the young green pea is a good antiscorbutic, loses this property as it matures, but regenerates it when sprouting. The oxidation-reduction or "respiratory" behavior of vitamin C *in vitro* here finds a clearcut relation to metabolism in the plant, while in animal metabolism its behavior in this direction is as yet somewhat overshadowed by the importance of its function in the making and maintenance of intercellular substance, as mentioned earlier in this chapter.

Among edible seed pods, *green peppers* have been found to be excellent, and *string beans* good sources.

Leaves, such as *cabbage, kale,* and *lettuce,* are also rich in vitamin C: they may be counted as excellent sources when eaten raw, and even though they lose a considerable proportion of their vitamin C in ordinary cooking, they are still fairly good sources when cooked. In *celery,* the leaves have been found to be even richer in vitamin C than the succulent stalks. *Turnip greens* and *watercress* are among the other edible leaves which have been demonstrated to be excellent sources of vitamin C.

Onion, an edible bulb, has also been found to be a good source of vitamin C: rich in the raw state, with variable cooking-losses which need not be large (Murphy, 1941).

Asparagus, a succulent growing tip, is highly potent when raw, but often loses much in ordinary cooking. Further research will doubtless show whether the cooking-loss *need* be large.

Among roots and tubers, *carrots, turnips,* and *potatoes* may be mentioned here. *Carrots* received considerable attention from Hess and his coworkers who emphasized the difference between old and fresh young carrots particularly after cooking. They found that 35 grams of old carrots sufficed to protect a guineapig from scurvy when fed raw but not after cooking, while in a parallel test with fresh young carrots 25 grams proved adequate for complete protection even after cooking. They pointed out that in such cases as this the fresh young vegetable may have a double advantage over the older and tougher, since in the first place the younger or fresher specimens tend to be richer in antiscorbutic vitamin to start with; and also, as the older, tougher vegetables require more prolonged cooking, they are apt to undergo a greater loss of vitamin C during the cooking process.

Largely as the result of this experience with carrots, Hess emphasized the view that vegetables must be expected to vary considerably in their content of vitamin C according to their freshness and age. While young carrots were much superior to old carrots in antiscorbutic value, he found that slightly green tomatoes contained less vitamin C than did those which were fully ripe. So far as fruits and vegetables are concerned, our present limited knowledge suggests that the degree of maturity at which each fresh fruit or vegetable is most palatable is about that at which it has greatest vitamin C value.

Potatoes, while containing vitamin C in distinctly lower concentration than do some other common foods, are yet of great importance as antiscorbutics because of the quantities in which they are consumed. Weight for weight, cooked potatoes are comparable as antiscorbutics with raw apples, and in most families the potato is consumed in much the larger quantity. Different investigators have varied greatly in their estimates as to the vitamin C in cooked potatoes: some say hardly any remains, while others say hardly any need be lost. Mayfield *et al.* (1937) are among the latter, finding even lesser losses for potatoes than were found in the same laboratory for string beans, cabbage, onions, or green peas (Mayfield and Richardson, 1939, 1940; Richardson and Mayfield, 1940).

Turnips have high vitamin C value when eaten raw. They and their juices have served as important antiscorbutics in wartime.

Among fruits, the citrus,—especially oranges and grapefruit,—and tomatoes, which are botanically fruit though classified commercially as a vegetable, are the sources of outstanding importance and qualified also for increasing prominence in the dietary on the grounds of economy and general acceptability. Milne, in his essay on fruit, gives first place to the orange, and returns to it for his peroration! Beside its many other virtues, the *orange* is one of the most potent and popular of antiscorbutics.

The *grapefruit* is about three-fourths as rich in vitamin C as the orange, and has a fine flavor all its own. Delicious also is a mixture of grapefruit and orange juices.

Tomatoes are somewhat less rich than grapefruit and distinctly less rich than oranges in their average vitamin C content. Like grapefruit and its juice, tomatoes hold their vitamin value well when preserved by cold storage or canning, and the canned product is economical and available almost everywhere at all seasons of the year. Often in recent years, citrus fruits have been about as cheap as canned tomatoes, but at times when oranges have been expensive the juice of canned tomatoes has been largely substituted for orange juice in infant feeding.

In very extensive experimentation in the Soil, Plant, and Nutritional Laboratory, the vitamin C content of vine-ripened tomatoes was found to be more favorably influenced by abundance of direct sunlight during the ripening period than by any other of the many factors studied. It should be kept in mind, however, that with some other foods, notably apples, the genetic factor ("variety" in the strict botanical or horticultural sense) has thus far showed greater influence upon the vitamin C content than has environment.

Tomatoes are also noteworthy for holding their vitamin C values well over a wide range of temperature. Thus Brown and Moser found no measurable diminution of the vitamin C content in 18 days storage at 6.7° C. Commercially canned and market-fresh tomatoes average about the same vitamin C content. For, those which are to be canned are usually grown under contract for the purpose, gathered at their precise best degree of ripeness, and then very promptly processed into air-tight cans.

TABLE 18. *Vitamin C in the Edible Portion of Typical Foods. Milligrams per 100 Grams*

Food	Range Within Which Average Will Probably Be Found
Orange (or juice)	49–56
Grapefruit (or juice)	35–41
Cabbage, raw	29–52
Cantaloupe	26–35
Turnip, fresh raw	19–33
Tomato (or fresh juice)	21–24
Peas, fresh young, green, raw	20–26
Beans, snap or string, raw	14–19
Potatoes, raw	11–17
Corn, sweet, raw	8–12
Peaches	7–11
Bananas	6–10
Apples (medium varieties)[a]	5–8
Celery (stalks)	5–9
Watermelon	6–7
Plums	4–7

[a] Varieties here averaged were: Astrachan, Baldwin, Ben Davis, Esopus, Golden Delicious, Gravenstein, King, Newton Wonder, Northern Spy, Rhode Island, Rome Beauty, Roxbury Russet, Spitzenburg, Stayman, Winesap, Winter Banana, and Yellow Newtown.

In view of confusing findings by other workers, Tressler and Curran (1938) made a special study of the causes of diminution of vitamin C content in bottled tomato juice. After heating the juice rapidly to 185° F., it was poured into glass bottles to three different levels: (*a*) entirely full, (*b*) within 2.5 cm. of the top, and (*c*) only to the shoulder (11.5 cm. head space). "The bottles were crowned immediately and permitted to cool without further processing, then stored in the dark at ordinary room temperature. . . .

Ascorbic acid is not lost more rapidly from tomato juice packed in bottles filled completely than from juice in cans similarly filled." A great loss occurs in either bottles or cans which are only partially filled. This is chiefly due to the contained air, and in these experiments seemed to come to rest after about 40 days of storage.

Apples are more variable and less potent than citrus fruits as antiscorbutics. Having been so widely cultivated, apples have become differentiated into well-marked varieties, some of which differ from each other as much, in their vitamin C content, as if they were different species. Several years ago Zilva discovered Bramley's Seedling to have outstanding vitamin C value among English apples; and more recently Maynard has recognized a New Zealand variety as a still richer source of this vitamin. Yet to recognize each variety separately in ordinary nutrition work would be prohibitively cumbersome. For present purposes therefore we present in Table 18 an average of the middle group of varieties.

Among the small-fruits, *black currants* have played an important part as antiscorbutics in Great Britain during the Second World War. *Strawberries* are (in season) a good source of vitamin C, and doubtless other berries both cultivated and wild have served human nutrition in this respect more significantly than has been appreciated. *Rose hips* are also reported very high in vitamin C.

In Table 18 the last column gives a *range* of usual values for each food included. One need not be trained in statistics to find interest in the fact that the statistical chances are at least 100 to 1 that the true mean value lies within the indicated range.

EXERCISES

1. Purchase oranges, grapefruit (or canned grapefruit juice), apples (noting the variety, if known), and bananas in your local market, recording the cost of each purchase and determining the weight of its edible portion. How do these fruits compare in pecuniary economy as sources of vitamin C?

2. Compare apples, bananas, oranges, and grapefruit (or its juice) as to the amount of vitamin C furnished (1) in each 100-Calorie portion; (2) per gram (or per 100 grams) of protein. Arrange these fruits (and perhaps others) in the order of their merit as a means of increasing the vitamin C value of a dietary with the least change in its total calories, or total protein, or both.

3. Prepare a critical compilation and discussion of all information

afforded by the library facilities available to you, on the extent of the losses of vitamin C involved in different recognized methods of cooking and serving potatoes. Taking account of all losses, what percentage of the vitamin C content of a raw potato probably actually enters the nutrition of the consumer? Could this be materially improved without undue change of household customs? If so, how?

SUGGESTED READINGS

BEDFORD, C. L., and M. A. MCGREGOR   1948   Effect of canning on the ascorbic acid and thiamine in vegetables. *J. Am. Dietet. Assoc.* **24**, 866–869.

BELSER, W. B., H. M. HAUCK, and C. A. STORVICK   1939   A study of the ascorbic acid intake required to maintain tissue saturation in normal adults. *J. Nutrition* **17**, 513–526.

BESSEY, O. A., and C. G. KING   1933   The distribution of vitamin C in plant and animal tissues. *J. Biol. Chem.* **103**, 687–698.

CLAYTON, M. M., and M. T. FOLSOM   1940   A method for the study of the availability for human nutrition of the vitamin C in foods, with an application to the study of the potato. *J. Home Econ.* **32**, 390–395.

CLAYTON, M. M., B. O. WELLS, C. GOOS, and E. F. MURPHY   1944   Ascorbic acid content of vegetables as determined by variety and method of processing. *Maine Agr. Expt. Sta. Bull.* No. 426, 306–311.

CRANDON, J. H. and C. C. LUND   1940   Vitamin C deficiency in an otherwise normal adult. *New Engl. J. Med.* **222**, 748–752; *Nutr. Abs. Rev.* **11**, 129.

CRANDON, J. H., C. C. LUND, and D. B. DILL   1940   Experimental human scurvy. *New Engl. J. Med.* **223**, 353–369; *Chem. Abs.* **35**, 1841.

CURRAN, K. M., D. K. TRESSLER, and C. G. KING   1937   Losses of vitamin C during cooking of Northern Spy apples. *Food Research* **2**, 549–557.

DODDS, M. L., and F. L. MACLEOD   1947   Blood plasma ascorbic acid levels on controlled intakes of ascorbic acid. *Science* **106**, 67.

EZELL, B. D., M. S. WILCOX, and M. C. HUTCHINS   1948   Effect of variety and storage on ascorbic acid content of sweetpotatoes. *Food Research* **13**, 116–122.

FARMER, C. J., and A. F. ABT   1938   Titration of plasma ascorbic acid as a test for latent avitaminosis C. Pages 114–147 of *"Nutrition: The Newer Diagnostic Methods."* (New York: Milbank Memorial Fund.)

FINCKE, M. L.   1940   The ascorbic acid (vitamin C) metabolism of college students: A cooperative study. *J. Am. Dietet. Assoc.* **16**, 325–328.

FINCKE, M. L., and V. L. LANDQUIST 1942 The daily intake of ascorbic acid required to maintain adequate and optimal levels of this vitamin in blood plasma. *J. Nutrition* **23**, 483–490.

GEDGOUD, J. L., V. M. WILDER, and J. A. HENSKE 1943 Significance of plasma ascorbic acid values in Nebraska children. *J. Pediat.* **23**, 39–49.

GUERRANT, N. B., and R. A. DUTCHER 1948 Further observations concerning the relationship of temperature of blanching to ascorbic acid retention in green beans. *Arch. Biochem.* **18**, 353–359.

HAMNER, K. C., L. BERNSTEIN, and L. A. MAYNARD 1945 Effects of light intensity, day length, temperature, and other environmental factors on the ascorbic acid content of tomatoes. *J. Nutrition* **29**, 85–97.

HANSEN, E., and G. F. WALDO 1944 Ascorbic acid content of small fruits in relation to genetic and environmental factors. *Food Research* **9**, 453–461.

HARDING, P. L., and E. E. THOMAS 1942 Relation of ascorbic acid concentration in juice of Florida grapefruit to variety, rootstock, and position of fruit on the tree. *J. Agr. Research* **64**, 57–61.

HESS, A. F. 1920 *Scurvy, Past and Present.* (Lippincott.)

HOLLINGER, M. E. 1948 Human utilization of ascorbic acid from mustard greens. *J. Nutrition* **35**, 73–81.

HOLMES, A. D., F. TRIPP, E. A. WOELFFER, and G. H. SATTERFIELD 1939 The influence of pasteurization on the ascorbic acid (vitamin C) content of certified milk. *J. Am. Dietet. Assoc.* **15**, 363–368.

KELLEY, L., M. JACKSON, K. SHEEHAN, and M. OHLSON 1947 Palatability and ascorbic acid retention of rutabaga, peas, and cabbage after holding on the steam table. *J. Am. Dietet. Assoc.* **23**, 120–124.

KING, C. G. 1936 Vitamin C, ascorbic acid. *Physiol. Rev.* **16**, 238–262.

KING, C. G. 1950 Vitamin C. *J. Am. Med. Assoc.* **142**, 563–565.

KING, C. G., and M. L. MENTEN 1935 The influence of vitamin C level upon the resistance to diphtheria toxin. I. Changes in body weight and duration of life. *J. Nutrition* **10**, 129–140.

KING, C. G., R. R. MUSULIN, and W. F. SWANSON 1940 Effects of vitamin C intake upon the degree of tooth injury produced by diphtheria toxin. *Am. J. Public Health* **30**, 1068–1072.

KING, C. G., and D. K. TRESSLER 1940 Effect of processing on the vitamin C content of foods. *Proc. Inst. Food Technol.* **1,** 123–132.

KIRK, M. M., and D. K. TRESSLER 1941 Ascorbic acid content of pigmented fruits, vegetables, and their juices. *Food Research* **6,** 395–411.

KLINE, A. B., and M. S. EHEART 1944 Variation in the ascorbic acid requirements for saturation of nine normal young women. *J. Nutrition* **28,** 413–419.

KRUSE, H. D. 1942 The gingival manifestations of avitaminosis C, with especial consideration of detection of early changes by biomicroscopy. *Milbank Mem. Fund Quart.* **20,** 290–323; *Nutr. Abs. Rev.* **12,** 490.

LANFORD, C. S. 1942 Studies of liberal citrus intakes. *J. Nutrition* **23,** 409–416; *Chem. Abs.* **36,** 3529.

MCCOLLUM, E. V., E. ORENT-KEILES, and H. DAY 1939 *The Newer Knowledge of Nutrition,* 5th Ed. (Macmillan.)

MCINTOSH, J. A., D. K. TRESSLER, and F. FENTON 1940 The effect of different cooking methods on the vitamin C content of quick-frozen vegetables. *J. Home Econ.* **32,** 692–695.

MENKIN, V., S. B. WOLBACH, and M. F. MENKIN 1934 Formation of intercellular substance by administration of ascorbic acid (vitamin C) in experimental scorbutus. *Am. J. Path.* **10,** 569–575.

MENTEN, M. L., and C. G. KING 1935 The influence of vitamin C level upon resistance to diphtheria toxin. II. Production of diffuse hyperplastic arteriosclerosis and degeneration in various organs. *J. Nutrition* **10,** 141–155.

METCALF, E., P. REHM, and J. WINTERS 1940 Variations in ascorbic acid content of grapefruit and oranges from the Rio Grande Valley of Texas. *Food Research* **5,** 233–240.

MEYER, F. L., and M. L. HATHAWAY 1944 Further studies on the vitamin C metabolism of preschool children. *J. Nutrition* **28,** 93–100.

MITCHELL, H. S., O. A. MERRIAM, and E. L. BATCHELDER 1938 The vitamin C status of college women as determined by urinary excretion. *J. Home Econ.* **30,** 645–650.

MOORE, E. L., C. D. ATKINS, E. WIEDERHOLD, and L. G. MACDOWELL 1945 Flavor and ascorbic acid retention in fresh Florida citrus juices. *J. Home Econ.* **37,** 290–293.

MURPHY, E. F. 1941 Ascorbic acid content of onions and observations on its distribution. *Food Research* **6,** 581–594.

MURPHY, E. F. 1942 The ascorbic acid content of different varieties of Maine-grown tomatoes and cabbages as influenced by locality, season, and stage of maturity. *J. Agr. Research* **64,** 483–502.

Murphy, E. F. 1944 The vitamin C content of Maine foods. *Maine Agr. Expt. Sta. Bull.* No. 426, 299–305.

Murphy, E. F., W. F. Dove, and R. V. Akeley 1945 Observations on genetic, physiological, and environmental factors affecting the vitamin C content of Maine-grown potatoes. *Am. Potato J.* 22, 62–83; *Nutr. Abs. Rev.* 15, 298.

Paul, P., B. Einbecker, et al. 1949 The nutritive value of canned foods. II. Changes in ascorbic acid of vegetables during storage prior to canning. *Food Technology* 3, 228–231.

Review 1943 Vitamin C saturation. *Nutrition Rev.* 1, 286.

Review 1945 Clinical scurvy in adults. *Nutrition Rev.* 3, 24–26.

Review 1945b Vitamin C and physical efficiency. *Nutrition Rev.* 3, 221.

Review 1947 Infantile scurvy. *Nutrition Rev.* 5, 90–91.

Richardson, J. E., and H. L. Mayfield 1940 The quality and vitamin content of green peas when cooked or home canned. *Montana Agr. Expt. Sta. Bull.* 381.

Richardson, J. E., and H. L. Mayfield 1941 Vitamin C content of winter fruits and vegetables. *Montana Agr. Expt. Sta. Bull.* 390.

Sharp, P. F. 1936 Vitamin C in pasteurized milk. *Science* 84, 461–462.

Smith, S. L. 1938 Vitamin C: Human requirements. *J. Am. Med. Assoc.* 111, 1753–1764.

Smith, S. L. 1939 Vitamin needs of man: Vitamin C. *U. S. Dept. Agriculture Year Book,* "Food and Life," 235–255.

Storvick, C. A., B. L. Davey, R. M. Nitchals, R. E. Coffey, and M. L. Fincke 1949 Ascorbic acid metabolism of older adolescents. *J. Nutrition* 39, 1–11.

Storvick, C. A., M. L. Fincke, J. P. Quinn, and B. L. Davey 1947 A study of ascorbic acid metabolism of adolescent children. *J. Nutrition* 33, 529–539.

Storvick, C. A., and H. M. Hauck 1942 Effect of controlled ascorbic acid ingestion upon urinary excretion and plasma concentration of ascorbic acid in normal adults. *J. Nutrition* 23, 111–123.

Todhunter, E. N., and R. C. Robbins 1940 The amount of ascorbic acid required to maintain tissue saturation in normal adults. *J. Nutrition* 19, 263–270.

Todhunter, E. N., R. C. Robbins, and J. A. McIntosh 1942 The rate of increase of blood plasma ascorbic acid after ingestion of ascorbic acid (vitamin C). *J. Nutrition* 23, 309–319.

Tressler, D. K., and K. M. Curran 1938 The cause of loss of vitamin C from bottled tomato juice. *J. Home Econ.* 30, 487–488.

Tressler, D. K., and J. C. Moyer 1941 Changes in vitamin C content of Bartlett pears in cold and gas storage. *Food Research* 6, 373–376.

Van Duyne, F. O., S. M. Bruckhart, J. T. Chase, and J. I. Simpson 1945 Ascorbic acid content of freshly harvested vegetables. *J. Am. Dietet. Assoc.* 21, 153–154.

Van Duyne, F. O., J. T. Chase, and J. I. Simpson 1945 Effects of various home practices on ascorbic acid content of potatoes. *Food Research* 10, 72–83.

White, B. H., and V. R. Goddard 1948 Green Chili peppers as a source of ascorbic acid in Mexican diet. *J. Am. Dietet. Assoc.* 24, 666–669.

Wiehl, D. G. 1942 Medical evaluation of nutritional status. VII. Diets of high school students of low-income families in New York City. *Milbank Mem. Fund Quart.* 20, 61–82.

Woods, E. 1935 The vitamin C content of the Russet Burbank potato of Idaho. *Idaho Agr. Expt. Sta. Bull. No.* 219; *Nutr. Abs. Rev.* 5, 967.

Wortis, H., J. Liebmann, and E. Wortis 1938 Vitamin C in the blood, spinal fluid, and urine. *J. Am. Med. Assoc.* 110, 1896–1899.

Yavorsky, M., P. Almaden, and C. G. King 1934 The vitamin C content of human tissue. *J. Biol. Chem.* 106, 525–529.

XII

THIAMINE (VITAMIN B$_1$)

Discovery and Identification of the Substance temporarily called Vitamin B and now named Thiamine

The existence of the substance now named *thiamine* was discovered both through studies of the disease beriberi and through experiments in normal nutrition. Here, as often, discovery was a process of gradual accumulation of evidence until finally it became convincing.

Beriberi manifests itself primarily as a nerve disease and usually appears first as a weakness and loss of neuromuscular coordination in the feet and legs, equally on both sides of the body. In formal terminology it is *a multiple peripheral neuritis*. It has been most prevalent in the Orient.

In 1878–1883, when the entire enlisted force of the Japanese navy was about 5000 men, each year's sick-lists showed from 1000 to 2000 cases of beriberi among them. Takaki, as a patriotic son of Japan and medical officer in her navy, could not reconcile himself to this enormous annual morbidity of 20 to 40 per cent from one disease. Careful study convinced him that it was not due to tropical climate, for British crews in tropical waters were not thus affected; nor to lack of care in sanitation, in which he found the Japanese as scrupulous as other sailors. He then obtained authority for a large-scale experiment with the ration. Two ships each carrying about 300 men were sent in succession over the same long cruise but with different rations. On the first ship, which was furnished with the then standard Japanese ration containing a greatly predominant amount of white rice, more than two-thirds of the men suffered from beriberi; while on the second ship, with a ration in which part of the white rice was replaced by barley, vegetables, fish, meat, and canned milk, only a few men developed beriberi, and these were found not to have eaten their share of the new foods. So convincing was the evidence, and so striking the contrast, that within a very short time thereafter Takaki was able to obtain a similar change of ration throughout the Japanese navy and this change was followed by a prompt decrease in beriberi cases, from a very high percentage to a mere fraction of one per cent.

The reported figures were as shown in Table 19.

TABLE 19. *Beriberi in the Japanese Navy (1880–1889)*

Year		Total Force	Cases of Beriberi	Percentage
1880	Old ration	4,956	1,725	34.81
1881	" "	4,641	1,165	25.06
1882	" "	4,769	1,929	40.45
1883	" "	5,346	1,236	23.12
1884	Ration changed	5,638	718	12.74
1885	New ration	6,918	41	0.59
1886	" "	8,475	3	0.04
1887	" "	9,106	0	0.00
1888	" "	9,184	0	0.00
1889	" "	8,954	3	0.03

Takaki received prompt and generous official recognition for this really great achievement in practically ridding his country's navy of this disease which had previously been so prevalent: he was promoted, made a baron, and appointed the permanent head of a Government hospital and training-school in Tokyo. Yet there was a long lag not only in popular but even in scientific and professional understanding of what he had accomplished.

Why was it so many years before the people of the Orient generally began to share the benefit from what had been demonstrated so clearly and acted upon so promptly in the Japanese navy? Takaki had really rid the navy of beriberi by changing the ration, and he had been explicit in saying so. He had even emphasized the fact that the fault in the older ration was nutritional. He had stated the facts as he saw them clearly and emphatically enough; but with world medical opinion, and so with the people generally, his statements remained ineffective because his explanation was inadequate. He attributed the superiority of the reformed ration simply to its higher protein content, which others rightly regarded as unconvincing. It was a time of great activity in the sanitary applications of the then new and brilliantly developing science of bacteriology; and naturally some advances in sanitation had been made in the same period in which Takaki had secured the reform of the ration. So with no adequate nutritional explanation at hand, it seemed to most medical men more probable that the diminished frequency of the disease in the Japanese navy was due to some sanitary cause, even though no infective agent had been discovered. Hence Takaki's work was largely forgotten, and most of those who had to deal with beriberi regarded it as probably due to some undiscovered infective agent.

Such was the view of the American Army Medical Officers when they took over the Philippines during and after the war with Spain. Their striking experience with beriberi in the Bilibid prison at Manila was, however, very influential in reviving the nutritional view of the disease.

When officers of the United States army took charge of this prison, they found what at first appeared to them as an abuse in the fact that the poor prisoners accustomed to live so largely upon rice had been fed with rice of low commercial quality, uneven in size and dark in color. This they promptly replaced by "high grade" rice, consisting of uniform, plump, well-polished, white kernels. Notwithstanding their attempts at better and more humane treatment of their prisoners, however, these officers were soon distressed by an epidemic of beriberi in their prison population.

The monthly record ran as shown in Table 20.

During the first several months of the epidemic every effort at further sanitary improvement was made, the responsible medical officers thinking at first only in terms of the theory that beriberi was due to infection. Failure of their earnest sanitary efforts led them to further study of the literature of beriberi, and in the light of the papers which Takaki had published several years before and which had been generally forgotten meanwhile, they finally began to think that the nutrition hypothesis might be worthy of trial. Accordingly, a change of ration was then made; and it was followed by practical disappearance of the disease in the course of about three months (Table 20).

It was at about the same time with this experience in the Bilibid prison that a nutritional interpretation was given to the observations first published by Eijkman, a Dutch physician working in the East Indies, upon "an illness of fowls similar to beriberi." He noticed that such a disease developed in fowls which lived in the bare yard of a prison hospital and subsisted almost entirely upon leftover rice from the prisoners' tables. In systematic trials he found that by confining fowls strictly to a polished-rice diet he could induce experimental beriberi with great regularity. Eijkman, however, did not at first explain the experimental disease in direct nutritional terms but rather upon the hypothesis of the presence of some unknown injurious substance; so that, as English writers afterward expressed it, "the pharmacological bias" at first prevented the nutritional significance from being seen. It was in papers published after the turn of the century and dealing with the work of Grijns as well as of Eijkman, that the experimentally induced disease was first clearly stated to be a *nutritional* polyneuritis.

TABLE 20. *Beriberi in the Bilibid Prison (1901–1903)*

Year	Month	Cases	Deaths
1901	November	2	0
Ration changed			
1901	December	52	2
1902	January	169	12
1902	February	1087	16
1902	March	576	15
1902	April	327	15
1902	May	310	19
1902	June	451	17
1902	July	233	33
1902	August	571	24
1902	September	522	31
Ration again changed October 20th			
1902	October	579	34
1902	November	476	8
1902	December	89	3
1903	January 1–15	4	0

Then followed about a quarter-century of very active search for the *antineuritic substance*. Several groups of investigators in different countries contributed toward the working out of methods for the separation of this substance and the study of its chemical nature. Funk in a paper published near the middle of this period proposed the name *vitamine*. Thus in this case the name was coined and proposed several years after the discovery of the existence and of some of the most important properties of the substance; and several years before its complete chemical identification.

It is to R. R. Williams that we feel most deeply indebted for knowledge as to the chemical nature of this substance, and preference is given to the name *thiamine* (or *thiamine chloride* or *hydrochloride*) which he proposed for it after its chemical identification had been completed. The structural formula may be found in textbooks of organic and biological chemistry, or on page 354 of Sherman's *Chemistry of Food and Nutrition,* Seventh Edition. The complete chemical name is obviously too long for everyday use. The name *thiamine* tells about as much of the chemical nature of the substance as can be conveyed in one short word. Because it is considered preferable that the name of each chemical individual shall suggest its chemical nature and shall not imply a therapeutic claim, *thiamine* is preferred to *aneurin* as the permanent name for the substance temporarily called vitamin B or B_1.

The American Institute of Nutrition, the American Society of Biological Chemists, and the American Medical Association's Councils on Foods and on Pharmacy and Chemistry are among those who have formally adopted and recommended the use of the name thiamine. At present the terms thiamine and vitamin B_1 are used interchangeably for the antineuritic substance once called anti-beriberi vitamine or vitamin B.

In 1911 Osborne and Mendel published the reports of their epoch-marking *Feeding Experiments with Isolated Food Substances* (Carnegie Institution of Washington, Publication No. 156, Parts I and II, 1911) and began their series of articles in *The Journal of Biological Chemistry,* Vol. 12 *et seq.* And in 1912 appeared the full account of the work by Hopkins which we noted in Chapter I.

While their work had originally been planned as a study of the nutritive values of individual proteins, Osborne and Mendel quickly perceived that purified protein and carbohydrate with butterfat and a good salt mixture lacked some nutritional essential which the water-soluble part of milk contained. This they supplied first by including in their experimental food mixtures generous proportions of what they called "protein-free milk," made by removing the coagulable proteins from whey and drying the clear filtrate. Soon they found that this nutritional need could be met also by the feeding of yeast, the material from which Funk was extracting what he called yeast vitamine. Then soon after this McCollum became convinced by his own experiments and those of Osborne and Mendel, that this water-soluble growth-essential was the same substance which prevented and cured beriberi. As he had already found that a fat-soluble factor was essential, McCollum now proposed the terms *fat-soluble A* and *water-soluble B*. But the catchy term "vitamin" had stuck, and in 1920 Drummond proposed (as noted more fully in Chapter XI) that the fat-soluble substance be called vitamin A; the water-soluble antineuritic substance, vitamin B; and the antiscorbutic substance, vitamin C.

In laboratory feeding experiments it came to be customary to use yeast as a source of vitamin B, and to attribute to vitamin B whatever of "vitaminic" values yeast was found to have.

To this extent, then, the term vitamin B covered also the other water-soluble vitamins contained in yeast and confused them with the antineuritic substance. Inasmuch, therefore, as the early literature of vitamin B belongs in part also to the other yeast vitamins, all these are sometimes collectively called the "B vitamins" or the "vitamin-B complex" or the "B group of vitamins."

Later, to distinguish it from the other members of the "B group" which were by then recognized to exist, the antineuritic substance (our present thiamine, but not structurally identified at that time) was designated vitamin B_1.

Nutritional Functions of Thiamine

This antineuritic substance (the original vitamin B, now vitamin B_1, or thiamine) has at least three other more or less specific nutritional functions: it is essential to growth, it has an important part in the maintenance of appetite, and it is concerned in at least one stage of carbohydrate metabolism.

An illustration of its relation to growth may be seen in Fig. 28. Seven rats of a litter were fed, one at a thiamine level but little above that required to prevent deficiency disease, and two each at three successively higher levels. Although all were healthy, the rate of growth was quite definitely determined by the thiamine intake, other conditions being uniform.

The effects upon growth and upon appetite may well be inter-

204   ESSENTIALS OF NUTRITION

connected; and to the favorite conundrum of Osborne and Mendel, "Does he eat more because he grows faster, or grow faster because he eats more?" the best answer is probably, "Both."

The relation to appetite is, however, specific in two senses: (1) While appetite may decline as the result of any of several vitamin deficiencies, no other known vitamin has such a prompt and apparently direct effect upon appetite as has thiamine. (2) The relation to appetite is also specific in the sense that it is a true effect upon appetite as a physiological condition and function of the

Fig. 28. Growth of healthy individuals as influenced by the level of thiamine, the food being allowed 'ad libitum.' (See text.)

body, and not merely a matter of making the food appetizing. For even when the vitamin is given separately the experimental animal will return with appetite, and often with dramatic promptness, to the same food which it has previously refused.

To what extent the weakening of the organism in thiamine deficiency is due to starvation from lack of interest in food is still a research problem; and to what extent and in what circumstances it is feasible and desirable to stimulate the appetites of patients by administration of thiamine concentrates is a problem for the physician. In good scientific literature one may meet the simple statement that this vitamin increases or stimulates the appetite; but sometimes there is a tendency to qualify this so sharply as to limit it to a statement that this vitamin restores an appetite which has declined for lack of it.

Stabilization of the appetite is helpful to the good growth and general wellbeing of children; and with adults, while growth is no longer concerned, there is still value in the toning-up and stabilizing of the appetite, of the digestive mechanism, and of the processes involved in the carbohydrate metabolism.

Peters and his coworkers at Oxford have especially studied the relation of thiamine to the process of metabolism. They found an abnormal accumulation of lactic acid and of the closely related pyruvic acid in the brain tissue of pigeons which had been kept on thiamine-deficient food; and also that sections of *such* brain tissue did not show the same power as did parallel sections from a normal brain, to oxidize glucose in a suitable respiration apparatus. Furthermore it was shown that, when thiamine was injected into polyneuritic pigeons, the brain tissue was restored to its normal power of burning glucose completely to carbon dioxide.

Williams and Spies emphasize the view that similar or analogous relationships exist in all the various tissues in which carbohydrate metabolism occurs; thus explaining the helpfulness of liberal thiamine intake in widely varied physiological and clinical conditions.

The work of Osborne and Mendel and that of Brodie and Mac-Leod showed that the thiamine content of body tissues may be influenced by that of the food.

More recently Harris, Leong, and Ungley[*] report that, as in the case of vitamin C so also with thiamine, the amount excreted in the urine reflects to some extent the level of intake and concentration of the substance in the tissues and fluids of the body; and that the thiamine content of the blood is lowered in conditions which involve either a diminished nutritional intake or an increased rate of destruction. The increased demand of pregnancy may also have the effect of lowering the level of thiamine concentration in the blood.

Harris and other English workers have given special attention to the relation of thiamine intake to the heart action. Experimenting with rats they found that shortage of thiamine in the food, with resulting incompleteness of carbohydrate metabolism and increase

[*] Harris, L. J., P. C. Leong, and C. C. Ungley. *Lancet* 1938, I, 539; Ungley, C. C. *Lancet* 1938, I, 981; Harris, *Vitamins and Vitamin Deficiencies*, Vol. I.

of pyruvic acid in the blood, slows the action of the muscles of the heart, often from the rat's normal rate of about 500 beats per minute to 350 or less.

This *experimental bradycardia* is quickly curable by injection of thiamine or by ingestion of food which contains it. Such experiments have even been made a method of estimating the thiamine values of foods.

Measures of Thiamine

The technique of measurement of the thiamine contents of foods and of artificial concentrates is subject to rather rapid change at present and need not detain us in our present study; for now that thiamine is readily available in pure form all methods for its determination in foods or other materials are of course standardized by control measurements with pure thiamine. And for the same reason we can now express the amount of thiamine contained in a food or desired in a diet in direct terms, just as we have done in the cases of protein, phosphorus, calcium, iron, and ascorbic acid; though the absolute amounts of thiamine concerned in our normal nutrition are so small that we sometimes use a unit of weight even smaller than the milligram.

The present custom is the one recommended by Williams and Spies, namely, the expression *in terms of micrograms or milligrams*. The microgram is the millionth of a gram, or the thousandth of a milligram. It is often represented by the Greek letter gamma (γ) or (we think preferably) by the abbreviation, mcg.

Human Requirements

Williams and Spies (1938) included in their monograph very careful estimates of the amounts of thiamine required to prevent beriberi; but more recently they, in common with nearly all students of the subject, have come to take a view which leads to a distinctly higher estimate of normal nutritional requirement than the earlier one of Williams and Spies. This newer view is based largely upon investigations made in Wilder's laboratory, in which volunteers have remained for relatively long periods on low-thiamine diets under the constant observation of physicians who gave special attention to the detection of evidences of slight deficiency through signs which under ordinary conditions might easily go unrecognized. Wilder writes of these symptoms as impairments of emotional stability and of mental and physical efficiency which precede the more noticeable signs of thiamine deficiency by weeks or months. After six months of such moderate restriction and having shown the milder symptoms for months with entire clearness to the physicians especially practiced in detecting them, there still was no sign of the characteristic symptoms of beriberi, such as polyneuritis and heart failure. Hence it is our present view that human requirement is to be judged not simply as the small amount which suffices to prevent beriberi, but as the larger amount required to prevent the much earlier signs of a relatively mild neurasthenia, plus a margin for physiological variability of individuals and for safety which practically aims at an *optimal* intake.* This optimal intake has been estimated by Wilder's group at not less than 0.5 nor more than 1.0 milligram of thiamine per 1000 Calories of a diet of ordinary composition.

It is perhaps to be regarded as an open question: how far the variations of individual views on thiamine requirement are due to differences of diagnostic methods and interpretation; and how far to actual physiological differences among normal people.

The Recommended Allowances of the Food and Nutrition Board of the National Research Council provide 1.2 milligrams of thiamine daily for a sedentary man or a moderately active woman, with allowances for people of other ages and activities set practically in parallel with their energy requirements as may be seen from the full table of Recommended Allowances in the Appendix.

Thiamine Contents of Typical Foods

Thiamine is of very widespread occurrence in the animal and vegetable kingdoms, and therefore in foods of both animal and plant origin unless these have been artificially refined or otherwise subjected to loss. Table 21 herewith gives the results of our study of available data on some typical foods, stated in each case in terms of a range which is intended as a reasonable estimate of the bounds within which the true average probably will be found. The Government's 1950 estimates of average values for a larger number of foods are included in the Appendix.

* See among Suggested Readings at the end of this chapter, Williams, (R.D.), Mason, and Wilder (1943).

TABLE 21. *Thiamine Contents of Typical Foods: Micrograms per 100 Grams*

Food	Range Within Which Average Will Probably Be Found
Foods of Animal Origin	
Beef muscle	80–180
Chicken (and fowl)	75–95
Lamb and mutton (lean)	120–250
Pork muscle	680–1150
Liver (of cattle, sheep, and swine)	250–400
Milk	40–65
Eggs	80–120
Egg white	trace
Egg yolk	250–350
Grain Products	
Oats (oatmeal)	345–770
Rice, entire	240–350
Rice, white (polished)	30–70
Wheat, entire	450–660
White flour (not enriched)	60–100
Enriched white bread	240
Dry Legumes	
Beans, pea or navy, dry	400–700
Beans, Lima, dry	400–700
Peas, dry	600–900
Peanuts	300–600
Other Vegetables and Fruits	
Apples	20–50
Bananas	40–80
Beans, snap or string	55–95
Cabbage	50–100
Carrots	60–140
Lettuce	40–60
Orange (or juice)	75–145
Peas, fresh young green	270–495
Potatoes	95–165
Spinach	95–155
Tomato (or fresh juice)	60–100

Meats exhibit a noteworthy species difference in that the average thiamine content of pork muscle exceeds that of beef muscle, though the data of Hughes (1941) indicate that this difference is somewhat smaller and more variable than has been widely believed. The few investigations thus far available do not show a corresponding species difference in the glandular organs and we have therefore averaged the data on the *kidney* and *liver,* respectively, from cattle, sheep, and swine together. These glandular organs show thiamine values intermediate between beef muscle and pork muscle.

The thiamine values of *milk* and of *eggs* are probably more stable. When comparing them with each other and with meats, the fact that milk is much more watery should be kept in mind. When milk is as liberally used as (for several nutritional reasons) is wise, it becomes one of the major sources of thiamine in the dietary, though this fact is often missed because of the high water content of milk.

Cereal grains and their milling and bakery products call for special attention, because while the seed as a whole is relatively rich in thiamine very much the largest part of this is rejected in the milling of refined wheat flour or rice. The replacement of the thiamine, so as to bring white bread to something approaching a whole-wheat level *in this respect,* can now be done in any of three ways: by returning wheat germ in the making of the bread; by the use of a specially developed high-vitamin yeast; or by adding thiamine itself to the white flour when milled or in breadmaking.

"Enriched" is the term authorized by the United States Food and Drug Administration to designate a white or near-white flour or bread which contains specified amounts of thiamine (and of such other things as may be prescribed by Federal regulation) whether this enrichment be effected by one or another of the three plans just mentioned or by combining them with each other or with new methods of milling which produce white or near-white flours of higher thiamine content than the white flours of the ordinary roller-mill process.

The legume seeds, *beans, lentils, peas,* and *peanuts,* rank near or with the whole-grain cereals as rich sources of thiamine. This is true even of *fresh young green peas,* notwithstanding their higher water content.

The *other vegetables* and *the fruits* show variations either way from an average of about 100 micrograms of thiamine per 100 grams of the edible material in the moist state in which most fruits and vegetables are marketed. It is a common mistake,—met even in some otherwise authoritative books, and often in oral discussion,—to treat the succulent fruits and vegetables as if, containing only about one part per million of thiamine, they were therefore nearly negligible sources. But because of their succulent character (and relatively low calories) fresh, including frozen and cold-stored, fruits and vegetables can be consumed in liberal quantities with pleasure and without fear of making the dietary too fattening. Moreover, our newest knowledge of nutrition tells us even more clearly than did the "newer knowledge" of a few years ago, that liberal use of such fruits and vegetables is so advantageous to health and efficiency as to be especially good dietetics and food economics. A normal adult dietary which gives due recognition to present-day knowledge will very probably contain two to three pounds of total fruit-and-vegetables in the course of a day, and when used in such quantities the fruits and vegetables as a group are among the major sources of thiamine in the dietary. A more abundant use of fruits and vegetables, the selection varying with individual preference and with market supply and price, is certainly one of the very best ways of improving the dietary in several of its mineral and vitamin factors.

Stability of Thiamine in the Storage and Preparation of Foods

Mature, dry, unbroken seeds seem to contain their thiamine in a relatively stable form and favorable environment. In one published report, the evidence of local records was accepted as showing that wheat taken from the bottom of a certain tight dry granary compartment was a century old. On feeding to experimental animals it was found to be a potent source of thiamine. Obviously there was no means of knowing just how much thiamine it had originally contained; but obviously also the thiamine of this wheat had shown good stability.

Like other thermolabile substances thiamine is more stable to heating in a dry state than in solution.

Thiamine, like vitamin C, is (other conditions being equal) distinctly more stable in a moderately acid than in a correspondingly alkaline solution.

In tomato juice, for instance, experiments at Columbia showed that the rate at which the destruction of thiamine occurred was gradually increased with rising temperature (thus correcting the early impression that the substance was "stable at 100° but destroyed at 130°"), while other work brought out clearly the destructive effect of additions of alkali on whichever side of the neutral point.

In one series of experiments, heating was always at the natural acidity of the tomato juice (pH = 4.3). At 100° C., this heating destroyed 20 per cent of the original thiamine in 4 hours; at 110°, 33 per cent; at 120°, 47 per cent; and at 130°, 55 per cent. Clearly there is here no sudden destruction, or even sudden rise in the rate of destruction, at any definite temperature. The chemical reaction which changes the thiamine into something else is increased in its rate as the temperature rises, but no more so than most chemical reactions. Another study showed also a destruction of 20 per cent of the thiamine of tomato juice when heated 4 hours at its natural acidity; when the acidity was about half neutralized before the heating, the destruction rose to 31 per cent; and when the juice had been brought barely over the neutral point (to pH 7.9) the destruction for the same time and temperature of heating was 70 per cent.

While thiamine and ascorbic acid thus show a similarity in their thermolability and susceptibility to alkali, we would not be justified in assuming from these facts similarity of behavior of vitamins in general; for Morgan has found that the impregnation of drying fruit with sulfurous acid diminishes the loss of vitamin C but increases the loss of thiamine.

In a study made by the U. S. Department of Agriculture, about 20 to 25 per cent of the thiamine of spinach, potatoes, and snap beans was destroyed when these vegetables were cooked by boiling, while additional amounts were dissolved away. Soda, added to preserve the green color of the snap beans, more than doubled the destruction of thiamine in cooking. Cooking carrots in boiling water or under steam pressure, and double-boiler cooking of rolled oats and whole wheat up to two hours, did not cause any measurable destruction of thiamine; but roasting pork loin destroyed 40 to 45 per cent of the thiamine present.

Baking losses as reported are now known to have been above the truth in some cases, because some of the methods used for determination of thiamine do not reveal the whole amount present in the baked product. In a special study made by the Food and

Drug Administration and reported in the official hearings upon the proposed new standards for bread, the baking losses ranged from too little to measure, up to about 15 per cent as a maximum, and averaged less than one tenth of the thiamine originally present in the dough from which the bread was made.

In an investigation of wheat germ muffins, it was found that there was no cooking loss of measurable degree unless soda was used, but with the use of soda there was a loss of 26 per cent of the original amount of thiamine. (For the full account, see Fincke and Little (1941) in the list of Suggested Readings below, which list also gives references to other studies of losses in cooking.)

Thiamine and the Enrichment Program

The trend of opinion has been and is favorable to liberal use of thiamine.

The argument runs that three causes operate to produce thiamine deficiency in the body: (1) low intake; (2) derangement of gastro-intestinal function which may diminish absorption; and (3) increased destruction or inefficiency of utilization in the tissues (with resulting relatively large individual differences of need).

The fact that a large proportion of the total food calories has very often been taken in the form of artificially refined foods containing little if any thiamine is unquestionable.

Whether a large proportion of people have abnormalities of digestion or metabolism which prevent their efficient absorption and use of thiamine, and therefore need considerably more than the normal, is a medical question which reaches beyond the scope of this book.

The comprehensive and critical review of clinical experience up to 1938, given by Williams and Spies in their *Vitamin B_1 (Thiamine) and Its Use in Medicine,* presents abundant evidence of favorable attitudes on the part of physicians; and leading physicians not only continue to make much use of thiamine therapeutically but have also cordially endorsed the movement to bring more thiamine into our daily dietaries through the use of Enriched flour and bread.

Williams and Spies (1938) also emphasized the view that deficiencies too mild to be recognized may nevertheless be cumulative in their weakening effects; that sometimes too, a diet followed because of a fear of digestive weakness is poor in thiamine and thus actually induces a slow degeneration of the digestive powers and perhaps also of the appetite; and moreover that "Because of custom or preconceived ideas as to what foods are good for them, or because of dependence upon appetite as a guide to the proper selection of foods, many people are likely to choose a poorly balanced diet," even when poverty is not a factor in their food selection.

The British Medical Journal pointed out editorially that in England the social custom of using the white bread which the present-day roller process of milling enables the baker to offer to his public has resulted in the unjustifiable situation that even the comfortably circumstanced typical Englishman of recent years was getting less thiamine than the half-starved paupers of a century ago; for while the latter were given only a semi-starvation ration it consisted largely of bread which had not been robbed of any of the natural constituents of the wheat. And a little later, the British quarterly *Nutrition Abstracts and Reviews* gave leading position to a review by Copping (1939) which recognizes frankly the strength of social custom and of the preference of the milling and baking interests for the products which are easiest for them, and explains that the interest of the public health requires a modification of the fashion of extreme whiteness ("fineness") in flour and bread.

Copping concludes: (1) that the change from the formerly standard flour which contained more of the wheat to the present-day white flour has resulted in the reduction of the nutritive value of the protein, in serious lowering of the content of calcium, phosphorus, and iron, as well as the nearly complete elimination of vitamin value . . . "all representing dead loss nutritionally"; (2) that in order to change back to whole-wheat flour it will be necessary both to educate the public and to overcome the inertia of the existing milling industry and flour trade; and (3) that "the advantages to be gained in national health would make it well worth while to overcome these difficulties."

So far as thiamine is concerned, the difficulty was greatly reduced when commercial production by synthesis made possible the restoration of this vitamin by adding the pure substance to the familiar white flour.

Enriched flour or bread as officially defined does not attempt restoration at every point, and in the case of thiamine there is no attempt to ensure that the restoration shall be entirely up to whole wheat levels. The basis chosen by the Food and Drug Administration was rather that the enrichment should be sufficient so that the new white flour should "carry its share" of the thiamine needed in our nutrition. Hence eating Enriched bread does not in itself "solve the thiamine problem"; but it is a worthwhile help. Those who insist that all the white bread they eat shall be enriched have taken a significant step in the right direction, and often this improvement may be sufficient to raise the diet to an excellent level of thiamine content if it is reasonably abundant and well balanced in other respects.

EXERCISES

1. Develop symptoms of thiamine deficiency in rats, pigeons, fowls, or chicks by means of a diet deficient in thiamine.
2. What is the thiamine content of each of the dietaries or weekly food orders which you have previously planned or recorded?
3. Arrange your "twelve to forty foods" in the order of their thiamine content: (a) per 100 grams of the edible portion; (b) per 100 Calories.
4. Which of the dietaries which you have previous studied provide as much thiamine as the Recommended Daily Allowances?
5. In your own home, or where you take your meals, is all white bread enriched? Is this also true of all white flour used in other ways?
6. By inquiry and observation in bakery and grocery shops, what proportion of the breadstuffs sold in your community would you judge to be enriched or whole-grain?
7. If all the breadstuffs consumed were enriched or whole grain, would you feel that no further thought need be given to either iron or thiamine in planning dietaries for normal people?

SUGGESTED READINGS

ARNOLD, A., and C. A. ELVEHJEM 1939 Influence of the composition of the diet on the thiamine requirement of dogs. *Am. J. Physiol.* **126**, 289–298.

BARNES, B., D. K. TRESSLER, and F. FENTON 1943 Thiamine content of fresh and frozen peas and corn before and after cooking. *Food Research* **8**, 420–427.

BRODIE, J. B., and F. L. MACLEOD 1935 Quantitative experiments on the occurrence of vitamin B in organs. *J. Nutrition* **10**, 179–186.

Conner, R. T., and G. J. Straub 1941 The thiamine and riboflavin contents of wheat and corn. *Cereal Chem.* 18, 671–677.

Copping, A. M. 1939 The nutritive value of wheaten flour and bread. *Nutr. Abs. Rev.* 8, 555–566.

Cowgill, G. R. 1939 The physiology of vitamin B_1. Chapter VIII in the American Medical Association volume, *The Vitamins, 1939*.

Daniel, L., and L. C. Norris 1945 The riboflavin, niacin and thiamin content of dried leguminous seeds. *J. Nutrition* 30, 31–36.

Daniels, A. L., M. L. Giddings, and D. Jordan 1929 Effect of heat on the antineuritic vitamin of milk. *J. Nutrition* 1, 455–466.

Editorial 1941 Induced thiamine deficiency. *J. Am. Med. Assoc.* 116, 707–708.

Elsom, K. O., F. H. Lewy, and G. W. Heublein 1940 Clinical studies of experimental vitamin B complex deficiency. *Am. J. Med. Sci.* 200, 757–764.

Elsom, K. O., F. D. W. Lukens, E. H. Montgomery, and L. Jonas 1940 Metabolic disturbances in experimental human vitamin B deficiency. *J. Clin. Invest.* 19, 153–161; *Chem. Abs.* 34, 5120.

Fincke, M. L., and R. R. Little 1941 The thiamine (vitamin B_1) values of wheat germ muffins. *J. Am. Dietet. Assoc.* 17, 531–534.

Hanning, F. 1941 The effects of long cooking upon the stability of thiamine in cereals. *J. Am. Dietet. Assoc.* 17, 527–530.

Hoffman, C., T. R. Schweitzer, and G. Dalby 1940 The loss of thiamine in bread on baking and toasting. *Cereal Chem.* 17, 737–739; *Chem. Abs.* 35, 528.

Holman, W. I. M. 1946 The amounts of (thiamine) in cereals and the extent to which they supply human requirements in various dietaries, *Nutr. Abs. Rev.* 15, 387–410.

Kelly, E., and T. Porter 1941 Effect of cooking upon the vitamin B_1 content of two types of beans grown in Michigan. *Food Research*, 6, 85–93.

Lane, R. L., E. Johnson, and R. R. Williams 1942 Studies of the average American diet. I. Thiamine content. *J. Nutrition* 23, 613–624.

McCollum, E. V., et al. 1939 *The Newer Knowledge of Nutrition*, 5th Ed., Chapters XVIII and XIX. (Macmillan.)

Melnick, D. 1944 A critique of values suggested as the thiamine requirement of man. *J. Am. Dietet. Assoc.* 20, 516–520.

Mendel, L. B. 1923 *Nutrition: The Chemistry of Life*, Chapter III. (Yale University Press.)

OSBORNE, T. B., and L. B. MENDEL 1923 The effect of diet on the content of vitamin B in the liver. *J. Biol. Chem.* **58**, 363–367.

REVIEW 1949 Effect of conversion processes on thiamine content of milled rice. *Nutrition Rev.* **7**, 125–126.

REVIEW 1949b Thiamine content of pork. *Nutrition Rev.* **7**, 238–239.

SANDELS, M. R. 1930 Experimental nutritional polyneuritis in the rat. *J. Nutrition* **2**, 409–413.

SHERMAN, H. C., and M. R. SANDELS 1931 Further experimental differentiation of vitamins B and G. *J. Nutrition* **3**, 395–409.

SOMERS, G. F., M. H. COOLIDGE, and K. C. HAMNER 1945 The distribution of thiamine and riboflavin in wheat grains. *Cereal Chem.* **22**, 333–340.

STEPHENSON, W., C. PENTON, and V. KOREŃCHEVSKY 1941 Some effects of vitamins B and C on senile patients. *Brit. Med. J.* **1941, II**, 839–844; *J. Am. Med. Assoc.* **118**, 1333.

SURE, B. 1944 Influence of sub-optimum doses of thiamine on urinary excretions of riboflavin. *J. Nutrition* **27**, 447–452.

VORHAUS, M. G., R. R. WILLIAMS, and R. E. WATERMAN 1935 Studies on crystalline vitamin B_1. Experimental and clinical observations. *J. Am. Med. Assoc.* **105**, 1580–1584.

WATERMAN, R. E., and M. AMMERMAN 1935 Studies of crystalline vitamin B. V. Effect of graduated doses on growing rats. *J. Nutrition* **10**, 35–44.

WERTZ, A. W., and C. E. WEIR 1944 The effect of institutional cooking methods on vitamin contents of food. I. The thiamine content of potatoes. *J. Nutrition* **28**, 255–261.

WILLIAMS, R. D., H. L. MASON, and R. M. WILDER 1943 The minimum daily requirement of thiamine of man. *J. Nutrition* **25**, 71–97.

WILLIAMS, R. R. 1939 The chemistry of thiamine. Chapter VII of the American Medical Association volume, *The Vitamins, 1939.*

WILLIAMS, R. R. 1941 Fortification and restoration of processed foods. *Industrial and Engineering Chem.* **33**, 718–720.

WILLIAMS, R. R., and T. D. SPIES 1938 *Vitamin B_1 (Thiamine) and Its Use in Medicine.* (Macmillan.)

XIII

RIBOFLAVIN, NIACIN (NICOTINIC ACID), AND THE PROBLEM OF PELLAGRA WITH ITS RELATED ILLS

Introductory Explanation

The science of nutrition of 1920 recognized vitamins A, B, and C. Since that time not only have several independent additions been made, but also there have been differentiations within the original concepts. Most especially is this true of vitamin B. We are not here concerned with questions as to how many members of the "B group of vitamins" there are, or as to all the different designations and concepts that have been more or less current in the course of the evolution of our knowledge up to its present point. Rather, this chapter is devoted to two of the more heat-stable vitamins of the B group. Each of these is now a well recognized specific nutrient; both are involved in the problem of pellagra and its related ills. Hence they are included together in this chapter. First we shall study riboflavin, its significance in nutrition and its quantitative distribution in foods, in much the same way that we studied thiamine in the preceding chapter; then we take up more briefly niacin (nicotinic acid) regarding which our quantitative knowledge is still too tentative to call for treatment on the same plan and scale. Finally we shall discuss the very important health problems of the prevention of pellagra and the other diseases in which shortages of one or both of these vitamins are involved.

Riboflavin

After yeast had been used for some years as an occasional experimental food in vitamin research, it was found to have a growth-promoting value (as an addition to certain laboratory diets) even after it had been heated to destroy its thiamine. Evidently it contained something of nutritional significance which is more stable toward heat than thiamine is.

This relatively heat-stable (thermostable) something was found also to be present, in relatively greater abundance than was thiamine, in milk; and likewise to a very significant extent in egg-white, which showed only traces of thiamine.

It had long been known that milk contains beside the orange-yellow fat-soluble substance which goes into the butter or cheese, a greenish-yellow water-soluble natural coloring matter, which was first called *lactochrome,* and later *lactoflavin.* And this lactoflavin now turned out to have nutritional effects agreeing with some of those of the "heat-stable fraction" of yeast. The explanation, or part of it, was found to be that the individual substance lactoflavin is one of the relatively heat-stable factors contained in yeast, in milk, and in some other foods.

This factor was also separated as a pure substance from egg white and found to be chemically the same whether obtained from milk, or egg, or any of a number of other sources. Very soon too it was synthesized in the laboratory and its chemical nature fully established. (The structural formula is shown on page 256 of the American Medical Association's "The Vitamins, 1939" and on page 372 of the Seventh Edition of "Chemistry of Food and Nutrition.")

Riboflavin is the name coined (after the molecular structure had been determined) to suggest as much of the chemical nature as a single short word can; and as being equally appropriate for the substance whether made synthetically or derived from any of its natural sources.

Riboflavin is widely distributed in both plant and animal tissues and is contained in relative abundance in milk and eggs, the means by which animals convey nutriment from one generation to the next. In this latter respect it may be considered the water-soluble analogue to the fat-soluble vitamin A.

In experiments with rats it has been found that riboflavin is essential both to growth and to normal nutrition at all ages. When the food is poor in riboflavin for any considerable length of time, digestive disturbances, nervous depression (different from the polyneuritis of thiamine deficiency), general weakness and lowering of tone, and an unwholesome condition of the skin with or without eye trouble, are apt to develop; the incidence of infectious disease is likely to be increased, vitality diminished, life shortened, and the prime of life curtailed by the unduly early onset of the aging process.

There is strong scientific probability that the effects of higher or lower riboflavin intake upon the life-history will be similar in their general trend and significance in the human family to those observed in rat families which (with a uniform hereditary background and with environmental factors alike in all other respects) have been fed for two or more generations on dietaries of different riboflavin content. Such experiments by Ellis and others in the Columbia University laboratories showed that when account is taken of the full-life and successive-generation effects, increasing benefits continue to result from increasing richness of the dietary in riboflavin, up to intake levels more than twice as high as that of minimal adequacy.

The best known function of riboflavin is that it combines with phosphoric acid and protein to form tissue respiratory enzymes which are importantly involved in the life processes of probably all active tissues. It therefore seems probable that the unrecognized effects of shortages of riboflavin in man are more widespread in the body than the symptoms which have yet been established clinically.

Quantitative Studies of Riboflavin Intake Levels

As we have seen in earlier chapters, there are some nutrients regarding which our new scientific knowledge agrees with the old adage that "enough is as good as a feast." Probably most students of nutrition, or at least the more open-minded and less tradition-bound among them, would agree that protein, fat, sugar, table salt, and cholesterol among other things may be thus regarded. In fact it has sometimes been taught as a principle that one can use to advantage only a small, if any, margin of nutriment above what one actually needs. But recent research has shown that there are other nutrients of which increased intakes continue to bring additional benefits, up to levels much above those which are demonstrably necessary as shown by the data of relatively short-time experiments. Among the nutrients thus possessed of potentialities for importantly constructive improvement of nutritional status above the levels

TABLE 22. *Adult Performance Plateaued, but Offspring Showing Added Benefit from Increased Intake of Riboflavin*

		On Diet with 3 Mcg. per Gram of Air-dry Food		On Diet with 10 Mcg. per Gram of Air-dry Food	
			Mean		Mean
Records of Original Animals					
Age of females at birth of first young,	days	(45)[a]	117	(46)[a]	120
Total number of young borne per female		(48)	29	(48)	24
Total number of young reared per female		(48)	16	(48)	16
Reproductive life of females,	days	(48)	251	(48)	228
Length of life,					
of males	days	(32)	673	(32)	671
of females	days	(48)	758	(48)	726
Records of Offspring					
Gain in weight during 28th to 56th days[b] of age,					
males	grams	(17)	88.5	(22)	97.1
females	grams	(19)	64.8	(23)	73.4
Gain in weight during 5th–7th week of age on riboflavin-free diet,					
males	grams	(19)	4.6	(19)	10.4
females	grams	(18)	4.3	(18)	9.7
Days of survival on thiamine-free diet from age of 28 days,					
males		(8)	33.1	(8)	38.9
females		(7)	35.6	(7)	44.6

[a] Number of cases shown in parenthesis.
[b] On maternal diet.

obviously needed for normal results—or as McCollum put it, cases in which there are, or may be, important differences between minimal-adequate and optimal nutrition—are calcium (Ch. VIII), vitamins A and C (Chs. XV and XI), and riboflavin (Table 22 herewith).

In Ellis' experiments, animals of like genetic and nutritional backgrounds were fed successively increased amounts of riboflavin.

The rate of growth increased with the riboflavin content of the food up to about 3 micrograms per gram of air-dry food. But 3 and 10 micrograms per gram of food resulted in practically identical growth curves and adult body weights. Other criteria yielded less regular results but in general the records of adult performance were essentially "plateaued" over a range of intake of 3 to 10 micrograms per gram of dry food. Nevertheless, the higher of these levels did show superior results when the experiments were carried into a second generation, as is shown by the last six lines of Table 22.

Riboflavin in Relation to Health and Disease

The Journal of the American Medical Association has spoken of riboflavin as being "necessary for the maintenance of the defense powers of the organism"; and several investigators have reported that riboflavin deficiency lowers the resistance of experimental animals to certain diseases.

Late in 1938 riboflavin deficiency was reported by Sebrell and Butler as a human deficiency disease (*ariboflavinosis*) and during the next two years many cases were reported, some occurring independently and some in conjunction with pellagra. (For examples of the medical evidence see Sebrell and Butler (1938), Sydenstricker, Geeslin, Templeton, and Weaver (1939), Kruse, Sydenstricker, Sebrell, and Cleckley (1940), Sydenstricker, Sebrell, Cleckley, and Kruse (1940), and Sydenstricker (1941), in the list of Suggested Readings below.)

Cheilosis (cracking of the lips at the corners of the mouth) and *vascularization of the cornea* are two definitely located lesions for which shortage of riboflavin appears to be, while not the sole, perhaps the most usual cause, and which have been repeatedly observed in people of various ages.

Spies and coworkers have reported riboflavin deficiency as probably the most frequent of dietary diseases in the child population with which they worked in the South, and the investigations of the Milbank Memorial Fund indicate a rather high incidence in New York City also, at least in low-income groups.

Very interesting were the cases found among members of a Southern hospital staff by Sydenstricker and coworkers (1940). These people chose their food at will from a satisfactorily supplied table and would not have been considered in any danger of nutritional deficiency, but on hearing that the research physicians were interested in cracked lips and "eyestrain" they offered themselves for examination and were found to show typical symptoms of shortage of riboflavin. The investigators considered that *dietary neglect* of milk, eggs, and green vegetables (although these were offered in the daily fare) was the cause of the riboflavin deficiency in these cases. Undoubtedly dietaries similarly poor in riboflavin are taken by very large numbers of other people because of poverty. Dr. Wilder has spoken of having met the folk-lore expression "poor folks' mouth" as a name for the cheilosis now recognized as a symptom of riboflavin deficiency.

China, India, and Africa have all reported areas of high incidence of human riboflavin deficiency.

In the United States probably the majority of cases of human riboflavin deficiencies either: (1) are in people who are simultaneously subjects of some other deficiency as well and are cured and recorded as pellagrins; or (2) are subclinical and go unrecognized, though lowering the health-plane, efficiency, and earning power of the victims.

Another reason for uncertainty, as to how prevalent riboflavin deficiency (*ariboflavinosis*) is in this country, lies in the fact that there may be other causes (also) for some of the conditions first attributed to shortage of this vitamin.

Inasmuch as this book seeks to serve in the field of health rather than of pathology, it is appropriate to emphasize here that, whatever may be the exact relation of this vitamin to one or another specific disease, there is no doubt that riboflavin is a very important factor in health. And this is true both for health as freedom from disease *and* for the upbuilding and maintenance of that higher health which is rightly regarded as a positive quality of life.

Measurement of Riboflavin

Now that riboflavin is available in pure form, the amount of this factor contained in food or required in nutrition can be expressed in terms of actual weight of riboflavin.

On the other hand we now know that riboflavin exists in plant and animal tissues, and thus in foods generally, both in the free state and in combinations of at least five to seven kinds. This fact complicated the development of simple *in vitro* methods applicable to all kinds of foods. Meanwhile measurements have been made by means of very carefully controlled *quantitative feeding tests* and more often recently by *microbioassay methods* based upon measurement of some activity of a specific microorganism in a medium in which riboflavin is the sole limiting factor.

All the methods just mentioned are sufficiently accepted so that data obtained by any of them are used interchangeably or collectively in considerations of riboflavin needs in nutrition and riboflavin values of foods.

Recommended Daily Dietary Allowances of Riboflavin

When the system of Recommended Allowances was being formulated in 1940-41, riboflavin was thought-of primarily as functioning like thiamine in combination with protein and phosphoric acid as a tissue respiratory enzyme—or a group of such enzymes. From that point of view it seemed likely that riboflavin requirement would tend to run parallel with thiamine requirement and with energy metabolism. Hence in the 1941-45 tables of Recommended Allowances those for riboflavin were set nearly parallel with those for thiamine at levels about 50 per cent higher.

In 1948, however, the functioning of riboflavin in the body's nutritional processes was more broadly conceived and the riboflavin requirements were set more nearly parallel with those for protein —as depending mainly upon age and size and as being largely independent of thiamine requirement or of the level of energy metabolism. For normal adult maintenance of men and women of average size, allowances of 1.8 mg. and of 1.5 mg., respectively, were recommended regardless of muscular activity, though (again as with protein) practical considerations of levels of intake often involve referring riboflavin level to micrograms per gram of air-dry food, just as protein level is often given as percentage of protein in the air-dry food.

Thus if the man receiving the recommended allowance of 1.8 milligrams of riboflavin, eats total food equivalent to 600 grams of dry food mixture per day, this will mean 3 micrograms of riboflavin per gram of dry food and can be compared with the amounts fed rats in studies of the effects of high *vs.* low levels of riboflavin, just as we can study and discuss high *vs.* low levels of protein intake in terms of percent of protein in the food mixture fed.

In neither case can we expect to translate the findings on one species directly into precise quantitative recommendations for another species; but the results of the animal experimentation may give valuable guidance as to whether the allowances recommended for human nutrition should be closely fitted to "rock bottom requirements," or would be more wisely set to allow more generous margins.

From the findings of large numbers of long-term experiments with laboratory bred and controlled rats, a representative series of which is summarized in Table 22, it appears that the general level of the 1948 Recommended Allowances corresponds with the minimal edge of the approximately optimal zone as indicated by the original or "first generation" animals—those receiving the assigned diet from infancy till natural death. When the offspring of such experimental families were continued on the respective family dietaries the objective records of performance indicate that optimal performance in the successive-generation type of test required a still higher level of riboflavin intake.

Thus there is here a general finding that the long-term type of research with objective evidence through entire life-times and into successive generations shows that riboflavin carries the potentiality of larger benefits than are fully revealed by experiments covering only short segments of the life cycle. There are also more specific benefits. Dr. C. G. King* emphasizes the fact that lessened incidence of at least one form of cancer has been found independently in three research laboratories. Bessey and coworkers found protection from rickettsial infections. Day and his coworkers found protection from a type of cataract—a finding of special interest in view of the connection between riboflavin level and incidence of senility.

There is doubtless also human significance in the observation by Street and Cowgill (1939) in the nutrition laboratory at Yale that a dog may continue in apparent good health on a riboflavin deficient diet for 100 to 140 days, but finally go into a collapse or rapid decline which however is curable by riboflavin if this is given in time.

Thus while experiments have been made in which well nourished young men have apparently maintained their health and fitness for work with riboflavin intakes materially below the levels of the

* *J. Am. Dietet. Assoc.* 25, 109 (1949).

1948 Recommended Allowances, the longest of such experiments were less than one per cent of a normal life-span, which is shown to be inconclusive as compared with large numbers of animal experiments extended through entire lifetimes and into successive generations.

Much well-controlled animal experimentation with species which are known to resemble the human in the nature of their nutrition processes has clearly shown both the long-term superiority of liberal intakes of riboflavin over intakes fashioned closely upon relatively short-term concepts of minimal adequacy. The more liberal intakes result in superior performances both in complete individual and family life histories and in respect to efficiency in meeting particular stresses. Thus György and Whipple found that liberal riboflavin supplies enhanced the efficiency of hemoglobin regeneration after experimental losses; and Ellis and Bessey found* riboflavin to be among the factors of which liberal supplies tend to superior blood hemoglobin values throughout normal life cycles including the stresses of reproduction.

Donelson and Macy (1932), investigating riboflavin before it had been given that name, found that, when the mother's diet is poor, her breast milk may not fully meet the riboflavin needs of the rapidly growing infant.

Bosse and Axelrod (1948) find that the rate and quality of wound healing are much better when the body is abundantly supplied, than when it is only scantily supplied, with riboflavin.

Shock and Sebrell (1946) have found that the total work output of the gastrocnemius muscle of the frog was significantly increased by addition of riboflavin to the perfusion solution.

As one studies the literature of nutrition of the past hundred years in the light of the knowledge of riboflavin gained in the past few years, and remembers that meat, eggs, and milk are all relatively rich in riboflavin, one is apt, if sufficiently openminded, to recognize a growing probability that riboflavin may have been really responsible for a significant share of the all-round bodily benefit which has been traditionally attributed to liberal intake of "animal protein."

Nutrition Reviews summarized† then recent work up to July 1943 essentially as follows: Rats on good diet showed in the first

---

* *Am. J. Physiol.* **113**, 582–585 (1935).
† *Nutrition Reviews* **1**, 267–268 (1943).

generation (the original experimental animals) no added benefit to their own growth performance and apparent nutritional status when the riboflavin content of their diet was increased from 3 mcg. to 10 mcg. per gram of dry food, but the offspring did show added benefit from the higher intake level, suggesting potentialities the full revelation of which required either broader search or longer-term experimentation or both. In 1935 Ellis and Bessey suggested that riboflavin is one of the factors contributing to the maintenance of a normal hemoglobin level, and in 1938 György, Robscheit-Robbins, and Whipple showed that regeneration of hemoglobin was hastened by dietary riboflavin. Ellis found that the intake level of 3 mcg. per gram of dry food-mixture supported the full plateau value of hemoglobin concentration in the blood. In some other way or ways, however, the three-fold higher intake level did bring added benefit to the young of the same families—the offspring of the same original experimental animals—notably in their better performance as shown objectively and quantitatively in the last six lines of Table 22. In just what way the body uses the extra riboflavin (which benefits the young while the adults appear, superficially at least, to be indifferent to it) is not yet clear. It has only doubtfully measurable effects upon the riboflavin content of muscle or of liver. The available data do not give us a clear concept regarding the excretion of riboflavin into the intestine or its absorption from different parts of the gastrointestinal tract. As interpreted by *Nutrition Reviews,* Sarett and Perlzweig* studied the effect of protein and B-vitamin levels of the diet upon the tissue content and balance of riboflavin (and niacin) in young male rats. " . . . Four diets, fed *ad libitum,* were used: (1) high protein (40 per cent)—high vitamin; (2) high-protein, low-vitamin; (3) low protein (8 per cent)—high vitamin; and (4) low-protein, low-vitamin . . . Riboflavin utilization (appeared) to be dependent not only on its intake but also on the protein level of the diet." This was confirmed and extended by the experiments of M. S. Ragan.

Beneficial results from dietary changes which increase our consumption of milk, eggs, and meat are apt to be attributed to increased intake of "animal" (or "first class") protein, whereas actually they may be due in greater degree to extra riboflavin than

* *J. Nutrition* 25, 173 (1943).

to extra protein. For the estimates of food consumption in the United States—both those obtained from studies of family food consumption and those which begin with statistics of food production and follow them through to "disappearance in channels of human food consumption at the retail level"—indicate that we habitually consume a considerably larger surplus of protein than of riboflavin, relative to our nutritional needs.

And this tends to go on indefinitely because the high animal-protein tradition (or "prestige" or "status value") makes many of us unduly credulous toward enthusiasm for high animal protein. Also worth keeping in mind is the evidence that the body can utilize protein to greater advantage when the dietary at the same time supplies liberal amounts of riboflavin, of calcium, or (best) of both calcium and riboflavin.

That the Recommended Allowances of 1948 provide only a very moderate margin over actual need of riboflavin is illustrated in the work of Braun, Brumberg, and Brezezinski, cited by Burke and Stuart (1948), in which of 900 pregnant women whose daily diets contained about 1.3 mg. of riboflavin, 21 per cent developed symptoms of riboflavin deficiency and were cured by riboflavin.

That it is also logical to provide a margin of riboflavin to meet stresses is illustrated by Warkany's evidence that higher margins of riboflavin intake tend to increase the proportion of normal pregnancies; and by King's emphasis (above noted) upon the evidence of three independent research groups that liberal intake of riboflavin tends to prevent the development of some types of cancer.

Sure, and also Mannering and Elvehjem, have emphasized the finding that a liberal proportion of riboflavin in the diet increases the efficiency of utilization of other nutrients.

In the April 1944 issue of *Nutrition Reviews* is a paper entitled, "Corneal vascularization in vitamin deficiencies," which concludes that, while riboflavin deficiency has been called the most common vitamin deficiency in this country, this judgment seems open to review in the light of further critical studies of the biomicroscopic method. Yet regardless of all questions of diagnosis, food consumption data show a high prevalence of dietaries of disturbingly low riboflavin content. This is one of several reasons for giving milk a larger place than it yet holds in the average American dietary.

Foods as Sources of Riboflavin

Plants form riboflavin beginning early in their lives. Even very young plants contain more riboflavin (in actual amount or in percentage of their dry matter) than the seeds from which they sprouted.

Somewhat as with vitamin C, though perhaps in a lesser degree, the young, juicy stage of development at which we most relish succulent foods for their "freshness" is also that at which they are best as sources of riboflavin. In general, too, the most actively functioning parts of the plant, the green leaves and growing tips, are relatively richest in riboflavin.

The riboflavin contents of a number of typical foods are shown in Table 23, expressed on the same basis as are the corresponding thiamine values in Table 21 (preceding chapter).

Perhaps the most important general differences in the quantitative distribution of these two vitamins are, that milk is relatively richer in riboflavin while wheat is relatively richer in thiamine, as are probably most of the seeds.

The green leaf foods, represented in Table 23 by kale and spinach, are also richer sources of riboflavin than of thiamine. Of the riboflavin content of fruits and vegetables generally we may say much the same as of their thiamine content, namely, that if the figures look low it is largely because of the high water content of these foods, and that when used as abundantly as they well may be, they become good sources.

Let us now consider some individual foods.

Beef and pork muscle, which will be remembered as differing in thiamine content, are seen to be very similar in the amounts of riboflavin which they contain. Liver contains, weight for weight, about ten times as much riboflavin as does muscle; and kidney is nearly as rich, in riboflavin, as is liver.

Milk, notwithstanding its high water content, contains only a little less riboflavin, weight for weight, than do the muscle meats. A quart of milk thus furnishes just about as much riboflavin as two pounds of *clear lean* meat.

Both cheese and whey are good sources. This is because an important part of the riboflavin of milk is "free" and goes into the whey, while another important part is so combined with protein as to stay in the curd in cheese making.

Eggs are distinctly richer in riboflavin than are the muscle meats. Even egg white, which contains only traces of thiamine, is a relatively rich source of riboflavin, though the yolk is still richer.

Whole wheat contains only about one-fourth as much riboflavin as thiamine. The germ or embryo is richer in both of these factors than is the entire grain. But as the germ constitutes only about two per cent of the weight of the grain, a large fraction of both thiamine

TABLE 23. *Riboflavin Contents of Typical Foods: Micrograms per 100 Grams*

Food	Range Within Which the Final Average Will Probably Be Found
Foods of Animal Origin	
Beef muscle	150–260
Pork muscle	180–265
Liver (of cattle and swine)	2000–4000
Milk	170–240
Eggs	250–350
Egg white	150–300
Egg yolk	300–600
Grain Products	
Wheat, entire	100–220
Wheat germ	600–800
Vegetables and Fruits	
Banana	45–80
Broccoli	200–500
Cabbage	50–80
Carrots	50–90
Kale	250–400
Orange or juice	28–62
Spinach	200–300
Tomato	37–50
Turnip	50–70

and riboflavin of wheat is rejected with the bran, even if the germ is retained with (or returned to) the white flour.

Among the vegetables and fruits the green leaves are outstanding, kale and spinach containing several-fold more riboflavin than do typical fruits and other-than-green vegetables; while cabbage and lettuce occupy an intermediate place.

It is also of interest to see how different types of food compare as contributors both of riboflavin and of other nutritional factors in representative dietaries.

Table 24 shows this as illustrated in Stiebeling's data for medium-cost dietaries as reported in the consumption studies made jointly by the Federal Departments of Agriculture and of Labor.

TABLE 24. *Relative Prominence of Certain Types of Food as Sources of Riboflavin and Other Nutrients*[a]
(*In dietaries costing $2.38–$3.00 weekly per food-cost unit*)

Food or Food Group	Per cent of Food Money Allocated	Calories	Protein	Calcium	Vitamin A	Vitamin C	Riboflavin
Meats and fish	25.5	12.9	36.2	2.7	7.1	0.7	32.2
Eggs	5.0	1.7	4.9	2.7	6.0	....	5.3
Milk, cheese, ice cream	12.1	9.8	16.0	60.7	13.9	5.3	34.2
Butter, cream	7.6	9.3	0.4	1.4	16.0	?	0.4
Other fats	3.0	7.8	0.5	0.1	0.8	....	1.1
Breadstuffs, cereals, bakery products	17.6	30.3	27.3	12.0	3.5	0.6	5.7
Sugar, sweets	4.2	12.4	0.1	2.1	....	....	....
Potatoes, sweetpotatoes	1.5	5.8	4.4	3.4	2.6	22.8	7.2
Dried legumes, nuts	1.8	2.9	5.3	3.4	0.2	....	0.8
Tomatoes	1.5	0.3	0.4	0.5	9.5	7.8	0.6
Citrus fruits	3.2	1.1	0.5	3.0	0.6	29.6	3.3
Green and yellow vegetables	3.9	0.8	1.4	3.4	33.7	12.8	3.7
Other vegetables	3.4	1.0	1.0	2.8	1.3	8.1	1.2
Other fruits	3.9	2.8	0.7	1.4	4.6	12.3	3.9

[a] Adapted from Stiebeling, Serial No. R409, Bureau of Labor Statistics, U. S. Dept. Labor (1936).

In this series of dietaries, milk (including cheese and ice cream) was the largest contributor of riboflavin, furnishing a little over one third of the total; meat (including poultry and fish) was second; and vegetables stood third. The importance of the vegetables is not fully apparent at a glance in Table 24 because they are there subdivided. Eggs contributed as large a proportion of the riboflavin as of the protein.

In another series of food consumption studies, milk furnished a little over half of the total riboflavin. In a very tentative estimate made at Columbia using data furnished by Williams (R.R.) for average food consumption of the people of the United States, milk and cheese furnished 44 per cent; meats, 19 per cent; eggs, 6 per cent; fruits and vegetables, 16 per cent; and breadstuffs and cereals, 15 per cent of the estimated total of 1.78 mg. riboflavin received per person per day.

TABLE 25. *Approximate Losses of Thiamine, Riboflavin, and Niacin on Cooking Foods. Examples selected from the data of Taylor and MacLeod:* Rose's Laboratory Handbook for Dietetics, 5th Ed. (Macmillan)

Food	Percentage Loss		
	Of Thiamine	Of Riboflavin	Of Niacin
Asparagus, fresh, boiled	25	5	15
Beans, green snap, boiled	35	20	25
Broccoli, all methods	25	10	20
Cabbage, all methods	35	20	20
Cauliflower, all methods	45	20	30
Eggs, all methods	20	23	25
Kohlrabi, all methods	25	5	15
Meat, broiling or frying	25	20	20
braising or roasting	45	20	25
stewing[a]	65	30	50
Onions, all methods	45	15	30
Peas, all methods	25	15	15
Potatoes, all methods	25	20	20
Sweetpotatoes, all methods	25	5	15
Turnip greens, all methods	35	20	20

[a] Research should show how to lower these losses.

Niacin (Nicotinic Acid) and Pellagra

The word *pellagra* signifies rough or inflamed skin. This is the outstanding symptom of a disease usually associated with poverty and with too great a dependence upon maize as a food.

The pellagrin, as the victim of this disease is often called, usually suffers not only with the skin trouble which gives rise to the name but also with mental or nervous disorders or depression, and with inflammation of the tongue and the lining of the mouth often extending to severe disorder of the digestive tract. One sometimes hears reference to "the three Ds of pellagra—depression, dermatitis, and diarrhoea." It is also considered by physicians in pellagrous regions that when either the nervous (mental) disturbance or the digestive disorder occurs with the characteristic dermatitis, the two symptoms together justify a diagnosis of the disease. A characteristic feature of the dermatitis of pellagra is that it occurs symmetrically upon, for instance, the backs of the hands, the ankles, the forearms, or the back of the neck. Often but not always, the dermatitis is most pronounced on some part of the body which is exposed to the sun. In its early stages it may resemble sun-burn.

Not until the first decade of this century was pellagra reported in the United States. Then the reports of its presence rapidly grew to an alarming frequency, especially in the South. Authorities of the United States Public Health Service consider that probably over 100,000 of our people have suffered from pellagra in each of several years.

Naturally, this disease has been much studied. It was found that an analogous condition, called "black-tongue," in dogs could be induced experimentally by pellagra-producing diet, and cured by such dietary improvements as were found to cure clinical pellagra.

Late in 1937, Elvehjem found that niacin (nicotinic acid or its amide) cures black-tongue, and immediately there followed a rapid succession of reports of its successful use in human pellagra, though this does not necessarily mean the entire cure of the pellagrin, as will be explained more fully below.

The substance which thus unexpectedly acquired such important nutritional interest, had long been known to chemists; and one who desires may readily "look it up" in books on organic chemistry. It was first described as one of the products formed when nicotine is broken down by laboratory treatment, and in this way came to be called nicotinic acid, an accidental name which now that the substance must often be referred to as a factor in food values becomes both inappropriate and somewhat absurd. Hence the new name niacin (niacin amide) has been coined by the Food and Nutrition Board of the National Research Council and adopted by the United States Food and Drug Administration for the designation of this substance as contained in food and as functioning in nutrition. Enriched flour and bread must contain specified amounts of niacin as well as of thiamine, riboflavin, and iron.

Recommended Daily Allowances of Niacin

At the time that the formulation of the "yardstick of good nutrition" was called for, the importance of niacin (nicotinic acid) was realized, but *quantitative* knowledge (both as regards nutritional need and natural distribution in foods) was uncertain, as is still the case in some respects.

The National Research Council has included in its recommended allowances a column for niacin in which all of the figures are simply ten times the corresponding figures for thiamine. Obviously these figures are to be regarded as provisional or tentative.

The Practical Prevention of Pellagra, and the Broader Nutritional Problem of Which This is a Part

Recent clinical evidence seems to leave no room for doubt that while niacin (nicotinic acid) cures the most outstanding symptoms of pellagra, the typical pellagrin is usually a sufferer from shortage not only of niacin but also of riboflavin.

Thus while riboflavin cannot prevent or cure pellagra without niacin, yet in practice the riboflavin content and the niacin content of the diet both have a bearing upon the occurrence and persistence of the disease. Liver and yeast, being relatively rich in both, naturally have a high place in therapeutic discussions of the disease. But such permanent and widespread reform of the food supply as is needed will probably be more effectively brought about in terms of the more staple or everyday foods of the general population.

The typical diet of the poor pellagrin consists so largely of pork fat, corn bread, soda biscuits and syrup, that it cannot be made nutritionally good by the addition of niacin alone. Even with liberal niacin and thiamine it would also need fruits, vegetables, and milk in some form to increase its content of calcium, vitamins A and C, and riboflavin, and possibly also to improve the character of its protein mixture. It is also to be kept in mind that enriched flour and bread carry only "their share" of certain nutrients and do not solve the problem of adequate nutrition.

In 1932, careful studies of food supplies and dietary practices in relation to the occurrence of pellagra were made with Florida families by Sandels and Grady, and with South Carolina families by Stiebeling and Munsell. In both States it was found that the families successful in warding off pellagra used dietaries containing a much higher proportion of milk than did the families in which one or more cases of pellagra occurred. Sandels and Grady further found a significantly larger consumption of succulent vegetables, and indications of a larger use of eggs, cheese, and fruit in the families which escaped pellagra. Stiebeling and Munsell reported results of relief distribution of certain foods to poor families in pellagra regions, with results which "afford a practical demonstration" that the addition of 2 to 4 ounces of dry skim milk, or 1 pound of evaporated milk, or $1\frac{1}{2}$ pints of canned tomatoes, or one-half pound of cured lean pork per person per day to the food supply "suffices to reduce greatly the incidence of pellagra among families which in times of stress subsist on a very monotonous and one-sided diet containing very little milk, lean meat, fish, or eggs."

Combining findings of the U. S. Department of Agriculture and of the U. S. Public Health Service, it appears that any one of the following in the daily dietary is nearly always effective for prevention of pellagra: a quart of milk or buttermilk; a pint of evaporated milk; one-third to one-half pound of dried skim milk, of lean meat, of canned salmon, of peanut meal, or of wheat germ; or one pound of fresh or canned collards, kale, green peas, or turnip greens; or two to three pounds of tomatoes, fresh, canned, or as juice.

Pellagra-prevention campaigns in the South have emphasized the home production of vegetables and the keeping of cows and chickens. An effective combination of pellagra-prevention and nutrition education was found by the Red Cross in the plan of lending a cow to the poor country family until better health and resultant increased earnings made it possible for the family to buy one.

Sebrell writes*: "The most important foods to add to the diet in (or for protection from) pellagra are milk, liver, lean meats, fish, eggs, tomatoes, green peas, and a variety of green and leafy vegetables, such as kale, mustard greens, turnip greens, and collards."

"It is very simple," he says in the same connection, "to state the remedy for endemic pellagra in this country. Here we have a rural disease known to be due to nutritional deficiency, caused by the cultivation of a money crop instead of food and forage crops. The remedy is obvious: The rural South must produce its own food supply."

* Sebrell, W. H., *Journal of Home Economics* 31, 534 (1939).

For the large, low-income, majority of the rural people of the South this will mean the home-raising of vegetables and poultry and the keeping of a family cow.

In the Kentucky mountains in adjacent neighborhoods both of which ate corn meal and in about equal amounts, one was freed from pellagra by persistent teaching of the health value of "the right kinds of food" which resulted in their planting gardens and keeping cows and chickens. (Kooser and Blankenhorn, 1941.)

Extensive field studies of food consumption and pellagra incidence and intensive experimentation upon human subjects in an institution for the insane, yielded consistent findings on the pellagra-preventive values of such staple foods as meat, eggs, and milk. But results of direct determination of niacin in foods of different types were sometimes in good accord with their previously established pellagra-preventive values, and sometimes not.

Thus analytical determinations of niacin in meat were as would be expected from the feeding investigations, while with milk the analytical data for niacin were much lower than would correspond. Somewhat embarrassingly it was pointed out that if children needed as much niacin as the Recommended Allowances imply, and if milk contained as little niacin as analysis seemed to show, then pellagra would "have to be" much more prevalent among children, largely milk-fed, than it actually is. The solution of this dilemma appears to lie chiefly in the fact that milk is favorable to the multiplication and activity of niacin-forming bacteria in the human digestive tract. By virtue of this bacterial action, the presence of a liberal amount of milk in the diet, either of a child or an adult, results in such person absorbing from the digestive tract more niacin than was contained in the food swallowed. Thus some foods, including milk, have niacin *values* materially higher than their niacin *contents*, while other foods do not. Briggs, Singal, and Sydenstricker[*] found that restriction of nicotinic acid (niacin) did not induce pellagra symptoms in either of two men who had previously been pellagrins, so suggested that intestinal biosynthesis of niacin may have been sufficient to meet their needs.

Thus a table of niacin contents of foods of different types, however accurate analytically, is unavoidably misleading nutritionally.

Hence it seems more scientific not to include such a table in the teaching text of this chapter. We do, however, include suggested

[*] *Journal of Nutrition,* 29, 338.

readings in which such data on the niacin contents of foods may be found if desired. And figures for niacin reproduced from Government tables, to which the above caution applies, are included in the Appendix of this book.

What Other B-Vitamins Are Likely to Be Limiting Factors in Human Health?

In our opinion it is too early to attempt an explicit answer to this question; and too late to ignore it. The next chapter aims to supply starting points for those desiring to study the question.

EXERCISES

1. Arrange your "twelve to forty foods" in the order of their riboflavin content, (a) per 100 grams of edible portion, and (b) per 100 Calories.
2. On the above showing, which of these foods would you consider of most practical importance as sources of riboflavin?
3. Which of these foods are important sources: (a) of riboflavin and calcium; (b) of riboflavin and vitamin C; (c) of riboflavin and vitamin A?
4. Taking account of the quantities in which they enter into well-balanced dietaries, (1) what familiar foods rival milk in importance as sources of protein, calcium, and riboflavin? (2) And which foods rival oranges in importance as sources of vitamin C and riboflavin?
5. Explain to what extent you have, in answering the preceding question, taken account of the potential as well as the present place of oranges in the food supply. What can you tell of the trend of citrus fruit production and prices?
6. Consult the most recent and authoritative medical publications available, as to whether the word pellagra now stands (1) for niacin deficiency *simply,* with any accompanying riboflavin deficiency regarded merely as an accidental complication, or (2) for the "complete clinical picture" for which it has hitherto stood, in which, while niacin controls the more outstanding symptoms, riboflavin is also a factor in the prevention and cure of the disease.

SUGGESTED READINGS

BESSEY, O. A., and O. H. LOWRY   1944   Factors influencing the riboflavin content of the cornea. *J. Biol. Chem.* 155, 635–643.
BESSEY, O. A., and S. B. WOLBACH   1939   Vascularization of the

cornea of the rat in riboflavin deficiency, with a note on corneal vascularization in vitamin A deficiency. *J. Exptl. Med.* **69**, 1–12; *Expt. Sta. Rec.* **81**, 311.

BURKE, B. S., and H. C. STUART 1948 Nutritional requirements during pregnancy and lactation. *J. Am. Med. Assoc.* **137**, 119–128.

CHELDELIN, V. H., and R. R. WILLIAMS 1943 Studies of the average American diet. II. Riboflavin, nicotinic acid, and pantothenic acid content. *J. Nutrition* **26**, 417–430.

COPPING, A. M. 1945 Some aspects of riboflavin nutrition in man. *Nutr. Abs. Rev.* **14**, 433–440.

DAVIS, M. V., H. G. OLDHAM, and L. J. ROBERTS 1946 Riboflavin excretions of young women on diets containing varying levels of the B vitamins. *J. Nutrition* **32**, 143–161.

DAY, P. L., W. J. DARBY, and K. W. COSGROVE 1938 The arrest of nutritional cataracts by the use of riboflavin. *J. Nutrition* **15**, 83–90.

DONELSON, E., and I. G. MACY 1932 Human milk studies. XI. Vitamin G in human milk. *Am. J. Physiol.* **100**, 420–425.

EBBS, J. H., F. F. TISDALL, and W. A. SCOTT 1941 Influence of prenatal diet on the mother and child. *J. Nutrition* **22**, 515–526.

ELLIS, L. N., A. ZMACHINSKY, and H. C. SHERMAN 1943 Experiments upon the significance of liberal levels of intake of riboflavin. *J. Nutrition* **25**, 153–160.

FEDER, V. H., G. T. LEWIS, and H. S. ALDEN 1944 Studies on the urinary excretion of riboflavin. *J. Nutrition* **27**, 347–353.

GUERRANT, N. B., and O. B. FARDIG 1947 The thiamine and riboflavin content of whole wheat, nonenriched and enriched flours and of breads made therefrom. *J. Nutrition* **34**, 523–542.

GYÖRGY, P., F. S. ROBSCHEIT-ROBBINS, and G. H. WHIPPLE 1938 Riboflavin increases hemoglobin production in the anemic dog. *Am. J. Physiol.* **122**, 154–159.

HAGEDORN, D. R., E. D. KYHOS, O. A. GERMEK, and E. L. SEVRINGHAUS 1945 Observations on riboflavin excretion by the adult male. *J. Nutrition* **29**, 179–189.

HANNING, F., B. A. SCHICK, and H. J. SEIM 1949 Stability of riboflavin in eggs to cooking and to light. *Food Research* **14**, 203–208.

HODSON, A. Z. 1940 The influence of dietary riboflavin on the content of the vitamin in chicken tissue. *J. Nutrition* **20**, 377–382.

INGALLS, R., W. D. BREWER, H. L. TOBEY, J. PLUMMER, B. B. BENNETT, and M. A. OHLSON 1950 Changes in riboflavin content of vegetables during storage prior to canning. *Food Technology* **4**, 258–263.

KRUSE, H. D., V. P. SYDENSTRICKER, W. H. SEBRELL, and H. M.

CLECKLEY 1940 Ocular manifestations of ariboflavinosis. *Public Health Repts.* **55**, 157–169.

LANFORD, C. S., B. FINKELSTEIN, and H. C. SHERMAN 1941 Riboflavin contents of some typical fruits. *J. Nutrition* **21**, 175–177.

MACLEOD, G., and C. M. TAYLOR 1944 *Rose's Foundations of Nutrition*, 4th Ed. (Macmillan.)

MANNERING, G. J., and C. A. ELVEHJEM 1944 Food utilization and appetite in riboflavin deficiency. *J. Nutrition* **28**, 157–163.

NOBLE, I., and J. GORDON 1949 Thiamine and riboflavin retention in bacon. *J. Am. Dietet. Assoc.* **25**, 130–133.

REVIEW 1947 Interaction of niacin and tryptophane in the diet. *Nutrition Rev.* **5**, 110–111.

REVIEW. 1947b Increasing the riboflavin content of hens' eggs. *Nutrition Rev.* **5**, 181–183.

REVIEW 1949 Metabolism of radioactive niacin and niacin-amide. *Nutrition Rev.* **7**, 166–167.

RODERUCK, C. E., M. N. CORYELL, H. H. WILLIAMS, and I. G. MACY 1945 Free and total riboflavin contents of colostrum and mature human milk. *Am. J. Diseases Children* **70**, 171–175.

SANDELS, M. R., and E. GRADY 1932 Dietary practices in relation to the incidence of pellagra. *Arch. Internal Med.* **50**, 362–372.

SARETT, H. P., and G. A. GOLDSMITH 1949 Tryptophan and nicotinic acid studies in man. *J. Biol. Chem.* **177**, 461–475.

SEBRELL, W. H. 1939 Public health implications of recent research in pellagra and ariboflavinosis. *J. Home Econ.* **31**, 530–536.

SEBRELL, W. H., and R. E. BUTLER 1938 Riboflavin deficiency in man. *Public Health Repts.* **53**, 2282–2284.

SEBRELL, W. H., JR., R. E. BUTLER, J. G. WOOLEY, and I. ISBELL 1941 Human riboflavin requirement estimated by urinary excretion of subjects on controlled intake. *Public Health Repts.* **56**, 510–519; *Nutr. Abs. Rev.* **11**, 128.

SINGAL, S. A., V. P. SYDENSTRICKER, and J. M. LITTLEJOHN 1948 The role of tryptophane in the nutrition of dogs on nicotinic acid-deficient diets. *J. Biol. Chem.* **176**, 1051–1062.

SNYDERMAN, S. E., K. C. KETRON, H. B. BURCH, O. H. LOWRY, O. A. BESSEY, L. P. GUY, and L. E. HOLT, JR. 1949 The minimum riboflavin requirement of the infant. *J. Nutrition* **39**, 219–232.

SPECTOR, H., A. R. MAASS, L. MICHAUD, C. A. ELVEHJEM, and E. B. HART 1943 Role of riboflavin in blood regeneration. *J. Biol. Chem.* **150**, 75–87.

STAMBERG, O. E., C. F. PETERSEN, and C. E. LAMPMAN 1946 Effect of riboflavin intake on the content of egg whites and yolks. Ratio of riboflavin in yolks and whites of eggs. *Poultry Sci.* **25**, 320–326; *Nutr. Abs. Rev.* **16**, 586.

STIEBELING, H. K., and H. E. MUNSELL 1932 Food supply and pellagra incidence in 73 South Carolina families. *U. S. Dept. Agriculture, Tech. Bull.* No. 333.

STREET, H. R., G. R. COWGILL, and H. M. ZIMMERMAN 1941 Further observations of riboflavin deficiency in the dog. *J. Nutrition* **22**, 7–24.

STRONG, F. M., R. E. FEENEY, B. MOORE, and H. T. PARSONS 1941 The riboflavin content of blood and urine. *J. Biol. Chem.* **137**, 363–372.

SURE, B. 1941 Riboflavin as a factor in economy of food utilization. *J. Nutrition* **22**, 295–301.

SYDENSTRICKER, V. P. 1941 The clinical manifestations of nicotinic acid and riboflavin deficiency (pellagra). *Ann. Internal Med.* **14**, 1499–1517.

SYDENSTRICKER, V. P., L. E. GEESLIN, C. M. TEMPLETON, and J. W. WEAVER 1939 Riboflavin deficiency in human subjects. *J. Am. Med. Assoc.* **113**, 1697–1700.

SYDENSTRICKER, V. P., W. H. SEBRELL, H. M. CLECKLEY, and H. D. KRUSE 1940 The ocular manifestations of ariboflavinosis. *J. Am. Med. Assoc.* **114**, 2437–2445.

TEPLY, L. J., W. A. KREHL, and C. A. ELVEHJEM 1945 Studies on the nicotinic acid content of coffee. *Arch. Biochem.* **6**, 139–149; *Nutr. Abs. Rev.* **15**, 80.

VAN DUYNE, F. O., J. T. CHASE, R. F. OWEN, and J. R. FANSKA 1948 Effect of certain home practices on riboflavin content of cabbage, peas, snap beans, and spinach. *Food Research* **13**, 162–171.

WARKANY, J., and E. SCHRAFFENBERGER 1944 Congenital malformations induced in rats by maternal nutritional deficiency. VI. The preventive factor. *J. Nutrition* **27**, 477–484.

WHITNEY, D. E., H. HERREN, and B. D. WESTERMAN 1945 The thiamine and riboflavin content of the grain and flour of certain varieties of Kansas-grown wheat. *Cereal Chem.* **22**, 90–95.

YUDKIN, J. 1946 Riboflavin deficiency in West Africa. *J. Trop. Med. Hyg.* **49**, 83–87; *Chem. Abs.* **41**, 2778.

XIV

OTHER WATER-SOLUBLE VITAMINS

Vitamin B_6 (Pyridoxine and related substances)

Fairly early in studies on the differentiation of the "B-complex" vitamins, a very striking ("acrodynia-like") dermatitis was produced experimentally in rats, and the active ingredient of preparations which cured or prevented the condition was designated as "vitamin B_6." In 1939, a substance which was called *pyridoxine** was shown to have the properties of vitamin B_6, and for a time the two terms were used synonymously. More recently, it has been found that two other distinct, though chemically related substances, designated, respectively, as *pyridoxamine* and *pyridoxal*, which occur naturally with pyridoxine, have vitamin B_6 activity and may even predominate over pyridoxine in animal nutrition. Hence, there is now a tendency to prefer the term "vitamin B_6" where the whole group of active substances is meant, and to reserve pyridoxine as the designation for one specific chemical substance.

Vitamin B_6 in combination with phosphorus occurs in several important body enzyme systems involved in the metabolism of proteins and amino acids. In another aspect of its functioning, vitamin B_6 appears to be somewhat interrelated with the nutritionally essential fatty acid factor, deficiency of which likewise provokes the "acrodynia-like" dermatitis in rats. In some way, and to an extent not yet well defined, provision of either one of these factors (vitamin B_6 *or* essential fatty acid) partially alleviates the effects on the skin of shortage of the other. Still another effect of the lack of vitamin B_6 is a severe anemia of microcytic, hypochromic type.

* The structural formulae for pyridoxine, pantothenic acid, and choline may be found in Chapter XXI of Sherman's *Chemistry of Food and Nutrition*.

The nature of vitamin B_6 deficiency in man, and whether it is apt to be encountered in practical nutrition, are still unanswered questions.

Vitamin B_{12}

In 1948, investigators in this country and in England isolated pink cobalt-containing crystals from liver, which were introduced as vitamin B_{12}. Within a short time this substance was shown to be identical with a number of differently named factors whose existence had been recognized in diverse studies. Thus, as already noted in Chapter IX, vitamin B_{12} was established as an *anti-pernicious anemia factor.* It proved also to be identical with *nutrient X,* discovered by workers in the Bureau of Animal Industry of the U. S. Department of Agriculture to be required for normal development in laboratory rats, and to be found in the non-fat portion of milk, in cheese, commercial casein, leafy foods and feeds, and in liver extracts, but not in the cereal grains or in the oil meals used for animal feed. Similarly, the chick-growth-promoting property possessed by various animal protein sources but lacking in vegetable protein sources, and ascribed to an *"animal protein factor,"* appears to be due in part at least to vitamin B_{12}. It should not, however, be inferred from the latter term that vitamin B_{12} is provided exclusively by foods of animal origin; for Hartman, Dryden, and Cary (1949) include lettuce, rice polishings concentrate, alfalfa, timothy, and Kentucky blue grass along with milk, skim milk, cheese, liver extracts, beef and pork muscle, and egg yolk as sources of nutrient X or vitamin B_{12} activity for the normal mammal. Their parallel listing of foods which do not show B_{12} activity includes: white, enriched and whole wheat flour, yeast, cornmeal, soybean meal, carrots, tomatoes, egg white, and butterfat.

Vitamin B_{12} is clearly required for normal nutrition in many species, including man. However, perhaps partly because intestinal microorganisms appear to synthesize appreciable amounts of it, perhaps partly also because the young of well nourished mothers may acquire significant body stores, the requirement becomes more quickly and strikingly apparent if the synthetic activities of the intestinal bacteria are checked, as by the use of certain "sulfa" drugs; or if a metabolic strain, so to speak, is imposed on the body. Examples of such "metabolic strains" were the feeding of diets of very high protein content by the Department of Agriculture investigators; and the experimental production of so-called "thyroid toxicity" by feeding thyroid or iodinated casein (containing thyroxine). The detrimental effects on growth of both of these types of treatment are counteracted by liberal dietary vitamin B_{12}. Whether comparable circumstances in man exaggerate the need for dietary vitamin B_{12} to the point where it becomes a factor in practical nutrition—aside from the anemias already noted—we do not as yet (1950) know. It is, however, of interest to point out that the case of vitamin B_{12} provides still another illustration of how supplementation with milk products greatly enhances the nutritive value of a diet consisting largely of grain and cereal products. It also exemplifies again how the well-being of the body may be conditioned in a positive way by the intestinal bacteria which it harbors.

Vitamin B_{14}

A newly discovered substance, extraordinarily active in stimulating red blood cell formation, and differing from vitamin B_{12} in not containing cobalt, has been reported under the name vitamin B_{14} by Norris and Majnarich (1949). They suggest such complex relationships for this as may require some years of research for complete clarification.

Vitamin M, Folic Acid, Pteroylglutamate (PGA)

Day, Langston and coworkers found that monkeys require, for the maintenance of a normal condition of their blood, something that is contained in yeast and had not been chemically identified. In recognition of the part played by the monkey in assisting this discovery they called the substance vitamin M. Through much research by workers in different laboratories employing different organisms it finally appeared that what met the need of the monkey (vitamin M), of the chick (vitamin B_c), found in leaves (folic acid) and also a nutrient factor named for a species of bacteria, were all the same thing—a substance whose chemical nature is best indicated by the name pteroylglutamate.

Though much remains to be learned about the relative importance of foods as sources of this factor, it appears that the outstandingly rich sources are fresh, deep-green leafy vegetables and liver; while muscle meats, milk and grain products, and vegetables with less intense green color are relatively much poorer in folic acid.

Folic acid is another of those factors which appear normally to be synthesized to a considerable extent by intestinal microorganisms. But, as commented in the discussion accompanying the National Research Council Recommendations, "the incidence of clinical deficiencies, however, affords evidence that intestinal synthesis should not be relied upon as a source of this nutrient."

Pantothenic Acid

In 1933 this name was given by R. J. Williams to a substance he had discovered to be (as the name was coined to convey) of extraordinarily wide distribution among organisms. It was later shown to be the active factor which had been sought in research on "bios" of yeast, "antidermatitis" (filtrate) factor for chicks, a liver filtrate factor for rats, and a growth factor for lactic acid bacteria.

As has been found for several other vitamins, pantothenic acid is an essential component of an enzyme system, in this case, of a system controlling acetylation* processes in the body.

Probably because of the very wide natural occurrence of pantothenic acid, no clearcut instances of pantothenic acid deficiency in man have yet (1950) been recognized.

Biotin

A sulfur-containing compound called *biotin* was recognized in 1941 as still another member of the "B-vitamin group." Its existence as a factor in mammalian nutrition was discovered through studies on "egg white injury," a curious disease developing in experimental animals fed large quantities of raw egg white. Supplying extra-generous amounts of "B-vitamins" (or of concentrates of biotin) prevents or cures this injurious action of egg white. An explanation of this was found in the presence in egg white of a protein called *avidin* (avidalbumin, antibiotin) which combines with biotin in a firm linkage from which the body cannot detach this vitamin essential to its normal functioning. In later studies,

---

* Such as the formation of acetyl choline, and the detoxification of certain drugs.

biotin deficiency was produced instead by feeding sulfa drugs which prevented intestinal synthesis of biotin. How apt this factor is to be of practical importance in human nutrition cannot yet be stated.

Choline ("Labile-Methyl Factor")

Choline (chemically, a methylated nitrogenous base) has long been known as a component of the phospholipids, lecithin and sphingomyelin, which are essential structural elements of the body and also importantly concerned in the metabolism of fats. Another compound, acetyl choline, is responsible for the conduction of impulses along the vagus nerve. Choline is thus of unquestionable significance in the body's functioning, yet only for about a decade has it been investigated by nutritionists as a possible limiting factor in certain diets. This is partially because choline differs from our usual concept of a vitamin in that the body appears able to form it if given extra-liberal amounts of such other normal dietary constituents as the amino acid methionine, from which may be transferred the methyl groupings required to build choline.

The process of transfer of a methyl grouping from one compound to another is known as transmethylation, and a methyl grouping which can be so transferred is known as a "labile methyl." The principal forms of "labile methyl" in a normal diet appear to be choline, methionine, and betaine; choline generally being the most important. The body uses labile methyl from whatever source interchangeably in such ways as the formation of creatine and the methylation of nicotinic acid prior to elimination by the kidneys. But, in addition, the body has a separate, specific need for choline as an intact chemical entity. Whether methionine, for instance, can fully replace choline in the diet depends upon whether there is available from the body's store of metabolic building blocks the residue which can accept "labile methyl" and become choline. In some (but possibly not all) species of experimental animals and apparently in man,[*] this substance is available. On the other hand, the compound (homocysteine) which, with "labile methyl," yields methionine is not normally available from other sources, hence choline cannot fully replace dietary methionine, though it can effectively "spare" it by assuming the "labile methyl" aspects of its functioning.

[*] See Simmonds and du Vigneaud, *J. Biol. Chem.* **146**, 685 (1942).

When insufficient choline is available (either as such in the diet or from other labile methyl compounds), growth of experimental animals is retarded and tissue damage may occur, including hemorrhagic changes in the kidney and abnormal accumulation of fat in the liver ("fatty liver"). Since this latter state sometimes progresses experimentally to cirrhosis, clinicians have naturally wondered whether the grave condition of liver cirrhosis in man may have its origin in a dietary deficiency and may be amenable to treatment with choline. No clearcut answer is yet possible.

Vitamin P (Rutin, Citrin)

It has been thought by some investigators that the effect of citrus fruit consumption upon the permability of the blood vessels involved more than could be explained in terms of vitamin C alone; so the presence of an additional "permeability factor," vitamin P, was postulated. Several naturally occurring substances are claimed to show this property, but although successful clinical use of such preparations has been reported by several workers, there is yet (1950) no clear consensus of opinion as to whether vitamin P should be regarded as a factor in normal nutrition.

EXERCISES

Write your own supplement to bring the foregoing chapter up to the date of your study of it.

To THE STUDENT.—It is consistent with the intention of the Exercise that you ask your librarian to borrow books from other libraries; but not that you deprive yourself of the experience of this search of scientific literature by trying to get the answer from another person.

SUGGESTED READINGS

Vitamin B_6 (Pyridoxine and Related Substances)

COOPERMAN, J. M., and C. A. ELVEHJEM   1944   The B-vitamin content of groats and rolled oats. *J. Nutrition* 27, 329–333.

DANIEL, E. P., O. L. KLINE, and C. D. TOLLE   1942   A convulsive syndrome in young rats associated with pyridoxine deficiency. *J. Nutrition* 23, 205–216.

DAVENPORT, V. D., and H. W. DAVENPORT   1948   Brain excitability in pyridoxine-deficient rats. *J. Nutrition* 36, 263–275.

Henderson, L. M., H. A. Waisman, and C. A. Elvehjem 1941 The distribution of pyridoxine (vitamin B_6) in meat and meat products. *J. Nutrition* 21, 589–598.

Kornberg, A., H. Tabor, and W. H. Sebrell 1945 Blood regeneration in pyridoxine-deficient rats. *Am. J. Physiol.* 143, 434–439; *Nutr. Abs. Rev.* 15, 285.

McHenry, E. W., and G. Gavin 1941 (Effect of pyridoxine on) the synthesis of fat from protein. *J. Biol. Chem.* 138, 471–475; *Chem. Abs.* 35, 3685; *Nutr. Abs. Rev.* 11, 227.

McKibbin, J. M., A. E. Schaefer, D. V. Frost, and C. A. Elvehjem 1942 Studies on anemia in dogs due to pyridoxine deficiency. *J. Biol. Chem.* 142, 77–84.

Review 1947 Present knowledge of vitamin B_6 in nutrition. *Nutrition Rev.* 5, 98–100.

Review 1949 Vitamin B_6 deficiency in the monkey. *Nutrition Rev.* 7, 184–186.

Review 1949b Metabolism of vitamin B_6 in man. *Nutrition Rev.* 7, 215–217.

Rosenblum, L. A., and N. Jolliffe 1941 The oral manifestations of vitamin deficiencies. *J. Am. Med. Assoc.* 117, 2245–2248.

Schlenk, F., and E. E. Snell 1945 Vitamin B_6 and transamination. *J. Biol. Chem.* 157, 425–426; *Nutr. Abs. Rev.* 15, 82.

Schneider, H., H. Steenbock, and B. R. Platz 1940 Essential fatty acids, vitamin B_6, and other factors in the cure of rat acrodynia. *J. Biol. Chem.* 132, 539–551.

Schwartzman, J., D. Dragutsky, and G. Rook 1941 Syndenham's chorea. Preliminary report of three cases successfully treated with vitamin B_6. *J. Pediat.* 19, 201–204; *Nutr. Abs. Rev.* 11, 475.

Smith, S. G., R. Curry, and H. Hawfield 1943 Vitamin B_6 deficiency anemia in the dog. *Science* 98, 520–522.

Spies, T. D., W. B. Bean, and W. F. Ashe 1939 A note on the use of vitamin B_6 in human nutrition. *J. Am. Med. Assoc.* 112, 2414–2415.

Spies, T. D., R. K. Ladisch, and W. B. Bean 1940 Vitamin B_6 (pyridoxin) deficiency in human beings. *J. Am. Med. Assoc.* 115, 839–840.

Street, H. R., G. R. Cowgill, and H. M. Zimmerman 1941 Vitamin B_6 deficiency in the dog. *J. Nutrition* 21, 275–290.

Vitamin B_{12}

Hartman, A. M., L. P. Dryden, and C. A. Cary 1949 The role and sources of vitamin B_{12}. *J. Am. Dietet. Assoc.* 25, 929–933.

Hartman, A. M., L. P. Dryden, and C. A. Cary 1949b A role

of vitamin B_{12} in the normal mammal. *Arch. Biochem.* **23**, 165–168.

LEWIS, U. J., U. D. REGISTER, and C. A. ELVEHJEM   1949   Vitamin B_{12} content of various organs and tissues of the rat. *Proc. Soc. Exptl. Biol. Med.* **71**, 509–511.

LUECKE, R. W., W. N. MCMILLEN, F. THORPE, JR., and J. R. BONIECE   1949   The effect of vitamin B_{12} concentrate on the growth of weanling pigs fed corn-soybean diets. *Science* **110**, 139–140.

NICHOL, C. A., A. E. HARPER, and C. A. ELVEHJEM   1949   Effect of folic acid, liver extract, and vitamin B_{12} on hemoglobin regeneration in chicks. *Proc. Soc. Exptl. Biol. Med.* **71**, 34–37.

REGISTER, U. D., U. J. LEWIS, H. T. THOMPSON, and C. A. ELVEHJEM   1949   Variations in the vitamin B_{12} content of selected samples of pork and beef muscle. *Proc. Soc. Exptl. Biol. Med.* **70**, 167–168; *Chem. Abs.* **43**, 3894.

REVIEW   1949   On the (problem of the) identity of vitamin B_{12} and the animal protein factor. *Nutrition Rev.* **7**, 136–137.

REVIEW   1949b   Castle's extrinsic factor and vitamin B_{12}. *Nutrition Rev.* **7**, 146–147.

REVIEW   1950   Growth promotion by vitamin B_{12} in children. *Nutrition Rev.* **8**, 139–141.

SCHAEFER, A. E., W. D. SALMON, and D. R. STRENGTH   1949   Interrelationship of vitamin B_{12} and choline, I, II. *Proc. Soc. Exptl. Biol. Med.* **71**, 193–196, 202–204; *Chem. Abs.* **43**, 6708.

WETZEL, N. C., W. C. FARGO, I. H. SMITH, and J. HELIKSON   1949   Growth failure in school children as associated with vitamin B_{12} deficiency—response to oral therapy. *Science* **110**, 651–653.

Vitamin B_{14}

NORRIS, E. R., and J. J. MAJNARICH   1949   Vitamin B_{14} and cell proliferation. *Science* **109**, 32–33.

NORRIS, E. R., and J. J. MAJNARICH   1949b   Action of enzymes on vitamin B_{14} and pteridine. *Science* **109**, 33–35.

REVIEW   1949   Vitamin B_{14}. *Nutrition Rev.* **7**, 164–166.

Vitamin M, Folic Acid, Pteroylglutamate

ALLFREY, V. G., and C. G. KING   1950   An investigation of the folic acid-protein complex in yeast. *J. Biol. Chem.* **182**, 367–384.

ASENJO, C. F.   1948   Pteroylglutamic acid requirement of the rat and a characteristic lesion observed in the spleen of the deficient animal. *J. Nutrition* **36**, 601–612.

BUYZE, H. G., and C. ENGEL 1949 Utilization of folic acid conjugate in man. *Nature* **163**, 135; *Chem. Abs.* **43**, 3895.

DARBY, W. J., E. JONES, H. F. WARDEN, and M. M. KASER 1947 The influence of pteroylglutamic acid (a member of the vitamin M group) on gastro-intestinal defects in sprue. A study of interrelationships of dietary essentials. *J. Nutrition* **34**, 645–660.

DAY, P. L., W. C. LANGSTON, and W. J. DARBY 1938 Failure of nicotinic acid to prevent nutritional cytopenia in the monkey. *Proc. Soc. Exptl. Biol. Med.* **38**, 860–863.

DAY, P. L., W. C. LANGSTON, W. J. DARBY, J. G. WAHLIN, and V. MIMS 1940 Nutritional cytopenia in monkeys receiving the Goldberger diet. *J. Exptl. Med.* **72**, 463–477.

DAY, P. L., V. MIMS, and J. R. TOTTER 1945 Relation between vitamin M and the *Lactobacillus casei* factor. *J. Biol. Chem.* **161**, 45–52; *Chem. Abs.* **40**, 1209.

DAY, P. L., V. MIMS, J. R. TOTTER, E. L. R. STOKSTAD, B. L. HUTCHINGS, and N. H. SLOANE 1945 The successful treatment of vitamin M deficiency in the monkey with highly purified *Lactobacillus casei* factor. *J. Biol. Chem.* **157**, 423–424.

DAY, P. L., and J. R. TOTTER 1948 Pteroylglutamic acid balance studies on monkeys. *J. Nutrition* **36**, 803–812.

FAGER, E. E. C., O. E. OLSON, R. H. BURRIS, and C. A. ELVEHJEM 1949 Folic acid in vegetables and certain other plant materials. *Food Research* **14**, 1–14.

JANOTA, M., and G. M. DACK 1939 Bacillary dysentery developing in monkeys on a vitamin-M deficient diet. *J. Infectious Diseases* **65**, 219–224; *Nutr. Abs. Rev.* **19**, 924–925.

JUKES, T. H., and E. L. R. STOKSTAD 1948 Pteroylglutamic acid and related compounds. *Physiol. Rev.* **28**, 51–106; *Chem. Abs.* **42**, 5523.

KRACKE, R. R., and W. H. RISER, JR. 1947 Folic acid (pteroylglutamic acid) studies: Hematologic remissions in pernicious anemia. *Proc. Soc. Exptl. Biol. Med.* **64**, 179–181.

KREHL, W. A., and C. A. ELVEHJEM 1945 The importance of "folic acid" in rations low in nicotinic acid. *J. Biol. Chem.* **158**, 173–179.

LANGSTON, W. C., W. J. DARBY, C. F. SHUKERS, and P. L. DAY 1938 Nutritional cytopenia (vitamin M deficiency) in the monkey. *J. Exptl. Med.* **68**, 923–940; *Nutr. Abs. Rev.* **8**, 938.

LOPEZ, G., T. D. SPIES, et al. 1946 Folic acid and sprue. *J. Am. Med. Assoc.* **132**, 906–911; *J. Am. Dietet. Assoc.* **23**, 362.

PRUSOFF, W. H., L. J. TEPLY, and C. G. KING 1948 The influence of pteroylglutamic acid on nucleic acid synthesis in *Lactobacillus casei*. *J. Biol. Chem.* **176**, 1309–1317.

Review   1947   Folic acid and pernicious anemia. *Nutrition Rev.* **5**, 115–116.

Spies, T. D.   1946   Folic acid for macrocytic anemia in relapse. *J. Am. Med. Assoc.* **130**, 474–477.

Weir, D. R., R. W. Heinle, and A. D. Welch   1948   Pteroylglutamic acid deficiency in mice: Hematologic and histologic findings. *Proc. Soc. Exptl. Biol. Med.* **69**, 211–215.

Pantothenic Acid

Coryell, M. N., M. E. Harris, S. Miller, H. H. Williams, and I. G. Macy   1947   Metabolism of women during the reproductive cycle: XIV. The utilization of pantothenic acid during lactation. *J. Lab. Clin. Med.* **32**, 1454–1461; *J. Home Econ.* **40**, 222.

Daft, F. S., W. H. Sebrell, S. H. Babcock, Jr., and T. H. Jukes   1940   Effect of synthetic pantothenic acid on adrenal hemorrhage, atrophy and necrosis in rats. *Public Health Repts.* **55**, 1333–1337.

Hegsted, D. M., and T. R. Riggs   1949   The pantothenic acid requirements of chicks receiving a purified diet. *J. Nutrition* **37**, 361–367.

Henderson, L. M., J. M. McIntire, H. A. Waisman, and C. A. Elvehjem   1942   Pantothenic acid in the nutrition of the rat. *J. Nutrition* **23**, 47–58.

Ihde, A. J., and H. A. Schuette   1941   Thiamine, nicotinic acid, riboflavin, and pantothenic acid in rye and its milled products. *J. Nutrition* **22**, 527–533.

Jukes, T. H.   1941   Distribution of pantothenic acid in certain products of natural origin. *J. Nutrition* **21**, 193–200.

Jukes, T. H., and L. W. McElroy   1943   Observations on the pantothenic acid requirement of chicks. *Poultry Sci.* **22**, 438–441; *Nutr. Abs. Rev.* **13**, 559.

Shaw, J. H., and P. H. Phillips   1945   Neuropathologic studies of pantothenic acid, biotin, and folic acid complex deficiencies in the chick. *J. Nutrition* **29**, 107–112.

Spies, T. D., S. R. Stanbery, R. J. Williams, T. H. Jukes, and S. H. Babcock   1940   Pantothenic acid in human nutrition. *J. Am. Med. Assoc.* **115**, 523–524; see also *J. Biol. Chem.* **135**, 353–354.

Biotin

Coryell, M. N., M. E. Harris, S. Miller, M. M. Rutledge, H. H. Williams, and I. G. Macy   1947   Metabolism of women during the reproductive cycle: XV. The utilization of biotin during lactation. *J. Lab. Clin. Med.* **32,** 1462–1469; *J. Home Econ.* **40,** 222.

"CURRENT COMMENT" 1942 Biotin deficiency in man. *J. Am. Med. Assoc.* **119,** 183.

GYÖRGY, P., C. S. ROSE, R. E. EAKIN, E. E. SNELL, and R. J. WILLIAMS 1941 Egg-white injury as the result of non-absorption or inactivation of biotin. *Science* **93,** 477–478.

LAMPEN, J. O., G. P. BAHLER, and W. H. PETERSON 1942 The occurrence of free and bound biotin. *J. Nutrition* **23,** 11–21.

SHULL, G. M., B. L. HUTCHINGS, and W. H. PETERSON 1942 A microbiological assay for biotin. *J. Biol. Chem.* **142,** 913–920.

SYDENSTRICKER, V. P., S. A. SINGAL, A. P. BRIGGS, N. M. DEVAUGHN, and H. ISBELL 1942 Preliminary observations on "egg-white injury" in man and its cure with a biotin concentrate. *Science* **95,** 176–177.

DU VIGNEAUD, V., J. M. SPANGLER, D. BURK, C. J. KANSLER, K. SUGIURA, and C. P. RHOADS 1942 The precarcinogenic effect of biotin in butter yellow tumor formation. *Science* **95,** 174–176.

Choline (Labile Methyl)

BEST, C. H. 1941 The significance of choline as a dietary factor. *Science* **94,** 523–527.

BLUMBERG, H., and E. V. MCCOLLUM 1941 Prevention by choline of liver cirrhosis in rats on high-fat, low-protein diets. *Science* **93,** 598–599.

GRIFFITH, W. H. 1941 The nutritional importance of choline. *J. Nutrition* **22,** 239–253.

MCINTIRE, J. M., B. S. SCHWEIGERT, and C. A. ELVEHJEM 1944 The choline and pyridoxine content of meats. *J. Nutrition* **28,** 219–223.

PATEK, A. J., JR., and J. POST 1941 Treatment of cirrhosis of the liver by a nutritious diet and supplements rich in vitamin B complex. *J. Clin. Investigation* **20,** 481–505; *Nutr. Abs. Rev.* **11,** 471.

Vitamin P

KUGELMASS, I. N. 1940 Vitamin P in vascular purpura. *J. Am. Med. Assoc.* **115,** 519–520.

RAPAPORT, H. G., and S. KLEIN 1941 Vitamin P and capillary fragility. *J. Pediatrics* **18,** 321–327; *Chem. Abs.* **35,** 3585; *Nutr. Abs. Rev.* **11,** 331.

RUSZNYÁK, S., and A. BENKŐ 1941 Experimental vitamin P deficiency. *Science* **94,** 25; *Nutr. Abs. Rev.* **11,** 423.

XV

VITAMIN A AND ITS PRECURSORS

General Relationships

Vitamin A itself is a colorless, fat-soluble substance found notably in milk, egg, and liver fats, and known to be essential both to the growth process and to the maintenance of normal conditions in the body at all ages. It has not been found in plants; but among the natural orange-yellow coloring matters of green and yellow vegetable tissues there are *precursors* of vitamin A, *i.e.*, substances which give rise to vitamin A in the animal body. These are named alpha-, beta-, and gamma-carotene, and cryptoxanthin.

Structural formulas for vitamin A and for these four precursors may be found, if desired, on pages 416 and 417 of the Seventh Edition of Sherman's *Chemistry of Food and Nutrition;* but for our present purpose it will suffice to remember simply the existence of the vitamin and its precursors as a group. For convenience the precursors are often referred to as "the carotenes," or even simply as "carotene."

While there are methods of making *in vitro* determinations of vitamin A and of "carotene" which serve certain purposes, the most general basis of comparison between foods of all kinds, or of summing up the contributions of foods of different kinds toward meeting the body's nutritional need, is in terms of *vitamin A values* determined by feeding experiments in which the body of the test animal converts the precursors into the vitamin in the same way as does our own.

It has been reported that vitamin A occurs in two forms (vitamins A_1 and A_2), the one predominating in the liver oils of salt-water, and the other of fresh-water fish; but they seem to be very closely related and of essentially the same nutritional character and potency, so we treat the two as one in everyday discussions of food and nutrition.

Vitamin A in Growth and Development

A good general first impression of the significance of the level of intake of vitamin A to growth and development is afforded by the quantitatively parallel photographs of twin brothers shown in Fig. 29. At four weeks of age, which we take as representing the

Fig. 29. Photographs of twin brothers, showing effects of different amounts of vitamin A in the food. (See text.) (Courtesy of The Forsyth Foundation.)

end of infancy in the rat, they were of the same size and indistinguishable in their appearance, both being smooth-coated, bright-eyed, alert, and of normal development for their age. From that time they were fed the same diet except that one received butter and the other did not, though the latter had always as much as he wished to eat of a mixture of vitamin A deficient foods which were all perfectly good of their kinds. At the time these rats were photographed they had reached an age corresponding to about seven years in a boy. The one which had plenty of vitamin A had continued to make a normal growth and development, while the one whose food had been otherwise adequate but very poor in vitamin

A is stunted in growth and muscular development, is dim-eyed, and sadly lacking in alertness. Here the shortage of vitamin A had been so severe as to show its effects upon health as well as growth.

In quantitatively controlled experiments with graded allowances of vitamin A* in an otherwise good diet, as in the experiments of Batchelder, the average growth data of which are summarized in Fig. 30, it may be clearly shown that even when there is no such severe shortage as to have any immediately visible effect upon health, the growth may still be limited by the level of vitamin A

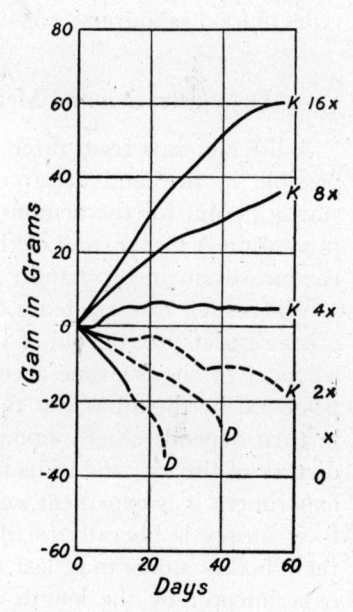

Fig. 30. Batchelder's average growth data from graded allowances of vitamin A.

value of the dietary. In these experiments of Batchelder, for example, the rats receiving the 8x and 16x levels of vitamin A per day did not show any differences in ostensible health though the ones receiving the more liberal allowance of vitamin A were making better growth.

Evidence obtained directly from human experience, first clinically and then by carefully controlled experimentation, shows extremely important relations of the vitamin A value of the food supply to the functioning of the eye,—a fact effectively used by Ham-

* Indicated by multiples of x at the right-hand margin of Fig. 30, in which D = died; K = killed.

bidge to introduce his general summary, and by Booher and Callison in their chapter on vitamin A, in the articles cited among Suggested Readings at the end of the chapter.

The sequence of the present text is first to describe the demonstration and measurement of vitamin A values as in controlled experiments with laboratory animals, then to summarize the effects of different levels of nutritional intake of this factor upon different organs of the body and upon the body and the life history as a whole, including positive health and longevity; and finally to consider the quantitative aspect of the values of different articles and types of food as sources.

Demonstration and Measurement of Vitamin A Values

A litter of rats from three to four weeks old, and as uniform as possible in size and apparent health and vigor, affords a good starting point for the demonstration of the influence of differences in vitamin A intake, and of the principle of the feeding method for the measurement of vitamin A values.

When such rats are fed a diet well adapted to their needs in all other respects but devoid of vitamin A value, growth continues for a longer or shorter time according to the body-store of vitamin A possessed by the animal at the beginning of the experiment, which in turn depends chiefly upon the vitamin A value of the previous dietary of the rat, and of its mother. For the purpose of the present experiment it is expedient *not* to use animals from a family whose food supply is liberally fortified with vitamin A; for in such case their bodily stores may last them so long as to inconvenience the experimenter by the length of time before the appearance of the effect of the experimental diet. The time thus required to use up the surplus previously stored in the body is called the depletion period.

When the body is sufficiently depleted of its surplus vitamin A, growth ceases and (with animals as young as here described) usually a loss of weight begins within the next few days, and at about the same time careful examination may begin to reveal incipient abnormalities, or diminutions of positive health.

Animals thus continued upon the vitamin A-free diet (the basal experimental diet alone) *beyond* the depletion period are sometimes spoken of as "negative controls." In contrast, the "positive controls" are animals (otherwise strictly parallel, of course) which are continued on the same basal experimental diet as the test animals, but with a supplement of sufficiently high vitamin A value to permit them to make fully normal growth and development. Other animals of the group, separated at the end of the depletion period, may be fed different amounts of some material whose vitamin A value is known or is to be ascertained, and in the latter case the work must be so planned as to provide strictly parallel cases, in sufficient numbers, of animals fed the material under test and of those fed the "reference material" whose vitamin A value is quantitatively known.

The International Unit (I.U.) of vitamin A value is a value equal to that of 0.6 microgram of pure beta-carotene. The standardized carotene was prepared by the Health Organization of the League of Nations and intended only for those having *official* need for it. A "reference codliver oil" whose vitamin A value has been compared with the International standard carotene is obtainable from the United States Pharmacopeia Organization, 43rd Street and Woodland Avenue, Philadelphia.

The United States Pharmacopeia (U.S.P.) Unit is so defined as to be identical with the International Unit. All of the numerical expressions of vitamin A value in this book are in terms of this unit.

As may be seen from Fig. 30 there is (when sufficient numbers of cases at each level are averaged) a fairly regular gradation of the weight curves according to the level of vitamin A fed; but the gain is, of course, not arithmetically proportional. The same data represented by this set of curves may be used to construct a "curve of response" representing the relation between the different levels of feeding and the corresponding gains in weight during a feeding-period of any length that the experimenter may desire. A test period of four weeks is now most generally chosen. (Coward's book, listed among Suggested Readings, discusses these points in detail.)

At the upper levels of vitamin-A allowance, as for instance at the 8x and 16x levels of the experiments represented by Fig. 30, the animals (as in the similar work with thiamine described in Chapter XII) will probably, at this early stage, appear equally healthy, with the difference in rate of growth and development as the only apparent result of the difference in vitamin A intake. At the other extreme, the negative controls sooner or later show evident illness with loss of weight and strength and development of one or more of the lesions mentioned in subsequent paragraphs as results of vitamin-A deficiency.

Nutritional Effects of the Level of Vitamin A Value of the Food Consumed

Rats of different colonies differ somewhat in the degree of shortage of vitamin A which must be imposed in order to bring about visible illness. It is reported from some laboratories that in order to keep their rats apparently healthy they must be fed enough vitamin A to support a gain of body weight of about 5 grams a week; while the rats of the Columbia colony almost invariably remain healthy when receiving enough vitamin A to permit a gain of 3 grams a week.

The Skeleton, the Muscles, and the Skin

A higher level of vitamin A intake during growth induces the probability that at a given age the body will not only be heavier but also more long and lithe, with better-formed bones and teeth, better muscular development and muscle tone, and a superior condition of skin "like the sleekness of a well-conditioned farm animal."

Even after such losses of the living impression as are involved in its transfer, first to the photographic plate, then to the engraver's block, and then to paper, the reader may still be able to see something of this difference between the twin brothers shown in Fig. 29 (earlier in this chapter).

McCollum considers a certain dryness of the skin as one of the earliest indications of a shortage of vitamin A. The observations of MacKay upon babies of the London poor indicated that a mild shortage of vitamin A was retarding their growth and making their skin less wholesome and resistant. This condition she was able to cure, by enriching the diet in vitamin A, before the development of any of the more drastic symptoms.

The Eye: Xerophthalmia and Nightblindness

In an experiment with laboratory animals such as was outlined above, xerophthalmia is usually the first noticeable characteristic symptom of the vitamin A deficiency. In work with cooperative human subjects a slight but detectable degree of night blindness (difficulty of adaptation of vision to diminished light) is now generally regarded as a delicate indication of an incipient deficiency of vitamin A.

The former is a special case of the general tendency of shortage of vitamin A to affect the mucous membranes, while the latter has to do with an independent function of vitamin A in the visual process.

Xerophthalmia (keratomalacia, conjunctivitis) is a condition of dry inflammation of the eye-lids and the outer surface of the eye which, soon after the discovery of vitamin A, was observed by Osborne and Mendel to be a frequent consequence of a shortage of this factor. The current explanation is that, under shortage of vitamin A, the cells of the lachrymal gland cease to pour out their normal secretion. The external eye thus becomes dry, bacteria multiply and are not washed away, the eyelids become congested and sometimes so swollen, sticky, and scabby as to close the eye. In extreme cases the cornea may be attacked and permanent blindness may result. Mori observed such an eye disease among children of the Japanese poor and found that it could be cured (if not too far advanced) by chicken livers, fish livers, or codliver oil.

Excessive exportation of butter from Denmark during 1914–1918 caused a shortage of vitamin A in the food of the poorer people with resulting high prevalence of xerophthalmia in Danish children as reported by Bloch and by Blegvad.

Xerosis conjunctivae and Bitot spots.—Kruse (1941) has especially studied the slight degrees of xerosis which precede the gross xerophthalmia just described and which may also develop into "Bitot spots" (tiny lumps or puckers on the conjunctival surface). He uses a method of biomicroscopic examination, description of which would lead beyond the scope of this book but which can be found if desired through the Suggested Readings listed at the end of the chapter. Such microscopic examination he regards as adequately objective and as permitting earlier detection of vitamin A deficiency than was previously possible. By combining this microscopic with skilled macroscopic examination of the conjunctivae, Kruse suggests that different stages or degrees of vitamin A deficiency can be distinguished, and that the earlier stages or milder degrees of vitamin A deficiency are thus found to be much more prevalent than hitherto supposed.

The Milbank Memorial Fund studies of *dietaries* of New York City *high school students* indicated that vitamin A was *their* most frequent deficiency; and correspondingly "changes in the conjunctiva associated with avitaminosis A were present in 88 per cent of 278 boys and 85 per cent of 216 girls" (Wiehl, 1942).

Follicular conjunctivitis has likewise been found prevalent among school children and attributable to shortage of vitamin A in their food inasmuch as the condition was cured by treatment with vitamin A. (If the medical account is desired see, in list of Suggested Readings below: Sandels, Cate, Wilkinson, and Graves, 1941.)

Nightblindness (hemeralopia), diminished ability to see clearly in a dim light, especially when the eye has recently been exposed to a bright one, is a defect of vision which has now been extensively investigated with results which show that vitamin A has a very fundamental role in the visual process, especially in the regeneration in the retina of the visual purple after its bleaching by bright light.

The chemical and physical mechanisms involved and the place of vitamin A in the process have been studied by several investigators including notably Hecht, Wald, and their respective coworkers. (To present this work in a fully explicit fashion would lead beyond the scope of this book. References to it are included among the Suggested Readings listed at the end of this chapter.)

The Respiratory System

As Bessey and Wolbach (1938) explained, the characteristic histological changes of vitamin A deficiency, found in many epithelial structures, consist of: (1) atrophy of some of the normal cuboidal surface cells of epithelium, (2) reparative proliferation of basal cells, and (3) differentiation of this new material into a stratified keratinizing epithelium. Many of the visible pathological features of the deficiency in man and animals, they explain, are the results of accumulation of keratinized epithelial cells in glands and their ducts and in other organs. This is true of xerophthalmia, which has already been considered.

The distribution of such keratinizing metaplasia and the sequence of its development as between, for instance, the eyes, the respiratory system, and the genito-urinary tract, tends to vary both with species and with the age at which the vitamin A deficiency is encountered. Bessey and Wolbach emphasized in 1938, as had Blackfan and Wolbach in 1933, the danger of vitamin A deficiency to the respiratory tract. They found that in the human infant the commonest and earliest appearance of epithelial metaplasia is in the trachea and the bronchi. Blegvad, following the histories of Danish infants who showed eye troubles due to vitamin A deficiency during 1914-1918, found that a large proportion of them ultimately died of respiratory disease.

The Genito-Urinary Tract

Osborne and Mendel found that phosphatic calculi ("bladder stones") developed in the urinary tracts of a large proportion of their vitamin-A deficient rats. The explanations offered have not been entirely harmonious. In a comprehensive review Clausen concludes that the factors involved are not clearly defined. The hypothesis most consistent with known chemical and histological factors would seem to be that the precipitation of phosphate may be induced by a local infection which in turn is attributable to an abnormality of the epithelium resulting from the vitamin A deficiency.

Atrophy of the testes and disturbances of the female reproductive system due to the keratinizing metaplasia already discussed have been observed in vitamin-A deficient human beings as well as in experimental animals.

Storage of Vitamin A in the Body

Vitamin A can be stored in the body to a large extent, and with far-reaching results.

As Bessey and Wolbach summarize it, most animals have a remarkable capacity for such storage, "illustrated by the fact that a rat may in a few days store enough vitamin A to supply its nutritional needs for several months." Usually over nine-tenths of the body's store of vitamin A is found in the liver, the amount thus stored depending upon the nutritional background,—how large a surplus the food has supplied and for how long. Lung and kidney tissue have much less than liver, but still measurable amounts; and it has been found that the level of vitamin A feeding influences the amount of vitamin A in the lung. Muscle contains so little as to be practically at the lower limit of measurability even when the level of nutritional intake of vitamin A is liberal. Adipose tissue may, however, contain a significant amount.

Agreeing fully with Bessey and Wolbach that the rat is able to store vitamin A in the body in sufficient amounts to meet nutritional needs for a relatively long time, we would also emphasize the fact that the limit of the body's capacity for storage of vitamin A is not quickly reached. Thus in one series of experiments* it was found that whether the opportunity for bodily storage was afforded by parallel additions of 1, 2, or 4 per cent of codliver oil to an already-adequate diet, or by feeding the diet fortified with 4 per cent of codliver oil for different lengths of time, in either case the body first stored rapidly from the surplus fed, but thereafter continued to add slowly to its store for as long a time as the experimental feeding was continued, and increasingly with the level fed up to the highest fortification tried. More recent work shows even more strikingly the

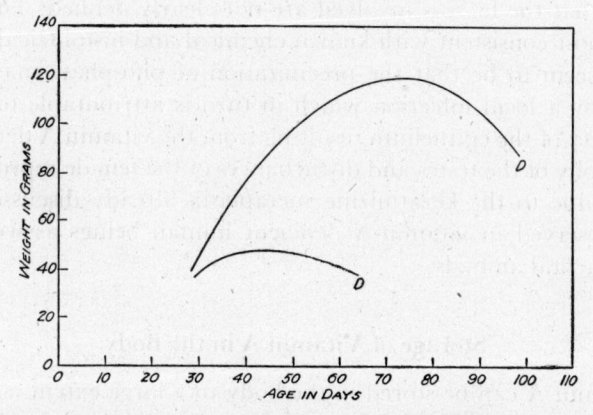

Fig. 31. Curves illustrating the effects of differing bodily stores of vitamin A. (See text.)

ability of the body to continue storing vitamin A throughout long-term experiments (Sherman and Trupp, 1949).

By the end of infancy, differently fed individuals of the same species and racial stock or strain may have quite different bodily reserves of vitamin A. Thus, in the experiments summarized in Fig. 31, young rats of the same colony but whose family dietaries consisted of (1) one-sixth dried whole milk with five-sixths ground whole wheat (Diet 16), and (2) two-thirds dried whole milk with one-third ground whole wheat (Diet 70), respectively, were transferred at the age of 28 days to the same vitamin-A-free diet. Those from Diet 16 with its approximately minimal-adequate vitamin A content had only sufficient body store to grow about 10 grams and to survive an average of 34 days, while those from Diet 70, which

* Sherman, H. C., and M. L. Cammack 1926 A quantitative study of the storage of vitamin A. *J. Biol. Chem.* 68, 69–74.

contains about four-fold more vitamin A than does Diet 16, had enough body store at the same age, to grow about 70 grams and survive an average of 65 days on the same vitamin-A-free diet. The difference in vitamin-A values between these two family dietaries is no greater than the differences which currently exist between many of those of American families (and often even between families of the same locality and same economic level) depending upon their different choices of food.

With older animals there is necessarily much less opportunity for growth to enter into the comparisons; but comparisons of rats taken at different ages from the same home dietary, which in this case

Fig. 32. Influence of the vitamin A content of the food on the rate of retention of vitamin A in the body. Curves I, II, and III show respectively the effects of 3, 6, and 12 International Units of vitamin A per gram of food. The figures given are average results for female rats. The relationship in the case of males was similar.

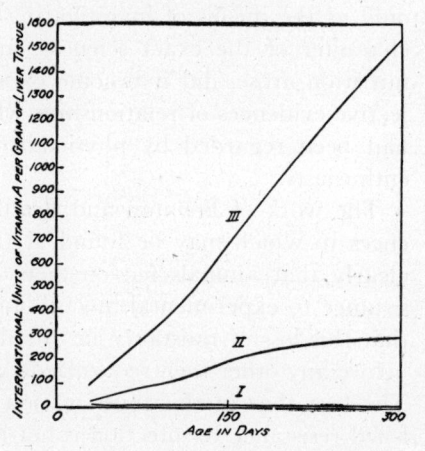

had about twice the minimal-adequate level of vitamin A, showed that the length of time they could survive upon a vitamin-A-free diet continued to increase with their age up to adulthood. While this mode of investigation is in itself perhaps less clear-cut and conclusive than the one above described, it is significant as evidence of yet another kind that the body continues for a relatively long time to add to its reserves of vitamin A if the food contains a surplus above immediate nutritional need.

Lack of complete realization of the full extent and significance of this phenomenon of widely differing bodily storage has undoubtedly sometimes been a cause of misinterpretation of human experience and of undue skepticism regarding the importance of the vitamin-A level in the human food supply.

Considering the evidence now available on the quantitative role which body storage can play in the growth and health of the rat, and taking account of the relative lengths of life in the two species, it appears that human subjects would have to be kept for years under strict observation in order fully to control the differing influence from their different nutritional backgrounds.

Relation to Frequency and Duration of Infection

Summarizing his special study of the subject, Clausen points out that the possibility of diet having influence upon the incidence, course, and final outcome of infection, is a comparatively recent idea, a development of twentieth-century science. In other words, only as the means of investigating infections came to take on the character of the exact sciences, and as the newer knowledge of nutrition arose, did it become experimentally possible to find objective evidences of relationships which before, if postulated at all, had been regarded by physicians as merely the views of a few enthusiasts.

The work of Boynton and Bradford (1931), and others, references to which may be found at the end of this chapter, showed clearly that animals fed on diets low in vitamin A had low resistance to experimental inoculation with infective organisms, and that this loss of resistance in rats deprived of vitamin A appeared before any other then recognized evidence of vitamin A deficiency. The fact that in this investigation rachitic rats showed undiminished resistance to infection is not necessarily inconsistent with the view that children who have been protected from rickets are less subject to respiratory disease. For protection from rickets has so generally been accomplished by means of the fish liver oils that the children thus protected have at the same time received important additions to their bodily reserves of vitamin A. Mellanby, in the very careful and extensive experiments which he made at the time that vitamins A and D were just beginning to be differentiated from each other, observed that pups fed diets poor in vitamin A showed an undue liability to pneumonia. Rats of many different colonies and strains, observed under conditions of laboratory control, have now been found by several investigators to suffer more from infections when kept on diets of low vitamin A value.

Discussions have not always distinguished between incidence, severity, and duration of infections. In one clinical investigation it was found that while extra vitamin A given to normally nourished people showed no certain effect upon the incidence or initial severity of "the common cold," it did measurably diminish the duration of infections of a given severity.

The work of McClung and Winters (1932) also showed clearly under well-controlled conditions a greater susceptibility to infection in those individuals whose diet is deficient in vitamin A.

Other (though not all) investigations indicate that, under conditions of everyday life, people receiving extra allowances of vitamin A have fewer days of disabling colds than in their previous experiences at the same season of year, *or* than in the parallel experience of people similarly placed in other respects but getting diets whose vitamin A value has received no special attention.

Doubtless the next few years will see further clarification of the questions which here we can discuss only in rather tentative terms or bring to notice through the Suggested Readings at the end of the chapter.

Meanwhile it seems safe to say that whether in a given case the benefit comes through diminished incidence, lessened severity, or shortened duration, there are doubtless many cases in which one who has regularly had a liberal daily intake and a rich bodily reserve of vitamin A suffers less from infections.

Reproduction and Lactation

Vitamin A is quite as definitely essential to reproduction as is the socalled anti-sterility vitamin (vitamin E). The latter received this designation because it was not known to be particularly concerned with general nutritional functions and not because it is any more vitally concerned in reproduction than is vitamin A.

For the support of successful reproduction and lactation the diet must furnish more vitamin A than is needed for even the most rapid growth. For instance, in the rat families studied by Sherman and MacLeod (1925) a diet of relatively low vitamin A value supported growth surprisingly well for some time but failed utterly when put to the further and more rigorous test of its adequacy to the successful launching of a second generation. On this low vitamin A diet the females (although not showing any outward signs of vitamin A deficiency) either bore no young or failed to rear any of the few that were born, while in parallel families of the same hereditary background and with diets entirely similar except that they contained more milk-fat, reproduction and rearing of young proceeded normally.

Full-life and Successive-generation Experiments

The investigations mentioned in the preceding paragraph were extended by Batchelder in a series of full-life and successive-generation experiments with rat families fed diets of systematically graded vitamin A content. Those at the minimal adequate level of vitamin A intake grew to normal size (though in the lower ranges of the normal zone), were successful in bearing and rearing young, lived to an age within the normal range of longevity without showing any specific sign of vitamin A deficiency, and left vigorous offspring. On a level of vitamin A intake twice as high, the performances in all these respects were again within the normal range, but the average record was slightly higher with respect to every one of the criteria just mentioned. Parallel animals on a level of vitamin A intake four-fold higher than that of minimal adequacy again made slightly better average records than those on the two-fold level. At a level eight-fold that of the minimal-adequate vitamin A requirement, the original animals showed no measurably different responses from those on the four-fold level; but the higher of these two levels seemed to confer a still further benefit upon the offspring. (It will be remembered from Chapter XIII that in the case of riboflavin—as here of vitamin A—when liberality of intake has been carried to the "plateau level" of adult response, further increments may still show further benefits to the offspring.)

More recently the Columbia laboratory with the aid of grants from The Nutrition Foundation has resumed and extended its experimental studies of the effects of different levels of vitamin A intake with results which permit of more positive and quantitative conclusions, especially as regards the relation of the vitamin A value of the diet to the length of life. Starting with a diet which previous and parallel work has shown adequate to the degree that rat families are still thriving upon it in the 72nd generation, it is found that doubling the vitamin A value of the diet increased the average length of these already normal lives. And moreover, on again doubling the vitamin A value of the diet there follow further improvements of life history to the extent that in terms of the original (adequate but suboptimal) level, quadrupling the original intake increased the already normal length of life: of males, 10.4 per cent;

and of females, 12.1 per cent. Moreover, in these same experiments, the socalled "useful life" (that part of the life cycle which lies between the attainment of maturity and the onset of senility) was increased in greater ratio than the life span itself.

Whatever form the final explanation may take, the fact is shown by experiment for vitamin A (as it has been also for vitamin C and for calcium) that the difference between minimal adequate and the optimal intake is much wider than had been supposed, or than is probable for many other factors in nutrition.

This means that the science of nutrition has greater constructive potentialities than hitherto supposed. Also, it meanwhile complicates the problem of quantitative standards of "requirement."

Human Requirements for Vitamin A

In view of the facts mentioned in the preceding paragraphs, the question, How much vitamin A value is required in human nutrition?, logically raises the further question, Required for what: for the maintenance of passable health with prevention of frank symptoms of deficiency, or for the support of the highest degree of nutritional wellbeing and positive health that each individual is potentially able to attain?

This distinction being relatively new, there are still many people, and perhaps even some influential ones, who regard it as more or less speculative. On the other hand, the reality of the difference is recognized as highly significant by those who sufficiently study the experimental evidence quantitatively. Thus it is gradually coming to be considered that the human requirement should mean not only what is needed for the prevention of specific deficiency symptoms, but further what is needed to permit a human population to realize fully the potentialities of its hereditary birthright.

Aykroyd and Krishnan,* as the result of special study, considered that the need for vitamin A value in human nutrition is higher than previously believed, and proposed allowances of 3000 to 5000 I.U. per child per day.

Booher, Callison, and coworkers† have found the minimum re-

---

* Aykroyd, W. R., and B. G. Krishnan   1936   *Indian J. Med. Research* 23, 741–745.

† Booher, L. E., E. C. Callison, and E. M. Hewston   1939   An experimental determination of the minimum vitamin A requirements of normal adults. *J. Nutrition* 17, 317–331.

quirements for the maintenance of the normal efficiency of the eye in the dark-adaptation test in five "ostensibly healthy" adults (three women aged 30 to 40; and two men aged 21 and 25 years) to vary from 1750 to 3850 I.U. per day when taken in the form of vitamin A itself, or 3010 to 7210 I.U. per day when taken in the form of carotene dissolved in cottonseed oil. Batchelder and Ebbs (1944) found evidence favoring the higher allowances while tentative findings of a British wartime study suggested that lower allowances might suffice.

When experiments show such a wide apparent range in even the minimum requirement, and it is still a matter of varying judgment among nutritionists how the optimal allowance shall be related to the minimum (or "rock bottom requirement") it is obvious that attempts to state human requirements in precise quantitative form must, for the present, be largely matters of judgment. The present writers favor the liberal allowances recommended by the National Research Council in 1948.

The Recommended Daily Allowances of the National Research Council Committee provide:

> 5,000 International Units for normal human adults, rising to 6,000 for women in the latter half of pregnancy and 8,000 during lactation;
> 1,500 such units for children under 1 year of age;
> 2,000, for children of 1 to 3 years;
> 2,500, " " " 4 to 6 " ;
> 3,500, " " " 7 to 9 " ;
> 4,500, " " " 10 to 12 " ; and
> 5,000–6,000 for young people of 13 to 20.

Whether these recommended allowances will seem sound investments will depend largely upon the degree of acceptance: (1) of the methods and criteria of Kruse which tend to show, by direct observations upon the human population, that slight deficiencies are more frequent and actual requirements therefore higher than hitherto supposed; and (2) of the evidence from full-life and successive-generation experiments with laboratory animals indicating that in the case of vitamin A there is a wide zone of beneficial increase between the minimal-adequate and the long-run optimal level of intake.

Vitamin A Values of Foods

The carotenes (and possibly other precursors or provitamins) formed in plants, and the ready-formed vitamin A contained in many food materials of animal origin, together constitute the source of the vitamin A which functions so importantly in our nutrition. One may, therefore, give much weight to the vitamin A values of foods in the planning of the dietary, or one may leave the responsibility for vitamin A very largely to the regular taking of fish-liver oils.

Probably the best plan is to give considerable weight to vitamin A values in the choice of foods or planning of food budgets, so that in satisfying our hunger we shall have ingested at least a minimal-adequate amount of vitamin A, and then (for "insurance" or "good measure" or for the further promotion of positive health) take fish-liver oil also, at least during the winter months.

The green leaf vegetables as a group and such yellow vegetables as carrots and the highly colored varieties of sweetpotatoes are rich in carotene and so are of high vitamin A value.

Grasses and other forage plants which (in America and Europe, at least) are not classified as human foods, are also of high vitamin A value, and in milch cows and laying hens the human family has very efficient servants for bringing into forms excellently adapted to our use (milk and eggs), the values of more fibrous leaves than we ourselves would care to eat. Muscles, however, take up extremely little vitamin A, even when the animal is abundantly supplied; so clear lean muscle meats are always of low vitamin A value. Liver is, weight for weight, usually a much richer source, but variable, depending upon how the animal has been fed. Adipose tissue usually contains more than clear lean but less than liver.

The cereal grains, and therefore their mill products, and bakery products (unless made with milk, butter, fortified margarines, or eggs) contain only insignificant amounts of vitamin A or of any of its precursors. This is also true of sweets and of most commercial fats and fatty oils.

So far, it has been possible to speak in general terms which are valid for general types of food. There are, however, other foods which are too variable to be accurately covered by these general statements.

Thus not only is the vitamin A value enormously higher in carrots than in turnips; but also in deep-yellow than in pale-fleshed sweetpotatoes, in Hubbard squash than in pale-fleshed summer squash, in loose-leaf than in tightly headed lettuce, in the green growing tip than in the white stalk of asparagus, and so in many other such cases. For example, Kramer, Boehm and Williams (1929) found the outer green leaves of lettuce to have 30 or more times as high vitamin A value as the white inner leaves from the same heads.

TABLE 26. *Vitamin A Values of Certain Foods*

Food	International Units per 100 Grams
Foods of Animal Origin	
Muscle meats	0–50
Liver (of cattle, sheep, and swine)	10,000–40,000
Milk	160–225
Butter	3300–4000
Eggs	1000–2000
Egg white	negligible
Egg yolk	3000–4000
Fruits and Vegetables	
Apples	40–100
Asparagus	300–1000
Bananas	300–430
Beans, baked	30–70
Carrots	4000–12,000
Greens (Dandelion, Escarole, Kale, Lambsquarters, Mustard, Spinach, Turnip tops)	3,000–20,000
Peas, fresh young green	680–1300
Potato	20–50
Sweetpotato (varying with color)	2000–7700
Fish liver oils	around 200,000

When comparisons are made of (*a*) the amounts of carotene(s) in vegetables as indicated by chemical analysis *in vitro* with (*b*) the vitamin A values as indicated by feeding experiments ("biological vitamin A values") the carotenes show availability values considerably below the theoretical; and lower for yellow roots than for green leaves. Experiments in the U. S. Department of Agriculture

TABLE 27. *Approximate Losses of Vitamin A Values on Cooking Foods. Examples Selected from the Data of Taylor and MacLeod,* "Rose's Laboratory Handbook for Dietetics," 5th Edition (Macmillan) (By permission of the authors and publisher.)

	Percentage Loss
Asparagus, fresh, boiled	25
Beans, green snap, boiled	25
other methods	20
Broccoli, all methods	20
Cabbage, all methods	30
Cauliflower, all methods	5
Okra, all methods	20
Onions, all methods	5
Peas, all methods	20
Sweetpotatoes	20
Turnip greens, all methods	25

showed 67 per cent availability for the carotenes of kale; 37 per cent for those of sweetpotatoes; and 34 to 41 per cent for those of carrots.*

EXERCISES

1. Arrange your "twelve to forty foods" in the order of, or in groups according to, their vitamin A values, (1) per 100 grams; (2) per 100 Calories.

2. Divide a litter of rats between three and four weeks old into two groups as nearly equal as possible in size and in the distribution of the sexes. To one group feed a diet[†] adequate (to the needs of rats) in all respects, and with its vitamin A supplied solely in the form of butter or butterfat. To the other group feed a diet similar except for the substitution of lard or cottonseed oil for the butter or butterfat. Several weeks may elapse before the nutritional effects of this difference in diets begin to appear.

3. If circumstances permit, duplicate the preceding Exercise with a parallel experiment using a litter of rats whose home diet has been distinctly richer or poorer in vitamin A value.

* *Journal of Nutrition,* **37,** 139–152 (1949).
† Either the diet prescribed in the U. S. Pharmacopeia directions for vitamin A testing, or a simplification of it adapted to individual circumstances may be used.

SUGGESTED READINGS

Batchelder, E. L. 1934 Nutritional significance of vitamin A throughout the life cycle. *Am. J. Physiol.* **109**, 430–435.

Batchelder, E. L., and J. C. Ebbs 1944 Some observations of dark adaptation in man and their bearing on the problem of human requirements for vitamin A. *J. Nutrition* **27**, 295–302.

Bessey, O. A., and S. B. Wolbach 1938 Vitamin A: Physiology and pathology. *J. Am. Med. Assoc.* **110**, 2072–2080; reprinted as Chapter II of *"The Vitamins, 1939."* (American Medical Association.)

Blackfan, K. D., and S. B. Wolbach 1933 Vitamin A deficiency in infants. *J. Pediat.* **3**, 679–706.

Booher, L. E., and E. C. Callison 1939 Vitamin needs of man: Vitamin A. *U. S. Dept. Agriculture Yearbook,* "Food and Life," 221–229.

Boynton, L. C., and W. L. Bradford 1931 Effect of vitamins A and D on resistance to infection. *J. Nutrition* **4**, 323–329.

Brenner, S., M. C. H. Brookes, and L. J. Roberts 1942 The relation of liver stores to the occurrence of early signs of vitamin A deficiency in the white rat. *J. Nutrition* **23**, 459–471.

Caldwell, A. B., G. MacLeod, and H. C. Sherman 1945 Bodily storage of vitamin A in relation to diet and age. *J. Nutrition* **30**, 349–353.

Callison, E. C., and E. Orent-Keiles 1947 Availability of carotene from carrots and further observations on human requirements for vitamin A and carotene. *J. Nutrition* **34**, 153–165.

Clausen, S. W. 1934 The influence of nutrition upon resistance to infection. *Physiol. Rev.* **14**, 309–350.

Cooley, M. L., J. B. Christiansen, and R. C. Koehn 1949 Vitamin A in mixed feeds: Chromatographic separation and estimation. *Anal. Chem.* **21**, 593–595.

Coward, K. H. 1947 *The Biological Standardization of the Vitamins,* 2nd Ed. (London: Ballière, Tindall, and Cox.)

Daniels, A. L., M. E. Armstrong, and M. K. Hutton 1923 Nasal sinusitis produced by diets deficient in fat-soluble A vitamin. *J. Am. Med. Assoc.* **81**, 828–829.

Drummond, J. C., et al. 1922 The origin of the vitamin A in fish oils and fish liver oils. *Biochem. J.* **16**, 482–485, 518–522.

Eddy, W. H., and G. Dalldorf 1941 *The Avitaminoses,* 2nd Ed. (Williams and Wilkins.)

Esh, G. C., and T. S. Sutton 1948 The effects of soya lecithin on the absorption, utilization, and storage of vitamin A and carotene in the white rat. *J. Nutrition* **36**, 391–404.

GLOVER, J., T. W. GOODWIN, and R. A. MORTON   1948   Conversion of beta-carotene into vitamin A in the intestine of the rat. *Biochem. J.* 43, 512–518; *Chem. Abs.* 43, 3899.

GOODWIN, T. W., and B. A. GREGORY   1948   Studies in vitamin A. VII. *Biochem. J.* 43, 505–512.

GUERRANT, N. B.   1949   Influence of age and of vitamin A intake on the storage of vitamin A in the liver of the rat. *J. Nutrition* 37, 37–51.

GUILBERT, H. R., C. E. HOWELL, and G. H. HART   1940   Minimum vitamin A and carotene requirements of mammalian species. *J. Nutrition* 19, 91–103.

HAMBIDGE, G.   1939   Food and life—a summary. *U. S. Dept. Agriculture Yearbook*, "Food and Life," 3–5.

HECHT, S., and J. MANDELBAUM   1939   The relation between vitamin A and dark adaptation. *J. Am. Med. Assoc.* 112, 1910–1916.

HICKMAN, K.   1946   Vitamin storage and utilization in the organism. *Nature* 158, 269.

JEANS, P. C., E. L. BLANCHARD, and F. E. SATTERTHWAITE   1941   Dark adaptation and vitamin A: Further studies with the biophotometer. *J. Pediatrics* 18, 170–194.

JOSEPHS, H. W., M. BABER, and H. CONN   1941   Studies on vitamin A: Relation of blood level and adaptation to dim light to diet. *Bull. Johns Hopkins Hosp.* 68, 375–387.

KRAMER, M. M., G. BOEHM, and R. E. WILLIAMS   1929   Vitamin A content (value) of the green and white leaves of market head lettuce. *J. Home Econ.* 21, 679–680.

KRUSE, H. D.   1941   Medical evaluation of nutritional status. IV. The ocular manifestations of avitaminosis A, with especial consideration of the detection of early changes by biomicroscopy. *Public Health Repts.* 56, 1301–1324.

LEHMAN, E., and H. G. RAPAPORT   1940   Cutaneous manifestations of vitamin A deficiency in children. *J. Am. Med. Assoc.* 114, 386–393.

LEONG, P. C.   1941   Vitamin A in blood and its relation to body reserves. *Biochem. J.* 35, 806–812; *J. Home Econ.* 34, 199.

LESHER, M., A. ROBINSON, J. K. BRODY, H. H. WILLIAMS, and I. G. MACY   1948   The effect of multivitamin supplements on the secretion of vitamin A in human milk. *J. Am. Dietet. Assoc.* 24, 12–16.

LEWIS, J. M., O. BODANSKY, K. G. FALK, and G. McGUIRE   1942   Vitamin A requirements in the rat. The relation of vitamin A intake to growth and to concentration of vitamin A in the blood plasma, liver, and retina. *J. Nutrition* 23, 351–363.

LEWIS, J. M., O. BODANSKY, M. C. C. LILLIENFELD and H. SCHNEIDER 1947 Supplements of vitamin A and of carotene during pregnancy: Their effects on the levels of vitamin A and carotene in the blood of mother and of newborn infant. *Am. J. Diseases Children* **75**, 143–150; *Nutr. Abs. Rev.* **17**, 226.

MACK, P. B., and A. P. SANDERS 1940 The vitamin A status of families in widely different economic levels. *Am. J. Med. Sci.* **199**, 686–697.

MACLEOD, G., and C. TAYLOR 1944 *Rose's Foundations of Nutrition*, 4th Ed. (Macmillan.)

MATTSON, F. H. 1948 The site of conversion of carotene to vitamin A. *J. Biol. Chem.* **176**, 1467–1468.

MCCLUNG, L. S., and J. C. WINTERS 1932 Effect of vitamin-A-free diet on resistance to infection by Salmonella enteritidis. *J. Infectious Diseases* **51**, 469–474.

MCCOLLUM, E. V., et al. 1939 *The Newer Knowledge of Nutrition*, 5th Ed., Chapters XII and XIII. (Macmillan.)

MELLANBY, E. 1947 Vitamin A and bone growth: the reversibility of vitamin-A-deficiency changes. *J. Physiol.* **105**, 382–399; *Nutr. Abs. Rev.* **17**, 91–92.

REVIEW 1943 Effects of vitamin A depletion in man. *Nutrition Rev.* **1**, 348–350.

REVIEW 1943b Bone overgrowth and nerve degeneration in vitamin A deficiency. *Nutrition Rev.* **1**, 419–422.

REVIEW 1944 Regulation and significance of plasma vitamin A level. *Nutrition Rev.* **2**, 176–178.

REVIEW 1944b Vitamin A and the nervous system. *Nutrition Rev.* **2**, 279–282.

REVIEW 1945 Dietary requirements. *Nutrition Rev.* **3**, 293–295.

REVIEW 1948 Comparative absorption, excretion, and storage of oily and aqueous preparations of vitamin A. *Nutrition Rev.* **6**, 248–251.

REVIEW 1949 Extra-hepatic conversion of carotene to vitamin A. *Nutrition Rev.* **7**, 169.

REVIEW 1949b Comparative activities of carotenoids in promoting growth and vitamin A storage in rats. *Nutrition Rev.* **7**, 180–182.

REVIEW 1949c Neurologic manifestations associated with vitamin A deficiency in young ducks. *Nutrition Rev.* **7**, 188–190.

REVIEW 1949d Vitamin A deficiency in man. *Nutrition Rev.* **7**, 234–238.

ROFSKY, H. A., and B. NEWMAN 1948 A study of the vitamin A- and carotene-tolerance tests in the aged. *Gastroenterology* **10**, 1001–1006; *Chem. Abs.* **42**, 7385.

SANDELS, M. R., H. D. CATE, K. P. WILKINSON, and L. J. GRAVES 1941 Follicular conjunctivitis in school children as an expression of vitamin A deficiency. *Am. J. Diseases Children* **62**, 101–114.

SHERMAN, H. C., and H. L. CAMPBELL 1945 Stabilizing influence of liberal intake of vitamin A. *Proc. National Acad. Sci.* **31**, 164–166.

SHERMAN, H. C., H. L. CAMPBELL, M. UDILJAK, and H. YARMOLINSKY (TRUPP) 1945 Vitamin A in relation to aging and to length of life. *Proc. National Acad. Sci.* **31**, 107–109.

SHERMAN, H. C., and F. L. MACLEOD 1925 The relation of vitamin A to growth, reproduction, and longevity. *J. Am. Chem. Soc.* **47**, 1658–1662.

SHERMAN, H. C., and E. N. TODHUNTER 1934 The determination of vitamin A values by a method of single feedings. *J. Nutrition* **8**, 347–356.

SHERMAN, H. C., and H. Y. TRUPP 1949 Further experiments with vitamin A in relation to aging and to length of life. *Proc. National Acad. Sci.* **35**, 90–92; *Chem. Abs.* **43**, 5096.

SHERMAN, H. C., and H. Y. TRUPP 1949a Long-term experiments at or near the optimal level of intake of vitamin A. *J. Nutrition* **37**, 467–474.

SMITH, M. C. 1930 A quantitative comparison of the vitamin A value of yellow corn and the grain sorghums hegari and yellow milo. *J. Agr. Research* **40**, 1147–1153.

SMITH, M. C., and L. OTIS 1941 Carotene analysis of vegetables and fruits as a basis for prediction of their vitamin A value. *Food Research* **6**, 143–150.

STEININGER, G., L. J. ROBERTS, and S. BRENNER 1939 Vitamin A in the blood of normal adults. *J. Am. Med. Assoc.* **113**, 2381–2387.

STEVEN, D., and G. WALD 1941 Vitamin A deficiency: A field study in Newfoundland and Labrador. *J. Nutrition* **21**, 461–476.

WALD, G. 1935 Carotenoids and the visual cycle. *J. Gen. Physiol.* **19**, 351–371.

WALD, G., H. JEGHERS, and J. ARMINIO 1938 An experiment in human dietary nightblindness. *Am. J. Physiol.* **123**, 732–746.

WALD, G., and D. STEVEN 1939 An experiment in human vitamin A deficiency. *Proc. National Acad. Sci.* **25**, 344–349.

WARKANY, J., and C. B. ROTH 1948 Congenital malformations induced in rats by maternal vitamin A deficiency. *J. Nutrition* **35**, 1–11.

WIEHL, D. G. 1942 Diets of high school students of low income families in New York City. *Milbank Mem. Fund Quart.* **20,** 61–82.

WOLBACH, S. B., and O. A. BESSEY 1941 Vitamin A deficiency and the nervous system. *Arch. Pathol.* **32,** 689–722; *Nutr. Abs. Rev.* **11,** 543.

YARBROUGH, M. E., and W. J. DANN 1941 Dark adaptometer and blood vitamin A measurements in a North Carolina nutrition survey. *J. Nutrition* **22,** 597–607.

XVI

RICKETS AND THE VITAMINS D

Straight, sturdy bones and sound teeth are among the most readily apparent and appreciated rewards of good nutrition. In an earlier chapter we have discussed the importance of providing liberal amounts of the inorganic elements which give these structures their characteristic strength and rigidity. Here we shall consider the rôle of a group of organic substances known as the vitamins D in assuring efficient utilization of the dietary calcium and phosphorus, in particular with regard to the development of normal bones. The teeth are given special consideration in Chapter XVIII.

Growth of Normal Bone

A detailed description of the physiological and histological processes of bone development would be inappropriate to this text. However, the relation of nutrition to these structures will become clearer if there is some understanding of the principal factors concerned in the formation of normal bone. Let us therefore consider briefly the sequence of events by which growth of a typical long bone is accomplished.

The main body or *shaft* of a long bone is known as the *diaphysis*. Separated from the shaft in young, growing individuals by a region of cartilage, but later becoming a part of the long bone, is a smaller bone, known as the *epiphysis* or *head*. Growth takes place by the continuous formation of new cartilage cells along the epiphysial margin. Normally, there is simultaneous degeneration of older cartilage cells along the diaphysial border. The cavities so formed are invaded by blood vessels from the marrow of the shaft, carrying inorganic elements which are deposited as relatively insoluble salts (chiefly of calcium and phosphorus) in the *matrix* or intercellular substance of the degenerating cartilage cells, forming what is known as the *zone of provisional calcification*. Accompanying the blood vessels are cells known as *osteoblasts* (bone-formers) which surround themselves with socalled *osteoid tissue,* into the matrix of which inorganic salts are laid down to form true bone.

All of the factors determining the deposition of bone salt are not understood. It is known that calcification cannot occur unless adequate supplies of calcium and phosphorus are available. But it is also clear that growing bone must have some special property, not shared by body tissues in general, by virtue of which precipitation of "bone salt" from blood of normal calcium and phosphorus content occurs in the bones but not in other tissues of the body.

The Nature of Rickets

Rickets is a condition, developing principally in infants and young children, in which the mineral metabolism is disturbed in such a way that calcification of the growing bones does not take place normally. In the majority of cases the failure of the bones to calcify appears to be due, not to any initial fault of the bone itself, but to some deficiency in the blood: for rachitic bones placed in normal blood serum usually begin at once to calcify; and a subnormal concentration in the blood of either calcium or phosphorus (or both) is generally found associated with rickets. However, Dr. Alfred Hess, one of the foremost authorities on the disease, observed indications that the primary deficit in *certain cases* of rickets concerned a *local* factor affecting the "anchorage" of the available calcium and phosphate in the end of the growing bone.

In rickets, the proliferation of cartilage cells and even of osteoid tissue continues, giving rise to a wide band of epiphysial-diaphysial cartilage. Calcification, however, fails to occur, and consequently no zone of provisional calcification is observed. Since these proliferative tissues do not become properly hardened by the deposition of bone salts, the strain of bearing the body weight causes enlargement of the ends of the bones. This gives rise to the familiar enlarged joints and row of beadlike swellings at the rib junctions commonly called the "rachitic rosary," which are among the prominent clinical signs of rickets. As the disease continues there may be loss of already deposited mineral salts from the shaft, with consequent further weakening of the bones. "Knock-knees" or "bow-legs" commonly develop as the result of such weakness, and, for mechanical reasons, are apt to be especially severe in the heavy, otherwise well nourished, infant and in the child who begins to stand at an unusually early age.

Although rickets itself is seldom fatal, it may result in permanent deformities, which, besides their sometimes tragic effects upon the appearance and happiness of the individual, are often responsible for grave physical misfortunes. Thus, malformations of the pelvis as the result of rickets in early life may persist into adulthood and cause injury at the time of childbirth to mother or child or both. In the opinion of Hess, these "constitute the foremost burden of rickets on the community." There are also indications of a heightened susceptibility to respiratory disease in severe rickets.

Discovery of the Antirachitic Factor

It has already been pointed out that the immediate cause of most cases of rickets appears to lie in a subnormal concentration of calcium ions or phosphate ions in the blood. Sometimes this low concentration may be traced to an inadequate mineral content of the diet. But, since mild rickets sometimes develops in infants fed almost exclusively on milk and thus liberally supplied with calcium and phosphorus, it is evident that the explanation of such cases must be sought in some further factor or factors controlling the *utilization* of these elements. This aspect, which has figured prominently in the history of both clinical and experimental rickets, may now be considered.

Many investigators had noticed the prevalence of rickets among children living in dark, crowded quarters, and the greater incidence of the disease in winter than in summer; and as early as 1822 a Polish physician, Jedrzej Sniadecki, clearly stated his belief that the exposure of the body to direct sunlight was of importance in both the prevention and the cure of rickets (or *English disease*, as it was commonly called in that day).*

This view of the significance of sunlight did not receive general acceptance until years later. Many careful students of the problem felt rather that other hygienic factors were primarily at fault in the dark, unsanitary quarters where rickets was so prevalent. In

* Mozolowski, W. 1939 Jedrzej Sniadecki (1768–1838) on the cure of rickets. *Nature* **143**, 121.

1890, however, Palm, an English physician who had practiced for some years in Japan, published the results of his correspondence with medical missionaries throughout the world to whom he had addressed queries regarding the occurrence or absence of rickets in their territory, the habits of the people, and the climatic and sanitary conditions. This remarkable survey revealed the complete absence of the disease in certain sections of the world where sunlight was abundant but where food and general hygienic conditions were extremely bad; and led Palm to the conclusion that the main etiological factor in rickets is a lack of sunlight.

About the time of the First World War, pediatricians discovered that, besides direct sunlight, artificial sources of ultraviolet light such as the mercury-vapor quartz lamp were effective for the cure of rickets in infants exposed to them under suitable conditions.

At just about the same time, studies on experimental rickets were lending support to the theory that a dietary factor was involved in the prevention and cure of this disease. Dr. (now Sir) Edward Mellanby observed the development of rachitic symptoms in puppies on a restricted diet, and showed that codliver oil was very effective, whereas lard was entirely ineffective, in preventing these abnormalities of the bones. Various investigators in this country induced rickets in rats by feeding diets of severely imbalanced mineral content, and showed that this experimental disease also could be largely prevented or cured by codliver oil. It was soon made evident that the fat-soluble dietary factor or vitamin here involved was different from that already recognized as related to growth and to the prevention of eye-symptoms; for, as shown by McCollum, even after this latter factor (vitamin A) had been destroyed by bubbling oxygen through hot codliver oil, the oil retained its antirachitic properties. The term "vitamin D" was, therefore, adopted for the antirachitic factor.

The reconciliation of these two seemingly divergent views as to the rickets-preventing agent followed the discovery in 1924, independently by Hess and by Steenbock, that exposure of many food materials to *ultraviolet light* endows them with the nutritional properties attributed to *vitamin D*. To the substance originally present in the food which the ultraviolet rays "activate," the name *provitamin D* was given. Further experimentation showed that it or a similar substance occurs in the sebaceous secretion of the skin, and that when the skin is exposed to direct sunlight or other source

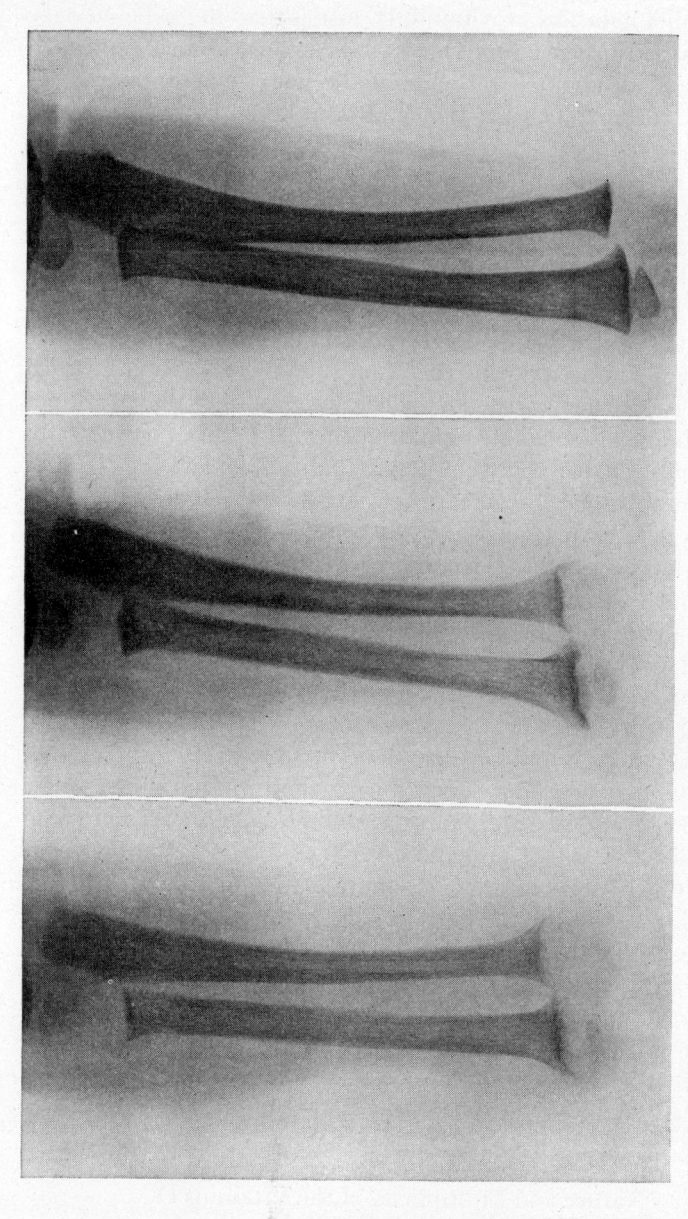

Fig. 33. Three photographs of the right wrist of the same girl. The first shows active rickets with marked flaring of the end of the long bone and fringing where calcification is retarded. The second shows increased calcification as the result of codliver oil and sunlight. The third shows a normal density of calcification and a smooth end of the long bone when further treatment had completed the healing. (Courtesy of Dr. Martha Eliot.)

of ultraviolet light this provitamin D, just as that in food materials, is transformed into vitamin D, which is in turn absorbed through the skin and distributed throughout the body, where it functions in exactly the same way as if it had been taken by mouth in fish liver oils or irradiated foods. Thus, the sunlight and the vitamin effects in rickets are but different aspects of the same phenomenon.

The statistics of rickets in Chicago which are cited in Rose's *Feeding the Family,* Fourth Edition (1940, page 170), illustrate the extent to which this branch of the newer knowledge of nutrition has solved its problem, and also give reassurance as to the mildness of most of the rickets recently diagnosed. In the Chicago examinations of pre-school children during the years 1926 to 1932, from 21 to 16 per cent revealed evidence of rickets, but in 1933 only 13.7 per cent of the newly examined children showed signs of rickets, and in 1935 only 7.1 per cent showed any indications and only 0.03 of one per cent showed severe rickets. Thus the incidence of such rickets as is to be regarded as really a disease in the usual sense of the word has been reduced to three cases per ten thousand children.

Park and associates (Follis, *et al.,* 1943) found *histologic* evidence of rickets in almost half of the children 2 to 14 years old whom they examined at autopsy, although only a few would have been judged rachitic by X-ray examination. Since these authors state that: "We doubt if (such) slight degrees of rickets ... interfere with health and development"; and further, since the possibility remains that the rickets may have developed during the terminal illness, these findings need not be regarded as alarming or as contradictory to the optimistic view just presented. Yet they do, as the authors conclude, "afford reason to prolong administration of vitamin D to the age limit of our study, the fourteenth year, and especially indicate the necessity to suspect, and to take the necessary measures to guard against, rickets in sick children."

Figure 33 shows X-ray photographs of the wrist of the same girl: (a) with active rickets of a degree now classified as "severe" (though not of such deforming severity as was common a generation ago); (b) when the rickets was healing; and (c) when it was healed.

Nature and Multiplicity of the Vitamins D

It is now well established that there are several vitamins D, two of which are important.

The provitamins which are converted to vitamins D by the action of ultraviolet light belong to the group of substances known as *sterols,* of which brief mention was made in Chapter II. Neither of the sterols occurring naturally in greatest abundance, *cholesterol,* found in animal fats, and *sitosterol,* in higher plants, is of significance as a precursor of vitamin D. But present in small amounts along with these are other, more highly reactive, sterols, notably *7-dehydrocholesterol*[*] in animal fats and *ergosterol* in both higher and lower plants, which are changed on exposure to light of suitable wave-length into potent antirachitic substances, designated, respectively, as *vitamin D_3* and *vitamin D_2* (or *calciferol*). These two products appear to be the forms of vitamin D of greatest importance in antirachitic foods and medicines, but a dozen or so chemical substances have been shown to have the calcification-promoting properties ascribed to "vitamin D."

Vitamin D_3 (activated 7-dehydrocholesterol) is the most prominent form of antirachitic vitamin in fish liver oils, irradiated milk, and irradiated animal products generally, and is believed to be the D-vitamin developed in the skin on exposure to ultraviolet light; whereas vitamin D_2 (activated ergosterol, calciferol) is the form widely used medicinally in preparations such as "viosterol," and is present also in irradiated yeast, in the milk of cows fed irradiated yeast (sometimes called "metabolized" vitamin D milk to distinguish it from milks fortified with this factor in other ways), and in minor proportions in certain fish oils. Eggs may contain predominantly either vitamin D_2 or vitamin D_3, depending on the feeding of the hen, but present trends in poultry husbandry are such as to increase the likelihood that vitamin D_3 will be the chief form present.

Nutritional Rôle of Vitamin D

As already indicated, vitamin D (if for convenience we may continue to speak in the singular in dealing with this factor) came to be known and has been studied largely through its involvement in the rickets problem.

Rickets (*rachitis*) is a medical term which does not always have exactly the same meaning in medical literature. Pathologists have

---

[*] For the sake of explicit identification of important substances a few somewhat technical chemical names are here given in the text. They need not be memorized. They may be found useful for reference in further reading.

until recently tended to follow Schmorl in defining rickets in terms of the histology of the growing ends of the bones, while pediatricians have more largely followed Park in defining rickets as a condition of retardation (or suspension) of the normal calcification of the developing bone.

As explained earlier in the chapter, the normal calcification (ossification) of the developing bone is essentially a building into the cartilaginous bone matrix of the crystalline bone mineral for which the chief ingredients are the calcium and the phosphate brought by the blood.

Fig. 34. Effects of very severe low-calcium rickets in contrast with normal twin brother. (Courtesy of the "Journal of Biological Chemistry.")

When the normal calcification of the growing and developing bone is retarded, an analysis of the blood quite regularly shows a subnormal concentration of calcium (calcium ion), or of phosphorus (phosphate), or both. It is logical to suppose that this subnormal supply of ingredients brought by the blood is in some sense a cause of the retardation of the calcification (ossification) process, although, as already mentioned, there may also (or in some cases) be a more "local" and less well defined factor involved.

This point of view recognizes both a low-calcium and a low-phosphorus type of rickets. Results of extreme (experimental) cases of low-calcium rickets are shown in Figs. 34 and 35. But only the low-phosphorus type shows the particular histology described in the classical work of Schmorl; so *some* writers have designated only the low-phosphorus type as true rickets.

How the subnormal concentration of calcium or phosphate ion in the blood comes about is not always clear. Such a shortage in the blood can sometimes but not always be attributable to a corresponding shortage in the food. More often, probably, it is attributable to a low "net absorption" of these elements: either too little getting in through the intestinal wall or too much passing out through the kidneys.

Vitamin D, whether taken as such or formed in the skin by irradiation with light of certain wave lengths (in the ultraviolet), tends to restore to normal the calcium or the phosphorus content

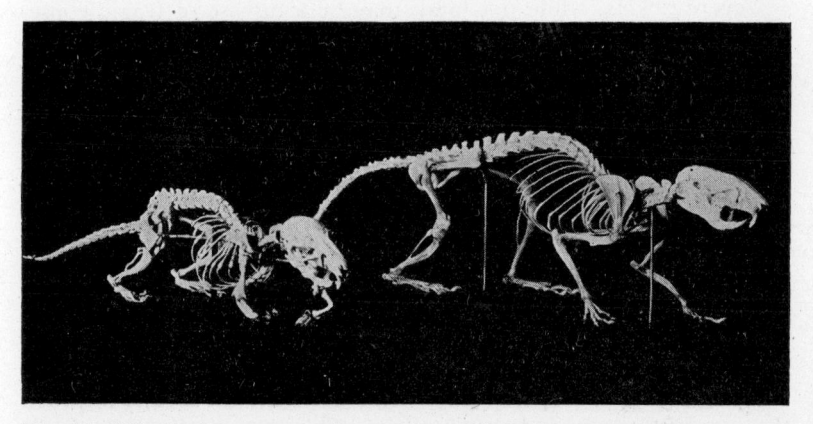

Fig. 35. Effects of very severe low-calcium rickets in contrast with a normal first cousin. Here with a dietary less drastically deficient, there appeared in the second generation the same skeletal difference as developed in the first generation in the case shown in Fig. 34.

of the blood, and the rate of calcification. As summarized in *Nutrition Reviews* for February, 1947, a present view is that "the action of vitamin D is to increase the 'net absorption' of the calcium and phosphate of the food, and is exerted in two ways. Directly, the vitamin D increases the permeability of the intestinal mucosa to calcium salts while leaving unchanged the permeability of other membranes. This leads to an increased serum calcium and consequently to a decreased activity of the parathyroid, thereby decreasing the rate of excretion of phosphate by the kidney. Vitamin D also appears to exert some direct effect on the calcification of growing bone; if large amounts of calcium and phosphate are supplied to the young rachitic animal by injection, then bone of normal density is laid down, but its histological structure is abnormal."

That so many of the mild cases of clinical rickets are of the low-phosphorus type is largely if not mainly attributable to the fact that during the age-range in which rickets is most common there is a rapid growth of muscle and thus the baby's developing bones and muscles are competing for the phosphorus which the blood brings. To keep in mind the fact that a large proportion of the cases of the condition which we call by a pathological name (rickets or rachitis) may with at least as much reason be viewed as a matter of the relative rates at which two normal processes are proceeding, may serve greatly to clarify one's scientific view of the situation.

Severe rickets, while not fatal, may be a disease of tragic consequences; but at the other end of the scale (confusingly still called by the same name) are the "clinical signs" which Park says are "notoriously deceiving and cannot be relied on" because in fact they are merely the signs that one physiological aspect of development is making slightly more rapid progress than another.

Perhaps the most helpful view is that presented by Jeans and Stearns in the 1938 meeting of the American Institute of Nutrition, namely, that children differ in the efficiency with which they assimilate the bone-building elements from their food, and that vitamin D in some ways helps to improve the cases of low efficiency.

These investigators also emphasize the fact that even at levels above that of rickets prevention additional vitamin D may improve the rate of growth and development. This has also been found in controlled experiments with laboratory animals (Sherman and Stiebeling, listed in Suggested Readings).

Jeans and Stearns, in discussing their findings that amounts of vitamin D over and above those required to prevent rickets may have a further beneficial effect upon the retention of calcium and the linear growth of the bones, point out that this effect may not be noted in each individual but becomes evident when large groups are observed. Thus, studies of calcium retention in infants given no additional vitamin D showed marked variability in calcium retention with a low average. When amounts of vitamin D up to that supposed to be sufficient to prevent rickets were given, the number of low retentions decreased, raising the average retention of the group. A further and significantly greater increase in average retention was obtained (again by raising the lower limit of the retention range) when two to three times as much vitamin D was given as is required to prevent rickets. In somewhat older children, past the age where rickets is most apt to occur, Jeans and Stearns found that some showed efficient utilization and others poor utilization of the calcium of milk when no added vitamin D was given; and that supplying vitamin D tended to improve the calcium utilization by the latter group, whereas it had little effect on the former. With adolescence, however, the need for vitamin D became "as universal and as great as in infancy." Indeed, Johnston (1948) holds that, during the period of rapid growth just before puberty, the need for vitamin D is probably twice as great as at any other time in life, except perhaps during the middle of the first year.

Measurement and Expression of Vitamin D Values

At the time this is written, the *International Standard* for vitamin D is a crystalline preparation of vitamin D_2; and the International *unit* of antirachitic activity is defined as that exhibited by 0.025 micrograms of this Standard material. The United States Pharmacopeia Standard has been a codliver oil preparation; but there is much sentiment in favor of replacing this with a crystalline product, preferably vitamin D_3.

Though chemical methods are now being worked out, principal reliance for the determination of vitamin D value still rests on tests with living things, prepared, fed, and examined in standardized ways. Since both types of method are undergoing development, those interested should consult the *current Pharmacopeia* and the *current volume* of the *methods* of the Association of Official Agricultural Chemists.

Sources

Irradiation.—Herodotus wrote that sunshine is a potent factor in skeletal development; and an ancient Roman medical aphorism calls the Sun the greatest of physicians. But the importance of sunshine had to be rediscovered by Sniadecki in 1822 (as noted above), and again by Huldschinsky in 1919. When in 1924 it was found that natural foods, and (soon after) that certain sterols specifically, can be rendered antirachitic by irradiation, there rapidly developed a high enthusiasm for irradiated foods, and for irradiated ergosterol as a specific against rickets. But since (as explained early in this chapter) it has been found that the antirachitic substance produced by irradiation of ergosterol, or other plant sterol, is not the same as the natural vitamin D produced by irradiation of our skins, there has been some shifting back of emphasis from the irradiation of our foods to the irradiation of our bodies with direct sunshine containing its natural proportion of ultraviolet rays or with its carefully determined equivalent. The amount of vitamin D which may be formed in the body varies widely with such factors as affect the amount of active radiation that reaches the provitamin D in the skin. Sunshine is richest in actinic rays at times of year when, and in latitudes where, the sun is most directly overhead. But much of this radiation may fail to reach persons living in smoke-palled areas, or in cities where crowded high buildings cut off much of the sunlight; and not all of the active rays can penetrate effectively the deeply pigmented skin layers of certain people. The benefit obtainable depends also directly on the amount of skin surface exposed, and thus varies both with the atmospheric temperature and with the habits of dress of the individual. Ordinary window glass stops most of the ultraviolet rays; but special glass which transmits them is now made, and is used in the construction of lamps which yield an indoor equivalent of "June sunshine" (*i.e.*, of the brighest natural sunshine, at ordinary altitudes, of our temperate zone).

The same rays which produce vitamin D in the skin also increase the circulation, thus bringing a fresh supply of the precursor into the skin-layers where the transformation is taking place, and carrying the new-formed vitamin D promptly away from any danger of over-irradiation and into the service of the body as a whole, and particularly of the bones and teeth.

Fish oils.—*Codliver oil* is outstanding in that it has been used as a remedy for rickets since the middle ages and is still universally prominent as a nutritional source of vitamin D. Liver oils from fish of the order Percomorphi (of which the blue fin tuna is a prominent member) are much richer in vitamin D, one of them having a reported concentration four hundred times that of ordinary grade codliver oil. As they are also very rich in vitamin A, such oils, available commercially as *Percomorph oil,* are becoming widely used. There are many persons for whom the fact that doses of this oil are measured in drops while those of codliver oil are measured in teaspoonfuls proves to be an irresistible advantage! *Halibut liver oil,* which is far richer in vitamin A than codliver oil, is only a few times more potent in vitamin D. For this reason, halibut liver oil to which viosterol has been added is frequently used where it is desired to give generous doses of both vitamins with a minimum volume of fishy-tasting oil.

The flesh of fish which contain much body oil, such as salmon, sardine, and herring, is a fairly rich source of the antirachitic vitamin.

Eliot, Nelson and coworkers (see Suggested Readings) have shown that an enormous potential source of vitamin D exists in the fat of salmon livers together with that of such other edible material as is trimmed off in preparing the standard-sized sections of salmon for canning. This mixture of liver and body fat, called *salmon oil*, is found to be comparable with codliver oil in vitamin A, and superior to codliver oil in vitamin D content. Thus the salmon canneries of the Pacific Coast will be able to furnish, as soon as consumers will take it, a very large supply of an oil which appears to be at least as rich a vitamin-source as is codliver oil.

Liver.—The liver appears to be a principal site of storage of vitamin D in the animals commonly slaughtered for food; and the consumption of calf, beef, lamb, and hog liver may thus be expected to contribute to the body supply of this factor. However, the amounts of vitamin D in liver depend upon the dietary and other management of the animal, and may vary down to practically zero.

Eggs.—Hess showed in 1923 that the yolk of one egg contained enough vitamin D to serve as a daily allowance for the prevention of rickets in babies. The diet of the hens and the amount of ultraviolet light they receive both influence the vitamin D content of the eggs produced. In recent years the practical advantages of including fish liver oils or other sources of vitamin D_3 in the diet of laying hens have been increasingly realized and the practice has unquestionably resulted in bringing to the market eggs of higher average vitamin D value than those which proved such effective antirachitics in the early work of Hess.

Milk and its products: "Vitamin D Milk."—The evidence varies greatly as to the vitamin D content of the fat of milk produced by cows on ordinary rations. *Vitamin D Milk* is the term generally used to indicate milk which has been enriched in its vitamin D value. Three methods of producing such vitamin D milk have been used commercially: (1) mixing into the milk a purified concentrate of natural (animal) vitamin, or, lately, of pure crystalline vitamin D_3 or D_2; (2) irradiation of the milk; (3) feeding irradiated material (usually irradiated yeast) to the cow. The first method gives a reproducible, high potency, and is increasingly preferred to the other two.

The practice of enriching milk with vitamin D is regarded with favor by most physicians and health commissioners, and has been given preferential endorsement by the Council on Foods of the American Medical Association in the following terms: "Of all the common foods available, milk is most suitable as a carrier of added vitamin D. Vitamin D is concerned with the utilization of calcium and phosphorus, of which milk is an excellent source. The Council has recently made the decision that for the present milk is the only common food which will be considered for acceptance when fortified with vitamin D."

"Vitamin D milk" is on regular delivery along with other fresh milk in many localities; and also a considerable part of the canned milk now offered in the retail market has had its vitamin D content enriched. In many cases, the vitamin D value is adjusted to 400 units per quart (of fresh bottled or reconstituted evaporated milk) so that the growing child who drinks his "quart of milk a day" is automatically assured the recommended intake of vitamin D.

An influential proportion of (though not all) pediatricians prefer vitamin D_3 to vitamin D_2, and also consider that vitamin D is best assimilated when consumed dispersed in milk.

Storage and Transfer

The body is able, when supplied with abundant vitamin D, to build up large reserve stores of this factor, which may be drawn upon in later time of need. Some pediatricians have indeed advocated the administration of large doses under medical supervision two or three times a year, instead of relying on the mother's day-to-day dosage with fish oil or other preparation. Others tend to regard this as unnecessary in view of the educational campaign of the past two decades which has so successfully reduced the incidence of rickets; and as possibly undesirable in seeming to relegate vitamin D to the role of a medicinal agent rather than a normal nutrient.

It was shown many years ago with experimental animals that the maternal organism shares its vitamin D with the offspring both before birth and later through the milk. A liberal intake of vitamin D during pregnancy and lactation thus serves the double purpose of giving the baby a body store of the vitamin and of assisting the mother to use her dietary calcium and phosphorus efficiently to meet the extraordinarily heavy demands of these periods.

Requirements

It follows from what has been said that the proportion of the total vitamin D required in metabolism which must be provided by the diet may vary enormously from individual to individual, depending on the opportunity which each has for synthesis of this factor in his body by irradiation.

Vigorous adults, leading a normal life, are thought to require little if any supplemental vitamin D, and no dietary allowance is made for them in the National Research Council recommendations. It is, however, suggested that: "for persons working at night and for nuns and others whose habits shield them from sunlight, as well as for elderly persons, the ingestion of small amounts of vitamin D is desirable."

For women in the latter half of pregnancy and for nursing mothers, supplemental vitamin D is recommended, 400 units being regarded as "most likely adequate . . . on the basis of available evidence."

The newer view that, in addition to infants, most growing children and all adolescents require liberal amounts to achieve satisfactory calcium retention is reflected by the extension to all age groups below adulthood of the recommendation that this be insured by supplying 400 units daily in the diet. The discussion accompanying the Recommended Allowances implies that enough vitamin D to promote maximal calcium retention is the objective; and states that 300 to 400 units per day have been shown to be ample for most infants; while the actual requirement at later ages has not been determined as accurately. "It is known, however, that 400 units daily is ample for good calcium retention in children when the milk intake is appropriate. . . . The total (daily) amount required in adolescence probably is no greater than in infancy." It is doubtful how much, if any, supplementary vitamin D is needed by adults living under normal conditions of diet and of exposure to sunlight.

It follows from what has been said above that no simple quantitative statement of the vitamin D requirement of human nutrition could as yet represent a complete consensus of opinion. For vitamin

D is formed in the body in widely variable amounts depending on the duration and effectiveness of the irradiation to which the skin is subjected. Then, too, the different molecular forms in foods and medicinal sources may vary (and, if so, to an extent not yet definitely measured) in their efficacy in human nutrition, and even the same chemical form may have different efficacy according to the medium in which it is taken. There are also differences of view as to the extent to which the amount required for optimal growth exceeds the amount required for the prevention of rickets; and it seems certain that under the same conditions some children need more than others.

EXERCISES: for instructors and students jointly

1. Induce rickets in rats by means of the Steenbock rickets-producing diet described in the current United States Pharmacopeia; or that of Zucker and coworkers in the paper listed among the Suggested Readings below. Arrange, if possible, for x-ray photographs. Otherwise, begin the experiment while the rats are small and see whether the rickets become obvious to naked-eye examination, either of the live rat or of its skeleton.

2. Induce low-calcium rickets by diet of low-calcium foods without provision for vitamin D either as such or as light. Save the skeletons of such rachitic rats as a permanent exhibit.

3. Examine the literature: (*a*) for evidence as to the relative values of vitamins D_2 and D_3 for children; (*b*) for advances in knowledge of any of the other vitamins D.

4. Compile and discuss current estimates of the vitamin D requirements of human nutrition.

SUGGESTED READINGS

AMERICAN MEDICAL ASSOCIATION 1939 *The Vitamins,* Chapters XXIII–XXIX. (American Medical Association, Chicago.)

ANNING, S. T., J. DAWSON, D. E. DOLBY, and J. T. INGRAM 1948 The toxic effects of calciferol. *Quart. J. Med.* **17,** 203–228; *Nutr. Abs. Rev.* **18,** 878.

BILLS, C. E., et al. 1937 The multiple nature of the vitamin D of fish oils. *J. Nutrition* **13,** 435–452.

BILLS, C. E. 1938 The chemistry of vitamin D. *J. Am. Med. Assoc.* **110,** 2150–2155; reprinted as Chapter XXIII, "The Vitamins." (American Medical Association, 1939.)

BLUNT, K., and R. COWAN 1930 *Ultraviolet Light and Vitamin D in Nutrition.* (University of Chicago Press.)

BUNKER, J. W. M., R. S. HARRIS, and L. M. MOSHER 1940 Studies in the activation of sterols. *J. Am. Chem. Soc.* **62,** 1760–1762.

BYFIELD, A. H., and A. L. DANIELS 1923 The rôle of parental nutrition in the causation of rickets. *J. Am. Med. Assoc.* **81,** 360–362.

DEVANEY, G. M., and H. E. MUNSELL 1935 Vitamin D content of calf, beef, lamb, and hog liver. *J. Home Econ.* **27,** 240–241.

ELIOT, M. M., E. M. NELSON, S. P. SOUTHER, and M. K. CARY 1932 The value of salmon oil in the treatment of infantile rickets. *J. Am. Med. Assoc.* **99,** 1075–1082.

FOLLIS, R. H. (JR.), D. JACKSON, M. M. ELIOT, and E. A. PARK 1943 Prevalence of rickets in children between two and 14 years of age. *Am. J. Diseases Children* **66,** 1–11.

GERSTENBERGER, H. J., and J. D. NOURSE 1926 Prevention of rickets in premature infants. *J. Am. Med. Assoc.* **87,** 1108–1114.

HESS, A. F. 1923 The therapeutic value of egg yolk in rickets. *J. Am. Med. Assoc.* **81,** 15–17.

HESS, A. F. 1929 *Rickets, Osteomalacia, and Tetany.* (Lea and Febiger.)

HOLMES, A. D., F. TRIPP, and G. H. SATTERFIELD 1941 Fish-liver and body oils. *Ind. Eng. Chem.* **33,** 944–949; *Chem. Abs.* **35,** 6385.

HUME, E. M. 1937 The relative potency of vitamin D from different sources. *Nutr. Abs. Rev.* **6,** 891–901.

JEANS, P. C. 1936 Vitamin D milks, with clinical discussion. *J. Am. Med. Assoc.* **106,** 2066–2069, 2150–2159.

JEANS, P. C., and G. STEARNS 1938 The human requirement of vitamin D. *J. Am. Med. Assoc.* **111,** 703–711; Chapter XXVI of "The Vitamins, 1939." (American Medical Association.)

JOHNSTON, J. A. 1948 Nutritional problems of adolescence. *J. Am. Med. Assoc.* **137,** 1587–1589.

LIGHTBOUND, T. 1948 Calciferol by intramuscular injection. *Lancet* **255,** 1010–1012; *Nutr. Abs. Rev.* **18,** 878.

MACLEOD, G., and C. M. TAYLOR 1944 *Rose's Foundations of Nutrition,* 4th Ed. (Macmillan.)

MCCOLLUM, E. V., *et al.* 1939 *The Newer Knowledge of Nutrition,* 5th Ed., Chapters XIV and XV. (Macmillan.)

MCKAY, H., M. B. PATTON, M. S. PITTMAN, G. STEARNS, and N. EDELBLUTE 1943 The effect of vitamin D on calcium retentions. *J. Nutrition* **26,** 153–159.

MIGICOVSKY, B. B., and A. R. G. EMSLIE 1947 Interaction of calcium, phosphorus, and vitamin D. *Arch. Biochem.* **13**, 175–183, 185–189.

MORGAN, A. F., H. E. AXELROD, and M. GROODY 1947 The effect of a single massive dose of vitamin D_2 on young dogs. *Am. J. Physiol.* **149**, 319–332, 333–339; *Nutr. Abs. Rev.* **17**, 369.

NELSON, E. M. 1939 The determination and sources of vitamin D. Chapter XXV of "The Vitamins, 1939." (American Medical Association.)

PARK, E. A. 1923 Etiology of rickets. *Physiol. Rev.* **3**, 106–163.

PARK, E. A. 1938 The use of vitamin D preparations in the prevention and treatment of disease. *J. Am. Med. Assoc.* **111**, 1179–1187; Chapter XXVII of "The Vitamins, 1939." (American Medical Association.)

PARK, E. A. 1940 The therapy of rickets. *J. Am. Med. Assoc.* **115**, 370–379.

REPORT OF THE COUNCIL ON FOODS 1937 Present status of vitamin D milks. *J. Am. Med. Assoc.* **108**, 206–207

REVIEW 1943 Prevalence of rickets in children. *Nutrition Rev.* **1**, 423–425.

REVIEW 1945a Prevention of rickets by single large doses of vitamin D. *Nutrition Rev.* **3**, 209–210.

REVIEW 1945b The effect of vitamins A and D on bone fracture healing. *Nutrition Rev.* **3**, 277–278.

REVIEW 1945c Toxicity following massive doses of vitamin D. *Nutrition Rev.* **3**, 313–314.

REVIEW 1946 The vitamin D content of human milk. *Nutrition Rev.* **4**, 157.

REVIEW 1947 Present knowledge of vitamin D in nutrition. *Nutrition Rev.* **5**, 35–37.

REVIEW 1947b Present knowledge of the relation of nutrition to dental caries. *Nutrition Rev.* **5**, 68–71.

REVIEW 1949 Rickets in premature infants. *Nutrition Rev.* **7**, 171–173.

SHERMAN, H. C., and H. K. STIEBELING 1929–30 Quantitative studies of the relation of vitamin D to deposition of calcium in bone. *Proc. Soc. Exptl. Biol. Med.* **27**, 663–665; *J. Biol. Chem.* **83**, 497–504; **88**, 683–693.

SHOHL, A. T. 1939 Physiology and pathology of vitamin D. Chapter XXIV of "The Vitamins, 1939." (American Medical Association.)

SHOHL, A. T., and S. B. WOLBACH 1936 The effect of low-calcium, high-phosphorus diets at various levels and ratios upon the production of rickets and tetany. *J. Nutrition* **11**, 275–291.

SMITH, M. C., and H. SPECTOR 1940 Further evidence of the mode of action of vitamin D. *J. Nutrition* **20**, 197–202.

STEARNS, G., P. C. JEANS, and V. VANDECAR 1936 Effect of vitamin D on linear growth in infancy. *J. Pediat.* **9**, 1–10.

STEENBOCK, H., *et al.* 1930–33 Vitamin D in nutrition. *J. Biol. Chem.* **87**, 103–126, 127–137; **88**, 197–214; **100**, 209–224.

TISDALL, F. F., and A. BROWN 1928 Seasonal variation in the antirachitic effect of sunshine. *Am. J. Diseases Children* **36**, 734–739.

ZUCKER, T. F., L. HALL, L. MASON, and M. YOUNG 1933 Growth-promoting rachitogenic diets for rats. *Proc. Soc. Exptl. Biol. Med.* **30**, 523–525.

XVII

OTHER FAT-SOLUBLE VITAMINS

Vitamin E

Although vitamin E is one of the longer-known vitamins, its existence having been recognized in the early 1920's, it is still not possible to define clearly the role of this factor in human nutrition; and for this reason a brief treatment only of it is appropriate to this book.

At least four chemically identified naturally occurring substances (known, respectively, as alpha-tocopherol, beta-tocopherol, gamma-tocopherol, and delta-tocopherol), as well as a number of related synthetic compounds, possess the activity ascribed to vitamin E.

The vitamins E are fat-soluble materials, found along with the fats in grains, vegetables, meat, milk, and butter, and doubtless occurring very widely among food materials of both plant and animal origin which have not been artificially refined. Toward heating and many other adverse influences, the vitamins E are among the most stable of the known vitamins. But treatments which cause the fat with which vitamin E is associated to become rancid result in rapid loss of this factor. An outstanding chemical property of vitamin E is its antioxidant action, which tends to "protect" or "stabilize" unsaturated fats (and certain other oxidizable substances) not only in food sources but also, to some extent, within the body.

Deficiency of vitamin E in rats manifests itself characteristically by reproductive failure in both sexes. In the deficient female, oestrus, ovulation, and impregnation of the ovum occur normally, but the fetus dies and is resorbed before maturity is reached. Treatment with vitamin E restores the ability of the female rat to bear normal young. In the male rat, on the other hand, deficiency of the vitamin may cause apparently irreparable degeneration of the germinal epithelium, with resulting complete and permanent sterility.

The effects of a lack of vitamin E are not, however, limited to the reproductive organs. The symptoms most prominent vary from species to species, and with the age of the individual, but in one or another species may include failure of growth, muscular dystrophy, injury to the central nervous system, interference with normal heart action, and possible endocrine disturbances.

Whether the counterpart of any of these conditions occurs in human beings is still controversial. The Council on Pharmacy and Chemistry of the American Medical Association, referring to reports of successful treatment of human reproductive disorders with vitamin E, has warned against regarding the value of vitamin E for man as fully established; and the Association has also emphasized the need for controlled clinical tests of the value of vitamin E in heart disease.

Dr. Pappenheimer emphasizes chiefly the importance of vitamin E to the muscles. *Nutrition Reviews* classifies it as a physiological antioxidant and warns against "the futility of supplying large amounts of vitamin E to aid in the recovery of muscle and nerve from lesions other than those actually arising from vitamin E deficiency." Vitamin E has also been called an oxidation-reduction catalyst.

Harris (1949) has presented an excellent full review of recent studies on vitamin E, both with experimental animals and clinical subjects, which includes much work still too controversial for mention here.

In any case vitamin E is so widely distributed among different types of food that there should be little likelihood of its being a limiting factor in human beings. Consequently, it seems unnecessary and quite possibly misleading to lay emphasis on vitamin E in practical consideration of food values.

Synthetic alpha-tocopherol acetate has been adopted as the International standard for vitamin E; and the International unit has been defined as the specific activity of 1 milligram of the standard preparation.

Vitamin K

Vitamin K ("Koagulations-Vitamin") was so named by the Danish workers Dam and Schønheyder to connote its relation to the coagulability of the blood, through which they had discovered its existence. When insufficient vitamin K is available there ensues a decrease in the blood concentration of *prothrombin,* one of the constituents necessary to the clotting process,* with resultant lengthening of the time required for coagulation. This condition of *hypoprothrombinemia* occurs quite frequently in human beings who have disturbances of the bile tract. In those cases, the diet, as a rule, is not primarily at fault, but, owing to lack of bile in the intestine, there is poor absorption of fat and hence of fat-soluble vitamin K. The remedy for such persons is either to inject vitamin K, or to feed it together with bile salts.

A considerable degree of hypoprothrombinemia appears to be common in newborn babies; and in some babies this is so very marked as to cause serious danger from hemorrhage. Though the reason for this condition is not fully understood it has been shown that administration of vitamin K to the newborn child (or even to the mother shortly before the birth) significantly raises the blood prothrombin value in the first days of life. One or the other of these precautionary measures has now been adopted by many obstetricians and maternity hospitals, with resultant sharp drop in the incidence of hemorrhage in the newborn.

To what extent, if any, there is a vitamin K problem in nutrition in the sense of feeding people we do not yet know. A very few cases have been reported of hypoprothrombinemia which seemed clearly to be the result of a lack of vitamin K in the diet. But vitamin K is so widely distributed among many different kinds of food (though especially abundant in green leaves) that we should expect dietary deficiency of this factor to be rare. In addition, it has been suggested that further quantities of vitamin K are normally formed by the intestinal microorganisms.

The National Research Council's circular on *Recommended Dietary Allowances,* Revised 1948, comments upon vitamin K in part as follows:

* The student wishing to review the current theories regarding the process of blood coagulation is referred to recent textbooks of physiology, or, for a fuller account, to Howell, W. H. 1935 Theories of blood coagulation, *Physiol. Rev.* **15**, 435–470.

"The requirement for vitamin K usually is satisfied by any good diet except for the infant in utero and for the first few days after birth. Supplemental vitamin K is recommended during the last month of pregnancy. When it has not been given in this manner, it is recommended for the mother preceding delivery or for the baby immediately after birth. . . . Pregnant women usually are found to have normal amounts of prothrombin in the blood, but many newborn infants have abnormally small amounts. Although little relation seems to exist between the amount of prothrombin in the blood of the mother and that of the infant at birth, the amount of vitamin K received by the mother is reflected quickly in the amount of prothrombin in the blood of her infant in utero. Seldom does the mother receive enough dietary vitamin K to prevent an important decrease in the prothrombin level of the blood of her infant during the first few days after birth . . . (and) the available evidence warrants increased attention to the vitamin K intake of the mother during the latter part of pregnancy . . . (hence) it is suggested that vitamin K be given to pregnant women during the last month of pregnancy."

Stamler, Tidrick, and Warner (1943) have reported* upon vitamin K and prothrombin levels with reference to the influence of age and of rapidity of growth.

Though we have here referred to vitamin K in the singular, it should perhaps be mentioned that at least two forms (K_1 or phylloquinone, and K_2) occur naturally, and that a number of chemically related synthetic products have also the antihemorrhagic properties of vitamin K.

Possibility of Other Vitamins

There is no general agreement as to how widely the term vitamin shall be used. And certainly there is no attempt to mention in this book "all the vitamins there are."

EXERCISES: for instructors and students jointly

Study the available literature published since the foregoing text was written (1950) and write a supplement bringing up to date such vitamin topics as may be chosen or assigned.

* *Journal of Nutrition,* 26, 95–103 (1943).

SUGGESTED READINGS

Vitamin E

BACHARACH, A. L., J. C. DRUMMOND, et al. 1940 *Vitamin E: A Symposium.* (Chemical Publishing Co.)

BICKNELL, F. 1940 Vitamin E in the treatment of muscular dystrophies and nervous diseases. *Lancet* **1940, I,** 10–13.

COUNCIL ON PHARMACY AND CHEMISTRY 1940 The treatment of habitual abortion with vitamin E. *J. Am. Med. Assoc.* **114,** 2214–2218.

EMERSON, G. A., and H. M. EVANS 1940 Successive generations of vitamin E-low rats. *Proc. Soc. Exptl. Biol. Med.* **45,** 159–162; *Chem. Abs.* **35,** 496.

EVANS, H. M. 1939 Aspects of the function of Vitamin E irrespective of its relation to the reproductive system. *J. Am. Dietet. Assoc.* **15,** 869–874.

GOETTSCH, M., and A. M. PAPPENHEIMER 1941 α-Tocopherol requirement of the rat for reproduction in the female and prevention of muscular dystrophy in the young. *J. Nutrition* **22,** 463–476.

HARRIS, P. L. 1949 Fat soluble vitamins. *Ann. Rev. Biochem.* **18,** 391–434.

HICKMAN, K. C. D., P. L. HARRIS, and M. R. WOODSIDE 1942 Interrelationship of vitamins A and E. *Nature* **150,** 91–92; *Nutr. Abs. Rev.* **12,** 365.

HOVE, E. L. 1946 Interrelation between alpha-tocopherol and protein metabolism: body weight and tooth pigmentation of rats. *Proc. Soc. Exptl. Biol. Med.* **63,** 508–511.

HOVE, E. L., and P. L. HARRIS 1947 Relative activity of the tocopherols in curing muscular dystrophy in rabbits. *J. Nutrition* **33,** 95–106.

HOVE, E. L., and P. L. HARRIS. 1947*b* Interrelation between alpha-tocopherol and protein metabolism. II. The increased utilization of casein produced by alpha-tocopherol, yeast digest, or xanthine in the rat-growth protein quality test. *J. Nutrition* **34,** 571–579.

JOHNSON, R. M., and C. A. BAUMANN 1948 The effect of alpha-tocopherol on the utilization of carotene in the rat. *J. Biol. Chem.* **175,** 811–816.

KAUNITZ, H., and C. A. SLANETZ 1948 Implantation in normal and vitamin E deficient rats. *J. Nutrition* **36,** 331–338.

KNOWLTON, G. C., H. M. HINES, and K. M. BRINKHOUS 1939 Cure and prevention of vitamin-E-deficient muscular dystrophy with synthetic alpha-tocopherol acetate. *Proc. Soc. Exptl. Biol. Med.* **42**, 804–809.

LEMLEY, J. M., R. A. BROWN, O. D. BIRD, and A. D. EMMETT 1947 The effect of mixed tocopherols on the utilization of vitamin A in the rat. *J. Nutrition* **34**, 205–218.

MACKENZIE, C. G., J. B. MACKENZIE, and E. V. MCCOLLUM 1940 Occurrence of tremors and incoordination in vitamin E-deficient adult rats. *Proc. Soc. Exptl. Biol. Med.* **44**, 95–98.

MACKENZIE, C. G., and E. V. MCCOLLUM 1940 The cure of nutritional muscular dystrophy in the rabbit by alpha-tocopherol and its effect on creatine metabolism. *J. Nutrition* **19**, 345–362.

MACKENZIE, C. G., and E. V. MCCOLLUM 1941 Muscular dystrophy in the absence of testicular degeneration in vitamin E deficiency. *Proc. Soc. Exptl. Biol. Med.* **47**, 148–152.

MATTILL, H. A. 1938, 1941 Vitamin E. *J. Am. Med. Assoc.* **110**, 1831–1837 (reprinted as Chapter XXX, "The Vitamins, 1939." American Medical Association); *Ann. Rev. Biochem.* **10**, 405–409.

MILHORAT, A. T. 1948 Effect of delta- and gamma-tocopherol on creatinuria in progressive muscular dystrophy. *Federation Proc.* **7**, 80–81.

NELSON, E. M. 1939 Vitamin E. *U. S. Dept. Agriculture Yearbook*, "Food and Life," pages 259–261.

NELSON, M. M., G. A. EMERSON, and H. M. EVANS 1940 Growth-stimulating activity of α-tocopherol. *Proc. Soc. Exptl. Biol. Med.* **45**, 157–158; *Chem. Abs.* **35**, 496.

PAPPENHEIMER, A. M. 1943 Muscular disorders associated with deficiency of vitamin E. *Physiol. Rev.* **23**, 37–50.

PAPPENHEIMER, A. M. 1948 On certain aspects of vitamin E deficiency. (A lecture.) (Springfield, Ill.: Charles C. Thomas.)

REVIEW 1945 Vitamin E as a physiologic antioxidant. *Nutrition Rev.* **3**, 17–19.

REVIEW 1946 Present knowledge of vitamins E and K in nutrition. *Nutrition Rev.* **4**, 324–326.

REVIEW 1947 Vitamins A and E and milk production. *Nutrition Rev.* **5**, 265–266.

SMITH, L. I. 1940 The chemistry of vitamin E. *Chem. Rev.* **27**, 287–329.

STONE, S. 1940 Treatment of muscular dystrophies and allied conditions: Preliminary report on use of vitamin E (wheat germ oil). *J. Am. Med. Assoc.* **114**, 2187–2191.

WHITING, F., and J. K. LOOSLI 1948 The placental and mammary transfer of tocopherols (vitamin E) in sheep, goats, and swine. *J. Nutrition* **36**, 721–726.

WHITING, F., J. K. LOOSLI, and J. P. WILLMAN 1949 The influence of tocopherols upon the mammary and placental transfer of vitamin A in the sheep, goat, and pig. *J. Animal Sci.* **8**, 35–40; *Nutr. Abs. Rev.* **19**, 55–56.

Vitamin K

BECK, A. C., E. S. TAYLOR, and R. F. COLBURN 1941 Vitamin K administered to the mother during labor as a prophylaxis against hemorrhage in the newborn infant. *Am. J. Obstet. Gynecol.* **41**, 765–776; *Chem. Abs.* **35**, 5163.

BRINKHOUS, K. M. 1940 Plasma prothrombin; vitamin K. *Medicine* **19**, 329–416.

BROWN, E. E., J. F. FUDGE, and L. R. RICHARDSON 1947 Diet of mother and brain hemorrhages in infant rats. *J. Nutrition* **34**, 141–151.

BUTT, H. R., and A. M. SNELL 1941 *Vitamin K.* (Saunders.)

DOISY, E. A., S. B. BINKLEY, and S. A. THAYER 1941 Vitamin K. *Chem. Rev.* **28**, 477–517.

FERRARO, A., and L. ROIZIN 1946 Hemorrhagic diathesis experimentally induced by deficiency in vitamin K. A histopathologic study. *Am. J. Pathol.* **22**, 1109–1179; *Nutr. Abs. Rev.* **17**, 100.

FIESER, L. F. 1941 The chemistry of vitamin K. *Ann. Internal Med.* **15**, 648–658.

KOVE, S., and H. SIEGEL 1940, 1941 Prothrombin in the newborn infant. *J. Pediatrics* **17**, 448–457; **18**, 764–770, 770–775; *Chem. Abs.* **35**, 6292.

QUICK, A. J. 1946 Experimentally induced changes in the prothrombin level of the blood. III. *J. Biol. Chem.* **164**, 371–376.

QUICK, A. J., and M. STEFANINI 1948 Experimentally induced changes in the prothrombin level of the blood. *J. Biol. Chem.* **175**, 945–952.

SCARBOROUGH, H. 1940 Nutritional deficiency of vitamin K in man. *Lancet* **1940, I**, 1080–1081; *J. Am. Med. Assoc.* **115**, 491–492.

SELLS, R. L., S. A. WALKER, and C. A. OWEN 1941 Vitamin K requirement of the newborn infant. *Proc. Soc. Exptl. Biol. Med.* **47**, 441–445; *Chem. Abs.* **35**, 6290.

SNELL, A. M. 1939 Vitamin K: Its properties, distribution, and clinical importance. *J. Am. Med. Assoc.* **112**, 1457–1459; see also *J. Am. Med. Assoc.* **113**, 2056–2059.

WARNER, E. D., T. D. SPIES, and C. A. OWEN 1941 Hypoprothrombinemia and vitamin K in nutritional deficiency states. *Southern Med. J.* **34**, 161–163; *Chem. Abs.* **36**, 1065.

XVIII

SOME RELATIONS OF FOOD TO THE TEETH

Introduction to "the Tooth Problem"

The formation of good teeth, and the maintenance of the health of the teeth and gums, present such special and such baffling problems that any attempt to treat this subject here will necessarily lack conclusiveness of scientific explanation.

Yet while the teeth and adjoining tissues are quite unique structures they still are a part of the bodily structure, and like the rest of the body they are considerably influenced by the food.

Some relations of food to good teeth are now sufficiently established to warrant our attention, even though we have not yet a clear consensus of opinion as to the precise explanation of all the facts.

Broadly speaking, a tooth is made up of three main sections: the *enamel* or outer covering, the *dentine,* and the *pulp*. In the perfect tooth, the enamel is hard, brittle, and semitransparent, and presents a smooth, lustrous appearance. It is non-cellular and is built up of prisms united by a densely calcified intermediate substance. The enamel forms a comparatively thin layer or cap over the dentine, which makes up the largest portion of the tooth. The dentine is a yellowish-white, translucent substance resembling bone, and consists of a non-cellular, homogeneous material traversed regularly by branched socalled dentinal tubes, which contain projecting outgrowths from the dentine-forming cells, together with nerves, some tissue fluid, and other organic matter. The innermost portion of the tooth, the pulp, is a soft tissue, composed largely of cells, blood vessels, and nerves. Its outer layer consists of *odontoblasts,* or dentine-forming cells; and in young, growing teeth there is always between the pulp and the (calcified) dentine a layer of uncalcified matrix, penetrated by fibers from the odontoblasts, which is the zone where further calcification is taking place. Normally, this zone is quite thin, but in an imperfectly calcified tooth, it may be wide and irregular and patches of uncalcified material known as "interglobular spaces" may remain as permanent defects in the resulting dentine. The imperfectly calcified tooth may also show defects of the enamel, varying from slight roughness to deep pits and grooves, and even in some cases to a complete absence of enamel over certain areas.

The term *hypoplasia* is frequently applied to such conditions of poor structural development of the teeth, which are to be distinguished from *dental caries,* or actual decay and disintegration of teeth already formed. The making of this distinction, however, should not be taken to imply that these two types of tooth trouble are entirely independent of each other, for even slight defects of structure may constitute a starting point for the development of caries. And complete perfection of tooth structure is not common.

Marshall (1939) considers it a "confirmed clinical and laboratory observation" that there is scarcely a tooth in man or lower animal which does not present areas of incomplete formation. Hence much depends upon the "personal equation" of the investigator in all studies of the incidence of tooth defects; for some will call a tooth defective while others, equally expert but of more tolerant temperament, will pass it as normal.

Marshall's view, following that of Fish, is that caries begins in a permeable crevice or fault area which after eruption of the tooth becomes filled with the fluid and suspended materials present in the mouth, which from time to time include food particles and bacteria. Among the latter are those whose products tend to corrode the tooth. If this corrosion is not too rapid, the slight irritation of underlying dentine which it causes may result in a sufficiently augmented calcification from within to erect an effective barrier against further invasion of the tooth by the caries.

Although attempts have been made to study the incidence of hypoplasia as such in human teeth in order to correlate this with what was known of the nutritional background, these efforts have frequently been confused by the difficulty of recognizing hypoplasia in the presence of caries. In studying this aspect, therefore, frequent use has been made of the puppy as an experimental subject: for, as Blunt and Cowan point out, the dog (unlike the rat or the guineapig) resembles the human being in that he forms two sets of teeth, temporary and permanent, which in their growth and development are readily comparable to those of man. Although hypoplasia resembling that of human teeth may be developed in dogs by dietary mistreatment, actual decay does not appear commonly in this species, and hence one may investigate the former condition practically uncomplicated by the latter.

Mrs. May Mellanby has reported extensive investigations of the teeth from the puppies with which her husband was studying experimental rickets. Her studies leave no doubt that tooth structure is markedly influenced by nutritional conditions prevailing at the time the tooth in question is being formed, whether before or after birth. There are indications, however, that the body resources of the mother may serve to a limited extent as a factor of safety, so that poor diet of the mother before birth is somewhat less disastrous in its effect on her child's teeth than is correspondingly poor diet of the infant after birth.

Some of the Causes of Tooth Defects

Because defects of structure are so closely connected with the caries problem, Marshall's classification, while offered in connection with his writings on caries, is broad enough for our present purpose. "For convenience" he groups the causes alphabetically as follows: A, anatomical; B, bacteriological; C, chemical; D, dietary; E, endocrine; F, failure in mouth hygiene; H, heredity. And he holds (1939) that the relative importance of these seven groups of factors varies "with age, environmental vicissitudes, habits, health, and probably other, as yet undetermined, agents."

Also it is to be remembered that these causes probably more often act two or more together than any one separately.

In fact the "chemical" causes are presumably results of bacteriological or dietary causes, or of such failures in mouth-hygiene as the use of corrosive dentifrices.

On the other hand, one may be born with some tooth defect or susceptibility to caries bacteria which cannot in any known way be connected with his heredity, and might therefore be classified as idiosyncratic or due to Chance (an alternative C for Marshall's classification in case you consider "chemical" as covered by other causes).

Kesel (1943) classifies the factors in the development of caries into two major divisions: (1) the exciting factors, which actually produce the lesion; and (2) the predisposing factors, which permit the exciting causes to exist and operate. The actual exciting causes are few, as viewed by Kesel, probably only two: first, bacteria within a plaque on the tooth surface capable of destroying tooth substance by the products of their metabolism; and second, material on the tooth surface or in the mouth capable of being converted into substances harmful to the tooth. Without these two conditions, Kesel believes, caries in all probability could not occur. Yet all individuals have bacteria on the tooth surfaces, and most of them, at times, have upon their teeth or in the mouth, materials that these bacteria could utilize to form acid. Since all teeth do not become carious, there must be other circumstances which determine whether or not damage to the teeth occurs. These are what Kesel calls the *predisposing* factors, and classifies into two groups: (a) factors which exert influence through systemic or nutritional channels, and (b) local factors, which have their effect through the immediate environs of the teeth.

Still another way of grouping factors which influence the teeth would be according to the stage at which they operate: whether during the period when the tooth is forming and maturing, or after it is erupted and fully developed.

As will be apparent in the discussion which follows, the factors and their modes of operation overlap so as to make clear differentiation and interpretation often difficult or impossible.

Empirical Evidence That Food Is A Factor

Some years ago a group of diabetic children, who had long been receiving special care as to diet, were found to have unusually good teeth.

A large-scale trial with abundant controls was later made by feeding a part of the population of a large orphanage with a diet containing (as had that of the diabetic children) "liberal amounts of milk, eggs, meat, fresh and canned vegetables and fruits, and codliver oil daily." This also led to a great decrease in the incidence of tooth defects among the children of like age in the same institution. Speaking of recent extensions of these studies, where caries was again strikingly arrested by dietary regulation, Boyd reported in 1942 that neither the high-fat nor the low-sugar content of the early diabetic diet appears to be essential to this effect on the teeth; and concluded: "We have been unable to attribute this favorable effect of the dietary regimen to any single constituent or characteristic of the diet."

It may perhaps be of interest to add the following incident which came to the knowledge of one of us while serving as a member of the advisory committee to a comprehensive dental research. One aspect of this research was to be a fairly large-scale attempt to improve the teeth of children in institutions, by certain nutritional enrichments of their dietary under conditions of experimental control, and with exceptionally careful and expert examination of the teeth before and after the dietary tests. A certain institution with a child population of about 400 seemed when first briefly visited to be a promising place for such experiment because the physical circumstances permitted of good control, the management was scientifically-minded and cooperative and the income of the institution was so meager that the proposed gift of "protective" foods for the nutritional experiment would have been extremely welcome. But the research dentist found in the first examination of these children's teeth that there was *so little room for improvement* that this group of children would not do for his investigation after all! And his explanation was that the institution, while financially in difficult circumstances, had for some years had a good dietitian so that the children had already had the benefit of the sort of diet he had intended to try,—and had only a fraction of the incidence of dental defects commonly found in American children of their age.

In this case the dietitian had been guided, not by any special theory as to the tooth problem, but by the general principles of the newer knowledge of nutrition. This institution population illustrated well the *trend* which Dr. Percy Howe expresses in the saying that, "*Generally,* good health and good teeth go together."

Undoubtedly, as the guidance of the newer knowledge of nutrition comes to be accepted more and more widely and wholeheartedly, dental health will be improved along with the health of the body as a whole. Yet we seem to meet enough people whose dental health is below the level of their general health, to constitute a scientifically valid indication that "there is something special about the teeth and gums." Does study of them indicate need of special emphasis on certain nutritional factors? Does it also (as some investigators believe) indicate that diet has other than strictly nutritional relations to the health of the teeth?

Individual Nutritional Factors

Calcium and *phosphorus* are such prominent ingredients of the chief tooth mineral that they must certainly be regarded as among the major nutritional factors concerned in the building of good teeth. This must be emphasized; for the fact that these elements do not tell the whole story, and the further fact that, once built into the tooth structure, they are not very readily withdrawn by the circulation, have resulted in too great a tendency to ignore them in recent discussions of the tooth problem. For the construction of good teeth, the body needs, on the one hand, abundant supplies of calcium and phosphorus as building material; and, on the other hand, abundant supplies of such vitamins as regulate the processes involved in building these particular tissues. The latter include vitamin D certainly, and, if observations on animals carry over to man, vitamin C and vitamin A as well.

That the calcium intake may indeed frequently be a limiting factor in tooth soundness was suggested by the finding of East (1941) in a survey of 109 cities in the United States, that hardness (richness in calcium carbonate) of the city water supply was associated with lower-than-average incidence of caries in the school children; and strikingly confirmed by extended studies among South African groups, where allowance was made in addition for a possible fluoride effect.

Vitamin D.—The essential similarity between the various calcified structures of the body, and the demonstrated importance of vitamin D to the development of the bones, lead naturally to the problem of the extent to which the teeth also are affected by this factor.

It has long been accepted that rickets occasions a *delay in dentition;* and Hess has cited an investigation in his clinic which showed that even in cases of extremely mild rickets teething was retarded, for "whereas about one-half the number of normal babies developed a tooth between the sixth and the ninth month, only about one-fourth of the infants with mild rickets had a tooth at this age." The eruption of subsequent teeth was likewise tardy. Clearly then the provision of vitamin D in a sufficient quantity to prevent all rachitic manifestations may be expected to hasten somewhat the time of appearance of the baby's teeth.

Proceeding now to a consideration of vitamin D in relation to dental caries, two questions suggest themselves: (1) to what extent does hypoplasia (of which, as Mrs. Mellanby's experiments showed, lack of vitamin D is one cause) predispose to caries; and (2) once the teeth have been formed (for better or worse), what protection, if any, against the inroads of tooth decay, may be hoped for from a liberal intake of vitamin D?

With regard to the first question, it would seem logical to expect that, whatever the underlying cause of caries, the damage, which involves essentially the solution of calcium salts by agents reaching them from outside the tooth, will be more severe to the hypoplastic tooth in which the protective coating of enamel may be less dense, or pitted and grooved (making mechanical removal of the destructive agent more difficult), or even totally lacking in spots; and in which the interglobular spaces of the dentine facilitate further penetration by the disintegrative fluid.

This reasoning is substantiated by the clinical experience that those teeth and portions of teeth which are in general most apt to be hypoplastic (perhaps because of the period of life at which they are calcified) are likewise in general most liable to dental caries. Thus, for example, Dick found in an investigation of the permanent teeth that, of the cases with carious teeth, the lower first molar was decayed in 80 per cent and the upper first molar in 30 per cent. The fact that the lower first molars decay out of proportion to the others "is to be attributed rather to the main part of the enamel of the crown having been laid down in the first two years of life when rickety conditions are operative." And May Mellanby, correlating structure with decay in individual teeth, found that those which were normal or nearly normal in structure had carious cavities in only a little more than one quarter of the cases, as compared with 85 per cent incidence of caries in distinctly hypoplastic teeth.

On the other hand, it is well known also that many hypoplastic teeth remain resistant to caries throughout life. Clearly, there are other factors to be considered in the problem of caries besides the structural quality of the teeth.

Administration of vitamin D was found by Mellanby and other workers to protect already erupted teeth significantly against the development of caries in preadolescent children, but there are suggestions that it may be less effective at later ages.

In the work of Boyd, Drain, and Stearns it appeared that a change of diet in the general direction indicated by the newer knowledge of nutrition reduced the rate of caries development in children, and that a further improvement was then effected by increasing the vitamin D intake to 600 units per day. This effect of 600 I.U. per day was, however, stated to be no greater than that observed in other work by them with 350 I.U. per day; so that the National Research Council's recommendation of 400 I.U. per day should permit an optimum effect of vitamin D on the teeth.

The vitamin D derived from sunshine may also affect importantly the soundness of the teeth. Thus, Mills (1937) found that, progressing northward across the United States, there was a steady increase in the frequency of caries among school children, which amounted in all to over 200 per cent increase from the Gulf of Mexico to the Canadian border. And East reported that the frequency of dental caries in various portions of the country varied inversely with the annual hours of sunshine enjoyed in the different regions.

According to the Council on Foods and Nutrition of the American Medical Association: "There is clinical evidence to justify the statement that vitamin D plays an important role in tooth formation. Likewise experimental evidence justifies the statement that vitamin D is a beneficial factor in preventing and arresting dental caries when the intake of calcium and phosphorus is liberal and the diet is adequate with respect to other nutrients."

Vitamin C.—In the days when severe scurvy was common, it frequently resulted in loss of teeth, though available records do not make clear in how far this was due to an effect upon the tooth itself and in how far to the condition of the gums and jaw bones.

In 1919, Zilva and Wells in England studied microscopic sections of the teeth of guineapigs subjected to shortage of vitamin C and came to the conclusion that the tooth is one of the first, if not the first, of the parts of the body to be affected by subnormal intake of this vitamin, and that profound changes may occur in the teeth even when the ordinary scorbutic symptoms are still so slight as to be almost or quite unrecognizable. (There were at that time no means of measuring the level of concentration of vitamin C in the body.) The typical effect upon the teeth was described as a fibroid degeneration of the pulp with a replacement of the fine structural organization by amorphous material. They also found similar effects of vitamin C deficiency upon the teeth of monkeys. They therefore emphasized the view that subclinical conditions of shortage of vitamin C may be more frequent than had been suspected and may reasonably be expected to injure the teeth.

Degeneration of the pulp tissue as a result of shortage of vitamin C has also been reported by several other investigators. In 1920 Howe of the Forsyth Dental Clinic and the Harvard Department of Pathology also found that scorbutic diets have a deleterious effect upon the teeth. He noted a marked decalcification and loosening of the teeth, with absorption of the alveolar processes as in pyorrhea; and emphasized the finding that if the condition was not too far advanced it could be cured by simple addition of orange juice to the diet. Others have also emphasized the good effects of orange juice upon the health of the teeth and gums. Höjer's very extensive studies, both experimental and clinical, seem to leave no doubt that even mild degrees of shortage of vitamin C are very important.

More recently, Boyle, Bessey, and Wolbach (1937) of the Harvard Dental and Medical Schools, in carefully controlled experiments with individual vitamin deficiencies, find that shortage of vitamin C may bring about a condition which upon full pathological investigation appears to be identical with one of the well-recognized clinical forms of pyorrhea: pyorrhea of the systemic type.

Particularly noteworthy is the further fact that these investigators then examined patients in the dental clinic and found definite correlation between this type of pyorrhea and a low concentration of vitamin C in the blood.

McCollum points out that dentine is derived from the mesoblastic tissue; and holds that the odontoblasts, which form dentine, are extremely sensitive to deficiency of ascorbic acid, so that if the tissues become depleted of this substance while the teeth are in process of growth, defective dentine will result.

Vitamin A.—Markedly abnormal tooth structure, involving especially the enamel, was found by Wolbach and Howe and later workers to be a prominent feature of vitamin A deficiency in experimental animals. McCollum *et al.* (1939) hold that the enamel-forming cells (ameloblasts) are derived from the same embryonic tissue (ectoderm) from which gum epithelium has its origin; and that they should therefore logically be expected, like other epithelium, to be extremely sensitive to deficiency of vitamin A.

Although the Committee on Survey of Literature on Dental Caries could (1946) find "no evidence except the one case described by Boyle to show that vitamin A deficiency in man resulted in a malformation of the teeth," and further, "no direct evidence that the addition of vitamin A to a diet will reduce the dental caries incidence," the evidence of animal experimentation strongly suggests that vitamin A is indeed a factor in the building of sound teeth, and points to the desirability of more controlled human observations.

Sugar Intake and the Teeth

The view was advanced by Bunting, Koehne, and others that an increased intake of sugar results in an increase in the number and severity of carious lesions in teeth already formed; and that this is due to the effect of soluble carbohydrate in promoting the multiplication in the mouth of types of bacteria which are specifically bad for the teeth.

Recent evaluations (Sognnaes, 1948; Shaw, 1949) of the effects of wartime diets, notably low in sugar and refined flour, on the teeth of European populations lead to the further suggestion that such diets may have an even more marked beneficial effect in promoting the development of teeth which are less susceptible to decay than teeth which form under ordinary peacetime conditions. For, observations on caries incidence among three quarters of a million school children examined in eleven European countries in the past forty years consistently point to a decreased incidence of tooth decay toward the latter part of, and following, both World Wars I and II. The decreased tendency to caries did not appear clearly until more than a year after the wartime diet was begun, and (in the case of World War I) it was still evident for several years after the close of the war and return to ordinary food habits. Moreover, the beneficial effect was most striking in young children and in *those teeth* of older children which developed and matured during the war years.

Such observations seem to indicate that the tooth structure itself —and not merely the environment in the mouth—benefited in some way by the enforced restrictions of wartime diet. Whether this came about directly as the result of a low sugar intake or because the quality of the diet improved when other "natural" foods had to be taken in place of the refined carbohydrate, or in some still other way, is not certain. However, animal studies cited by Shaw (1949) confirm the belief that a high sugar intake is specifically bad for the teeth.

Favorable Effects of Certain Fruits and Vegetables

The eating of fruit, particularly raw fruit such as apple, or taking orange or grapefruit juice, at the end of a meal or soon after, or at bedtime, is considered by some investigators to induce "a bacteriostatic condition in the mouth."

Precise explanation of this benefit is not yet entirely clear. It may be a combined effect of several factors no one of which sufficiently predominates over the others to be readily demonstrated in an outstandingly convincing way.

In the case of such a soft-fibrous texture as that of a raw apple (or of celery) the mechanical effects of moderate massage of the gums, and of leaving the surfaces of the teeth scrubbed free from food particles, are in themselves beneficial. The "savory" property of such a raw food or of a citrus fruit juice doubtless also means a physiological stimulation of the cells which pour their more or less bacteriostatic secretions into the mouth. Again, some investigators have emphasized the view that the mild acidity of a fruit or fruit juice is helpful in keeping the tooth surfaces free from plaques and in affording a wholesome stimulation of the mucous membranes of the mouth, in contrast to the unnatural and drastic "cleansers" of some tooth pastes, which may be injurious.

Fruits and vegetables generally, and milk, cream, and ice cream, tend to the ensurance of good intakes of calcium, phosphorus, vitamin A, and vitamin C; while eggs are a good source of phosphorus, vitamin A, and vitamin D. Hence liberal use of these foods may reasonably be expected to aid both the development and maintenance of sound tooth structure and a healthy condition of the gums.

Fluorides and the Teeth

Opinions may differ as to whether any discussion of the relation of fluorides to the teeth is appropriate to a nutrition textbook, or whether this should be regarded as purely a public health problem. For this reason, a brief account only will be given here of the findings which recently have attracted much attention from the dental profession and the general public.

The discovery by Smith, Lantz, and Smith (1931) of the cause of mottled enamel is of closely related interest to the influence of food upon teeth and also illustrates the important fact that the methods of long-time feeding trials under strict laboratory control developed in nutrition research may also be uniquely useful in solving problems of the relation of our intake to our health which may be other than strictly nutritional.

Upon careful investigation by Margaret Cammack Smith, chief of research in human nutrition, University of Arizona, the defect of human teeth known as mottled enamel was found to be due, not to a nutritional deficiency, but to injury of the teeth by the fluorine of the local drinking water. Later, surveys showed that mottled enamel is endemic in many regions throughout the world, and is invariably associated with drinking water containing about 1.5 or more parts per million of fluorine. Communities nearby but with fluorine-free water supplies, have natives free from this disfiguring defect of the enamel. Studies of the teeth of migrants into and from high-fluoride regions indicate that this effect of fluorides operates during the developmental period only and is not reversible: teeth are mottled or not depending on the fluoride intake while they are being formed: and, once mottled, they remain so.

A decade or so ago, however, a different sort of emphasis began to be directed to the fluorine problem, *viz.*, whether a certain intake of the element may not be beneficial in protecting the teeth against decay, whether perhaps there may be more water supplies with suboptimal levels than with excessive concentrations of fluoride. H. T. Dean, at the National Institute of Health, and others, amassed impressive statistical evidence that tooth decay is less extensive among natives of communities where the drinking water contains fluoride than among those of fluoride-free districts, and that this "protective" effect may be noted even on fluoride levels below those which produce mottled enamel. Persons who had resided in "fluoride localities" during the period when their teeth were developing were found to retain a *relative* immunity to tooth decay through years of subsequent residence in fluoride-free areas. Application of fluorides, several times a year, to the surface of the teeth, especially in young subjects, was reported by several dentists to reduce the incidence of new caries strikingly. How this effect is produced is not certain, but evidence has been presented suggesting (*a*) that fluoride hardens the enamel and makes it more resistant to acid erosion; (*b*) that it decreases the number of mouth bacteria supposed to be harmful to the teeth; and (*c*) that it may furthermore diminish acid formation by these bacteria.

Such observations have led naturally to the question whether it may be possible to reduce the tooth decay of whole communities by simple addition of fluoride to the public water supply. Simultaneously arises the question whether even small amounts of a potentially toxic material such as fluoride may be ingested day in and day out without risk of injury to other body organs. A comprehensive investigation of both questions is under way under the auspices of the New York State Department of Health in the two communities of Newburgh and Kingston, New York. These neighboring cities are of similar size, population groups, economic status, have common sources of food supply, and, until May of 1945, the water supplies of both were "fluoride-free." Dental examination of all school children 5 to 12 years old revealed the same situation in both cities—an incidence of 21 decayed, missing, or filled (DMF) teeth per 100 *permanent* teeth. Since May, 1945, fluoride has been added to the Newburgh water supply, bringing the level up to 1.0-1.2 parts per million, while the Kingston water supply has remained "fluoride-free." At the time of writing (late 1950) a report has just been made of the effects of the first three years' exposure of fluorine on the teeth of the Newburgh school children: a reduction of 30 per cent in the number decayed, missing, or filled (from 21 to 15 DMF/100 permanent teeth). In the control city of Kingston, the incidence remains the same as three years earlier (21 DMF/100 permanent teeth). As would be expected, the protective effect was greatest among the younger children, but it was still significant among the older groups whose permanent teeth had presumably erupted before the fluorine exposure began. No undesirable systemic effects have as yet been detected, but it may be many years before final judgment as to the safety of water fluorination can be reached. Meanwhile, even the most enthusiastic supporters of the policy admit that it cannot be expected to eliminate all caries, and nutrition will undoubtedly continue as a factor.

In Conclusion

From the strictly nutritional viewpoint, there appear to be at least five factors important to good teeth and gums: calcium, phosphorus, and vitamins D, C, and A. If much of the nutritional investigation of dental problems seems inconclusive, this is probably largely due to attempts to fasten upon *the* factor where in reality a combination of factors may be involved. Approached more broadly, the evidence is strong and fairly clear: such choice of food as the newer knowledge of nutrition teaches is unquestionably advantageous to the teeth.

There is also strong evidence that nutrition is not the only way in which food affects the teeth.

Hence, high intakes of protective foods and a low consumption of sugar are both important.

Boyd (1942) recommends the following daily diet for the normal child: "1 quart milk; 1 or 2 eggs; two 4-ounce servings of succulent, leafy, and root vegetables; two 4-ounce servings of fruit, one of which should be orange or other raw fruit (tomato may be used as a substitute); one serving meat, fish, fowl, or liver; 1 teaspoon codliver oil; and supplementary foods such as potatoes, starches, bread and other cereal products, sweets and fats, in amounts sufficient to complete the caloric requirement for full activity."

The Forsyth Dental Clinic is reported as finding that caries incidence decreased 79 per cent in that part of its child population which followed a dietary of the sort just outlined, while among children of the same age and locality on unreformed diet it increased 13 per cent.

Among the few conclusions which Marshall considered to be justified, by a critical examination of the extensive literature of caries up to 1939, was that dietary supervision has reduced the number of carious teeth, and that the application of the newer knowledge of nutrition during pregnancy and lactation is beneficial to both mother and child.

In a more recent (December 1946) survey of the literature by a special committee of the National Research Council, it was also concluded that: "there is a strong association between diet and the susceptibility to dental caries. Arrest of dental caries activity and reduction in the initiation of new lesions can be maintained for long periods by adherence to a fully adequate dietary regimen." Although this Committee further pointed out that, of specific nutritional factors, only an adequate intake of vitamin D and a good retention of calcium and phosphorus had yet been demonstrated beyond doubt to have a part in caries control in man, leaving many questions still open, we are inclined to share the optimistic view of McCollum that: "At any rate we now know how to produce good teeth as respects structure and how to preserve them in considerable measure from decay. We may confidently expect that further researches will within a few years see complete unanimity of opinion as to the factors which operate to cause caries-susceptibility. Nutritional research has scored a great achievement in the field of dental science."

EXERCISE

After study of the available literature, including that later than the suggestions listed below, write a paper of from 200 to 500 words supplementary to the foregoing chapter.

SUGGESTED READINGS

AST, D. M. 1950 (Progress report on Newburgh fluorine project.) *Am. J. Public Health* **40**, 716–727.

BOYD, J. D. 1942 Nutrition as it affects tooth decay. *J. Am. Dietet. Assoc.* **18**, 211–215.

BOYD, J. D. 1943 Prevention of dental caries in late childhood and adolescence. *J. Am. Dental Assoc.* **30**, 670–680.

BOYD, J. D., and C. L. DRAIN 1928 The arrest of dental caries in childhood. *J. Am. Med. Assoc.* **90**, 1867–1869.

BOYLE, P. E. 1941 Effect of various dietary deficiencies on the periodontal tissues of the guineapig and of man. *J. Am. Dental Assoc.* **28**, 1788–1793; *Chem. Abs.* **36**, 1364.

BOYLE, P. E., O. A. BESSEY, and S. B. WOLBACH 1937 (Vitamin C and pyorrhea.) *Proc. Soc. Exptl. Biol. Med.* **36**, 733; *J. Am. Dental Assoc.* **24**, 1768–1777.

Committee on Survey of Literature on Dental Caries 1946 *Nutrition and Dental Caries.* Mimeographed Draft Report, Food and Nutrition Board, National Research Council, Washington, D. C.

EAST, B. R. 1941 Association of dental caries in school children with hardness of communal water supplies. *J. Dental Research* **20**, 323–326; *Chem. Abs.* **36**, 1086.

HOWE, P. R., R. L. WHITE, and M. D. ELLIOTT 1942 The influence of nutrition supervision on dental caries. *J. Am. Dental Assoc.* **29**, 38–43.

Howe, P. R., R. L. White, and M. Rabine 1933 Retardation of dental caries in outpatients of a dental infirmary. *Am. J. Diseases Children* **46**, 1045–1049.

Jay, P. 1940 Role of sugar in the etiology of dental caries. *J. Am. Dental Assoc.* **27**, 393–396; *Chem. Abs.* **34**, 2445.

Kesel, R. G. 1943 Dental caries: Etiology, control and activity tests. *J. Am. Dental Assoc.* **30**, 25–39.

Marshall, J. A. 1939 Dental caries. *Physiol. Rev.* **19**, 389–414.

McCay, C. M., and L. Will 1949 Erosion of molar teeth by acid beverages. *J. Nutrition* **39**, 313–324.

McCollum, E. V., et al. 1939 *The Newer Knowledge of Nutrition*, 5th Edition, Chapter XXVII. (Macmillan.)

McKay, F. S., H. T. Dean, W. D. Armstrong, B. G. Bibby, and D. B. Ast 1945 Fluorine in Dental Public Health: A Symposium. (New York Institute of Clinical Oral Pathology.)

Phillips, P. H. 1950 Relation of nutrition to good teeth. *J. Am. Dietet. Assoc.* **26**, 85–88.

Shaw, J. H. 1949 Nutrition and dental caries. *Federation Proc.* **8**, 536–545.

Smith, M. C., E. M. Lantz, and H. V. Smith 1931 The cause of mottled enamel, a defect of human teeth. *Arizona Agr. Expt. Sta.*, Bull. 32.

Sognnaes, R. F. 1948 Analysis of wartime reduction of dental caries in European children. *Am. J. Diseases Children* **75**, 792–821.

XIX

NUTRITIONAL CHARACTERISTICS OF FOOD COMMODITIES

Foods may properly be grouped in different ways according to the purposes in view. "The basic seven" was and is a useful device for giving emphasis to certain main types of foods; and guidance toward the choice of balanced diets by consumers who need not be versed in nutritive values. For fuller considerations, and especially such as involve the finding of common ground of understanding between nutritionists and agricultural economists, the most advantageous plan seems to be that of *classifying all foods into from ten to twelve groups,* taking account both of nutritional characteristics and of economic or commodity relationships, either in production or consumption or both.

Ten food groups may well be: (1) the cereal grains and their products; (2) mature legumes and nuts; (3) potatoes and sweetpotatoes; (4) green and yellow vegetables; (5) citrus fruits and tomatoes; (6) other fruits and vegetables; (7) milk and its products other than butter; (8) meats, fish, poultry, and eggs; (9) butter and other fats; (10) sugar and other sweets. A frequent modification of this is to treat eggs separately, making a total of 11 groups. Less frequently, butter is treated as separate from other fats.

In the terms of the agricultural economist, the grains, vegetables, and fruits are "primary" or "direct food crops" coming directly from the soil into human consumption; while milk, meat, poultry, and eggs are "secondarily derived" by the "processing" of crops through animals; and fats and sugars are in a third economic category because to so large an extent they are products of industrial technology as well as of agriculture.

In this chapter, we shall consider the nutritional characteristics, place in the diet, and some of the commodity relationships of each of the ten food groups just listed. The order of this listing affords, in our opinion, the clearest sequence in thinking of the place of each food group in the dietary when we assume that full use is made of each group in its turn as here arranged.

A governmental study of the distribution of the food expenditures of American families among these ten food groups, and the contribution of each of these groups to the chief different factors of nutritive value of the total dietary or food supply, is shown in Table 28.

The student is advised to refer back to this table frequently in the following study of the nutritional characteristics and economy of each food group.

TABLE 28. *Relative Cost and Contributions to Nutritive Value of Diet: 10 Food Groups (American Family Dietaries, 1942: U. S. Dept. Agriculture)*

Food Group	Percentage of Total Food Cost	Calories	Protein	Calcium	Iron	Vitamin A Value	Thiamine	Riboflavin	Vitamin C
1. Grain products[a]	11	30	28	12	21	[b]	22	9	0
2. Dry beans, peas, nuts	1	3	5	3	11	[b]	6	3	0
3. Potatoes, sweetpotatoes	3	5	3	2	7	6	8	4	13
4. Citrus fruits, tomatoes	6	2	1	3	4	7	6	2	35
5. Green and yellow vegetables	5	1	2	5	8	39	6	5	31
6. Other vegetables and fruits	8	4	2	3	6	6	3	5	13
7. Milk and its products other than butter	17	14	23	65	7	15	8	43	6
8. Meat, fish, poultry and eggs	30	13	33	5	31	16	37	28	1
9. Butter and other fats	10	19	2	[b]	2	11	4	1	0
10. Sugar and other sweets	3	8	[b]	2	3	[b]	[b]	[b]	1
Miscellaneous	2	1	1	[b]	[b]	[b]	[b]	[b]	[b]
Food adjuncts	4	No attempt to estimate nutrients in these								

[a] 35 per cent of flour counted as enriched.
[b] Less than 0.5 per cent.

Grain Products

Cereal grains and their milling and bakery products are still the staff of life in the sense that this food-group contributes a larger proportion of nutriment to a larger part of the world's people than does any other.

As the late Sir Frederick Hopkins summarized the historic place of these foods in our diet: "Circumstances have to be very exceptional indeed when the growing of cereals does not yield an energy supply for the worker at less cost and with less relative effort than any other method of food production. Economic and social factors usually tend to make bread by far the most convenient form in which the cereals can reach the individual consumer. The nations of the West have acquired the habit of demanding a well-piled loaf, and for this the special properties of wheat gluten seem necessary. Hence the reliance on wheat in the West."

Stiebeling and Phipard (1939) found in their comprehensive study of American family food consumption that, "in all regions, and whatever the level of food expenditure, the largest share of the calories was derived from the grain products."

It was, of course, because flour and bread are consumed in such amounts by so large a majority of the people, that attention was attracted to this food-group as a practicable means of improving broadly and promptly "the nutritional environment in which our people live," through the enrichment "program," or "movement."

Six cereal grains—rice, wheat, corn (maize), oats, barley, and rye—are important in human nutrition. Their relative prominence is subject to wide geographic variation, partly due to climate and partly to differing preference of different peoples. When corn and oats are referred to as "feed" grains, it does not mean that they lack suitability for use as human food; but rather that (in the United States, at least) our normal crops of corn and oats so greatly exceed the amounts desired for human food that large quantities remain for animal feeding.

Outstanding characteristics of the grain products are: their acceptability and cheapness as sources of food calories and protein; and also (in their whole grain or enriched or restored forms) as sources of iron, thiamine, and niacin. Nutritionally they need supplementation in calcium, vitamins A and C and in riboflavin; and to make a diet fully satisfactory for growth, reproduction, or lactation the grain protein needs moderate supplementation with some protein or proteins richer in lysine and tryptophane. In addition to its strictly nutritional characteristics, this food-group aids the digestive process by conferring a favorable texture upon the food mass and its residue in the alimentary tract.

Present-day conditions therefore make it logical for nutrition-conscious people to consider anew whether we may not advocate a somewhat larger place for grain products in American dietaries than that to which they had sunk by about 1940.

During the year 1940–41 the National Research Council reestablished its Committee on Food and Nutrition (later renamed Food and Nutrition Board) and sponsored its collaboration with the Food and Drug Administration and the milling and baking industries. The resulting Enrichment Program or Movement has been fully recorded by R. M. Wilder and R. R. Williams in their bulletin entitled, "Enrichment of Flour and Bread: A History of the Movement" published by the National Research Council.

Awakening realization of the nutritional desirability of enriching white bread led to studies of other enrichments as well as the one for which the name Enriched was officially authorized. Under the title, "What the Consumer Should Know About Bread," Professor C. M. McCay of Cornell has reviewed in the *Journal of Home Economics* of April 1949 several ways of increasing the nutritive value of bread by incorporating in the flour or dough such protein concentrates as soy flour, non-fat dry milk solids, dry yeast, wheat germ, corn germ, and dry whey. McCay concludes that bread is "a superb medium" for these special protein concentrates and that "the difference in cost between a very poor bread and one of very high nutritive value ranges only between one half and one cent per pound loaf."

For some years before the initiation of the movement for enriching flour and bread with thiamine, riboflavin, niacin, and iron there had been a general trend toward a wider and larger use of milk, and especially of skim-milk powder ("non-fat dry milk solids") in bread-making. Such addition of significant amounts of milk solids obviously enriches the bread in its protein and calcium as well as some of its vitamin values. The process to which the term enrichment has been officially assigned is not a rival project but a further step. We should stimulate consumer demand for bread which has been enriched in both ways. According to Prouty and Cathcart

(1939) a considerable proportion of the white bread made in the United States in recent years has contained enough of milk solids to double its earlier calcium content. Mineral salt mixtures used as "yeast food" in bread-making also increase the calcium content of the resulting bread. Another means of enrichment of bread in vitamins of the B group is the use of specially grown yeast of extra high vitamin content. And always it is open to the consumer to demand bread from which less of the nutriment has been removed in the milling process, or to which the germ has been returned.

Mature Legumes and Nuts

Mature legumes and nuts are grouped together as direct food crops rich in proteins and thiamine. They doubtless deserve a larger place in our dietaries than we have yet learned to give them.

In their production, ordinary dry beans are much like a grain crop; and are, indeed, sometimes grouped with grains in agricultural discussion. They are, however, almost twice as rich in proteins as are the cereal grains. And soybeans (dry) are almost twice as rich in protein as are ordinary beans. The protein both of ordinary and of soy beans, needs cooking to make it readily digestible; and the nutritive value of bean protein is often under-rated because of feeding experiments in which it was fed raw. More recent research has shown that the protein of beans, when cooked as it is for human consumption, need not be discriminated against either on grounds of digestibility or of the nutritive value of the amino acid mixture which these proteins yield upon digestion.

Every food protein yields a somewhat different mixture of amino acids—not so much different in kind as in the quantitative proportions in which the same kinds of amino acids are present. The one which is present in smallest amount, relative to the need of the person or animal being fed, is called the *limiting* amino acid. This term may be used whether we are speaking of an individual protein or of the protein mixture contained in a food or a diet. Thus according to present-day knowledge, the "limiting" amino acid of beans is cystine-plus-methionine, while that of wheat is lysine. Thus the proteins of beans and those of wheat (or flour) have supplementary value to each other and the serving of Boston brown bread with baked beans is good nutritional practice. Hence also we see that it is entirely consistent to make baked beans (or a thick pea soup) the "main dish" of the largest meal on some days, while on other days or at other meals a different protein food may be chosen to balance or supplement the wheat or bread protein.

Because no one of the essential amino acids is apt to be entirely lacking from any natural food it is better to speak of the amino acid which is present in relatively smallest amount as the *limiting* amino acid, *rather* than to say that the food protein is "deficient" in it.

The proteins of ordinary beans, of soybeans, of peas, and of such nuts as have been sufficiently studied to permit a judgment, certainly of peanuts, all have proteins very similar to those of meat and all can be used as nutritionally good alternatives for meat to a much larger extent than they yet are in the United States. Also these are all protein-rich crops which American farmers can readily produce more abundantly as rapidly as consumers will buy them. These facts were thoroughly studied from many viewpoints, especially during the Second World War, and may be emphasized with confidence.

Peanut butter spread on white bread tends to restore the protein, vitamin, and some of the mineral values of the whole wheat grain which are rejected in the milling process.

The peanut, of course, is a legume comparable with peas, beans (including soybeans), and lentils. Most other nuts ("real" nuts as some fanciers say) are botanically fruits and agriculturally tree crops. The culture of nut trees and the consumption of nuts might well be increased.

Table 29 (beyond) shows the approximate amounts of each of the amino acids now called *essential* in the sense explained in Chapter VI, in each of several foods and food-proteins. These are the data of Horn, Jones, and Blum, published by the United States Department of Agriculture in 1950.

The high nutritive value of beans is true also of peas (dry, or as dry-equivalent of fresh or canned peas) and these two legumes may well be considered as alternative "meat substitutes." *Alternatives* is the better word, but the continued use of the word substitutes is a true indication that a prejudice still exists.

Nuts are an alternative toward which there is less of active prejudice than toward beans, but most of us still do not take nuts as seriously as they deserve, as one of the main protein-rich food groups. The well-deserved popularity of peanut-butter sandwiches might advantageously serve as an introduction to a much larger use of nuts in American dietaries. A generous dish of mixed nuts or of fruit-and-nut salad can well be the main dish of luncheon or dinner and an interesting and labor-saving way of diversifying the diet.

Thus there are good reasons, nutritional and economic, for giving increased emphasis to this food-group in American dietaries. One can confidently expect that money thus spent will bring much more than its *pro rata* share of nutrients. If increasing acquaintance of consumers with these facts increases the consumer demand for beans, peas, soy-bean products, peanuts, and peanut butter, American agriculture can readily supply the increased demand with little if any increase of price. These are crops which are relatively easy to grow and to handle and which tend to increase the fertility of the soil because they "fix" nitrogen from the air in the form of compounds available to other plants as well as themselves. Careful investigations made during the Second World War showed clearly that only easy adjustments favorable to agriculture would be involved in meeting even a largely increased demand for the foods of the legume group.

Potatoes and Sweetpotatoes

These two foods are not closely related botanically—which is the reason for making sweetpotato a single word. And to bracket them together may seem odd from the viewpoint of the fact that sweetpotatoes are an important source of vitamin A while (ordinary) potatoes are not. But from the viewpoint both of agricultural production and household use, they are sufficiently of the nature of alternatives (as foods chiefly grown for their calorie values, and characterized by high carbohydrate content) to warrant their being bracketed as one of the 10 or 11 groups into which we find it helpful to classify all of our important foods.

If a single term were being chosen to characterize this food group, it would probably be *starchy*. In this respect they are like the grains, and some students of food-supply problems count together the starchy seeds, roots, and tubers as foods of relatively low cost and low "protective" value on which the peoples of some areas are forced largely to live, and from which, when economically able, they tend to shift toward diets higher in protein and fat, and perhaps more diversified in other respects also.

But potatoes and sweetpotatoes are not such "one-sided" foods as most people probably suppose them to be. In the average of the presumably representative American family dietaries summarized in Table 28, it may be seen that an investment of 3 percent of the food money in this food-group brought a return of 5 percent of the calories; 3 percent of the protein; 2, of the calcium; 7, of the iron; 6, of the vitamin A value; 8, of the thiamine; 4, of the riboflavin; and 13 percent of the vitamin C. Thus the investment in this food-group brought a return which was not only large in proportion to its cost but also fairly well distributed over the different main factors in the nutritive value of the diet.

Green and Yellow Vegetables

Green and yellow vegetables are grouped together because of their relatively high vitamin A values. We say "values" rather than "contents" because, as previously explained, these foods contain not vitamin A itself but precursors (or provitamins A)—notably carotenes—which the body transforms into vitamin A and then uses in the same manner as if it had received the vitamin A directly from the food itself. The fact that the chief precursors are named carotenes for the carrot makes it easy to remember that high vitamin A value is characteristic of most yellow as well as all green vegetables. In the latter, however, the yellow color is hidden by the presence of the intensely green chlorophyll.

The economy of this food-group compared with others, as sources of vitamin A, is illustrated in Table 28. In the American dietaries there summarized, the expenditure for green and yellow vegetables was only 5 percent of the total food expenditure, yet it brought 39 percent of the total vitamin A value. This group also supplied 5 percent of the calcium, 8 percent of the iron, 6 percent of the thiamine, 5 percent of the riboflavin, and 31 percent of the vitamin C. As we saw in Chapter XV that liberal intake of vitamin A is very beneficial to health and longevity, a food group so rich in vitamin A value and which also contributes importantly to several other factors of nutritive value, is one which might well be promoted to a larger place in our dietaries. Experts of the U. S. Department of Agriculture have recommended that production and consumption of this food-group be increased promptly by 15 to 20 percent which, they report, would be a very practicable adjustment which the growers of these foods could easily make just as rapidly as there is prospect of sufficient consumer demand.

Early in the era of the newer knowledge of nutrition McCollum emphasized the efficiency of green leaves in supplementing seeds and their products in the dietary; and attributed this to the relative richness of the green leaf foods in both calcium and vitamin A value. Quinn and coworkers showed that vitamin A value accompanies greenness not only in leaves but also in green peppers and green beans. The green and yellow vegetables are quite varied both botanically (as to the kind and the organ of the plant) and in nutritional character. Illustrations are as follows:

Beans, green snap or string, succulent green pods with immature seeds, have shown 600 to 1200 International Units of vitamin A value per 100 grams. This is a value worth taking into account, though much below those of typical dark green leaves. *Broccoli* comprises flower buds together with accompanying twigs and leaves. This total edible portion has shown 3000 to 7000 I.U.* per 100 grams. If, as is sometimes done, the leaves are rejected, about two-thirds of the vitamin A value is thereby lost; the other third is in the flower buds, the twigs having only traces. The leaves are also richer than either the flower buds or the twigs in riboflavin and calcium, while the flower buds are the richest in phosphorus. Broccoli is easily grown in home gardens, and is now also a fairly staple market commodity. The plant branches freely and not only does each branch produce a head or spray of flower buds but when these are plucked at the succulent stage successive crops are borne through a long season. *Cabbage* varies from a loose bunch of green leaves of good vitamin A and C value to a tight head, most of which is nearly colorless and of but little vitamin A value, which however contains a worthwhile amount of vitamin C. *Carrots* contain carotene not masked by chlorophyll so the intensity of the characteristic color is roughly proportionate to the vitamin A value. This has been reported from 2000 to 12000 I.U. per 100 grams, increasing with the growth of the carrot. *Collards* are an important vegetable in the Southern states; but as yet (1950) are not much brought to the Northern markets. They might be described as something midway between green cabbage and kale. *Kale* is a deep green leaf food of high vitamin A value and vitamin

---

* I.U. stands for International Units of vitamin A value. This unit has been defined in Chapter XV.

C content. It is hardy, and rapidly replaces the leaves harvested from it so that it is available fresh throughout the entire year. Its vitamin A value, and its vitamin C and calcium content are all high. Its nutritive values are outstanding and deserve to make it the green leaf food of choice. Its superiority to spinach has been explained in Chapter VIII. Its vitamin A value is of the order of 7,000 to 20,000 International Units per 100 grams. *Turnip greens* are comparable with kale. *Watercress* consists too largely of stem to equal kale and turnip greens, but is very pleasant to eat raw and can be a worthwhile source of calcium, vitamins A and C, and riboflavin. In the famous experiments (described below) of Dr. H. C. C. Mann in which various foods were tried as supplements to the diet of a boys' school, milk stood first and watercress second in outcome.

Citrus Fruits and Tomatoes

Citrus fruits and tomatoes are likely to retain the high esteem they now enjoy as rich and reliable sources of vitamin C, even though we are learning that potatoes, sweetpotatoes, and leaf vegetables can readily be so handled as also to constitute important sources of this vitamin. This is true because we now have good evidence that we derive added benefit from increased intake of vitamin C up to several times the amount which is needed to protect from manifest scurvy. Also these foods are now such well-established staples that there is little danger of disturbingly large fluctuations in market supplies or in cost to consumers.

Other Fruits and Vegetables

Other fruits and vegetables, while not such outstanding sources of individual nutrients, are good all-around contributors to the mineral content and vitamin values as well as to commendable diversification of diet. They also contribute to the body's good intestinal hygiene, and its alkaline reserve for the insurance of neutrality of body fluids and tissues.

Liberal use of a wide range of these other fruits and vegetables usually makes the dietary as a whole both more palatable and nutritionally better-balanced than the American average. We are also advised that a larger consumer demand for these other fruits and vegetables tends to a better-balanced agriculture.

When each of the six food-groups of the preceding paragraphs is studied (preferably in the sequence suggested at the beginning of this chapter) from the point of view of making full use of what it offers, probably each student will find good reasons for giving each of these six food-groups a somewhat larger place in the diet than it is at present generally given in American dietaries. This is partly because our American food habits have hitherto been more or less tradition-bound and partly because today's newer knowledge of nutrition affords us much clearer and fuller guidance to good use of food resources than has ever been available before. And one who now plans a food budget in this way will probably be surprised to find in what a large degree nutritional needs can advantageously be met from the six food-groups which are economically the "direct food crops." Very probably the only nutritional factors seeming to need further attention will be animal protein, calcium, and riboflavin; and of all of these milk is an outstanding source. This is also true of all the staple products of milk except butter.

Milk

Milk (with its products other than butter) thus becomes the logical seventh food-group of the present classification. It stands in a class by itself in the economy and efficiency with which it makes good such low points as may remain when present-day knowledge has been applied to the problem of making full use of the foods of the six preceding groups. For the past forty years the science of nutrition has emphasized in its non-technical teaching, the saying that: "The dietary should be built around bread and milk." This teaching has shown beneficial results in an increased per capita consumption of milk, while at the same time the more recent research has shown still stronger scientific support for such emphasis as in the supplementary relations of milk proteins to those of grains and other seeds, the benefits of liberal amounts of food calcium, and the discovery of the existence and nutritional importance of riboflavin, of which (as of calcium) milk is the largest supplier in typical American dietaries.

According to the official estimates of the U. S. Department of Agriculture, the total supply of milk in the United States in 1948 was 118,300,000,000 pounds. Of this, it was estimated that 44 per cent was used for the factory production of dairy products, so that presumably about half of the milk produced or a little over one pint a day for each person comes into human consumption as fluid milk and cream. Nutritionally it makes little difference whether milk is consumed as such or in such forms as canned or dried milk, ice cream, and cheese. But butter making is apt to involve a large loss to human nutrition of the skimmed milk from butter manufacture. Gradually, however, dried skimmed milk is being brought more fully into human consumption. There should be no interference between a growing use of fresh milk and cream on the one hand and (on the other) milk products other than butter.

With some fluctuations from year to year, the per capita production and consumption of milk in the United States has been increasing for a generation and will probably continue to increase with growing knowledge of the nutritional importance of liberal consumption of milk as such or in the form of its staple products other than butter.

A February 1950 estimate of city consumption of milk and its products other than butter as milk equivalent was $4\frac{1}{2}$ quarts a person a week.*

Dr. H. C. Corry Mann's experiment of 1922–26 with English school boys, is of great interest and significance. Its problem was: Whether a typical English dietary, which had been planned and adopted "with every consideration for the welfare of those to be nourished by it" would be improved by increasing the proportion of what were beginning to be called "protective foods"—milk and green leaf vegetables—and, if so, to what nutrient factor would the improvement be due?

That is, starting from a baseline dietary which was "medically adjudged" to be adequate according to the nutritional knowledge of 1922, could improved results in human nutrition be obtained by simple supplementary feeding guided by the "newer knowledge" then beginning to be suggested by nutritional research?

The subjects of this investigation were English boys living in a village-type boarding school 11 miles from London where 500 to 600 boys between 7 and 11 years of age lived continuously, each boy for 11 to 12 months of each year. This school-village comprised 19 cottages and a central dining hall. Each cottage housed about 30 boys. And the boys of each house had their own dining table.

* U. S. Dept. Agriculture, Food Consumption Surveys of 1948, "Dairy Products in City Diets," Commodity Summary No. 6.

Boys of House No. 1 received the regular diet of the school and served as the direct control group for each of seven other groups as follows:

Each boy of House No. 2 received the regular diet plus a supplement of 1 pint of extra milk a day (388 Calories); those of House No. 3 received essentially the same number of supplementary Calories (350 a day) of sugar; those of House No. 4 received 387 Calories of supplementary butter a day; those of Houses Nos. 5 and 6 each received a supplement of $\frac{1}{2}$ to $\frac{3}{4}$ ounce of watercress daily; those of House No. 7 received a daily supplement of casein, equal to the amount of protein in the pint of extra milk which was fed to each boy of House No. 2; and those of House 8 each received daily 379 Calories of vegetable margarine (vitamin-free fat) a day. With all other conditions very carefully held uniform, the boys receiving the supplement of extra milk did best; and those receiving the watercress, second best.

The discussion in the official report of the experiment is centered mainly upon the effects of the supplementary milk as shown by comparison of the boys receiving it with those of the control group (House No. 1) as well as with the boys in the school as a whole.

The boys receiving the supplement of extra milk made very significantly better gains both in height and weight, and in "fitness" and "spirit."

As the results from Houses Nos. 3, 4, 7 and 8 indicated that the benefit from the milk supplement could not be attributed to carbohydrate, fat, fat-soluble vitamin, or protein, the investigators concluded that the clearly demonstrated superiority of the milk supplement must have been due to "something more specific to the milk." In terms of known nutrients, and in view of the fact that the second best records were made by the boys receiving watercress, the "specific" factor may well have been the combined increments of calcium and riboflavin.

The advantage of increasing the proportion of milk, even in an already adequate diet has also been very conclusively shown in experiments continued throughout entire lives and successive generations of suitable animals of relatively short natural life cycle.

Using rats as experimental animals, the nutrition laboratory of the Columbia University department of chemistry studied the effects of different quantitative proportions of wheat and milk in dietaries which, for the sake of certainty of interpretation, were simplified to consist of these two foods with table salt and distilled water. It was found that five-sixths ground whole wheat with one-sixth dried whole milk (Diet A) made an *adequate* food supply, but that a mixture of two-thirds ground wheat and one-third dried milk (Diet B) was *better*. Compared with those on Diet A, the animals on Diet B showed more rapid and efficient growth and development (corresponding to the freshmen entering college taller yet younger), higher adult vitality, and a longer prime of life. While general attention was attracted by the fact that the adult life expectation or "life cycle" was extended by about ten per cent, it is chiefly worthy of emphasis here that undoubtedly the "health as a positive quality of life" was higher at every age.

In terms of the set-up of the original experiment, the variable factor in the dietary was the quantitative relation of its two major ingredients: wheat, taken as typical of foods furnishing energy at low cost; and milk, as representative of the "protective" foods needed to "balance" the dietary.

Greater prominence of milk in the food supply of the individual, the family, or the nation means enrichment of the diet in its calcium content, and practically always in its riboflavin content and vitamin A value also. And these are among the nutritional factors which we know to possess large areas of beneficial increase above the level of mere adequacy. Thus milk is the food most likely to be effective in meeting the actual need of a deficient diet; and also when the diet is already adequate, milk is the food most likely to be effective in building to higher levels of positive health.

Because, for Americans and Europeans at least, the calcium intake depends chiefly (Fig. 36) upon the consumption of milk in some form (including cheese, cream, and ice cream), and because calcium is probably more often deficient in the dietary than any other chemical element, and certainly falls below *optimal* amount in many present-day dietaries, the explanation of the importance of a liberal use of milk tends to be given largely in terms of calcium. That milk is a highly evolved vehicle for meeting the calcium need in nutrition is further illustrated by the fact that its other constituents are such as to enable it to convey calcium with outstanding efficiency, a quart of milk actually containing more calcium than does a quart of limewater (saturated solution of calcium hydroxide).

CHARACTERISTICS OF FOOD COMMODITIES 331

And it must never be supposed that the calcium tells the whole story. For milk contains all the factors known to be needed in the nutrition of the mammalian species, and in view of the experiments of Osborne and Mendel it doubtless contains also any such essential factors as may be still awaiting discovery. The cases of riboflavin and of vitamin B_{12} have been completed since their work was published. Obviously these recent discoveries confirm the general viewpoint which this discussion as a whole affords.

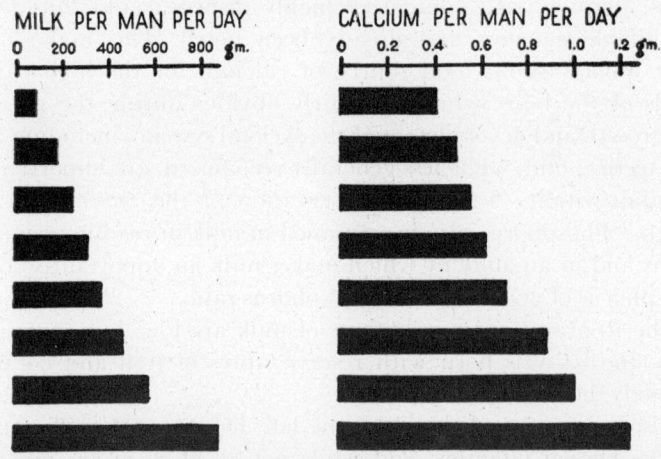

Fig. 36. The relation of milk consumption to the calcium content of the dietary. Here the 224 American dietaries previously mentioned were arranged in order of milk consumed and their calcium contents averaged in eight groups of 28 dietaries each.

Milk is the one article whose sole function in nature is to serve as food, and the one food for which there is no fully satisfactory substitute.

Mrs. Rose wrote*: "No other food can so well serve as the foundation of an adequate diet, because no other reinforces (the diet) at so many points." And again,† "Milk is particularly adapted to offset the total lack of minerals in fats and sugars, and the serious mineral deficiencies of white flour, hominy, polished rice, and other refined cereal products so widely used in American dietaries."

The milk of different species differs somewhat, and some methods of preserving milk may diminish its vitamin C and, perhaps, (in less degree) its thiamine content; but all the generally recognized com-

* *Foundations of Nutrition*, 3rd Ed., p. 389.
† *Ibid.*, p. 391.

mercial forms of milk resemble each other much more closely than does any other food approach milk in nutritional characteristics.

In addition to the outstandingly efficacious amino-acid make-up of its natural mixture of casein and lactalbumin, milk also has other nutritional characteristics which in the long course of mammalian evolution have become fixed, doubtless because of their "survival value" in the promotion of growth and development, health and efficiency.

Its uniquely rich content of highly dispersed and thus readily assimilable calcium has already been noted. This makes it the most advantageous food source of calcium for the high calcium needs of the body which are fairly obvious during the period of the growth and development of the skeletal system (including bones and teeth); and, while less generally recognized, are important also to adult vitality and "the preservation of the characteristics of youth." Phosphorus also is contained in milk in readily assimilable forms and in an amount which makes milk an important source of phosphorus of good calcium: phosphorus ratio.

The iron and copper contents of milk are low, but correspondingly the baby is born with reserve stores of iron and copper in the body, largely in the liver.

Also, as was emphasized by the late Dr. Mendel, milk contains all the known vitamins, and while not all of them are present in milk in as high a proportion as we want them, it is probable that milk contains a larger number of the vitamins in reasonably well-balanced proportion than does any other one food.

While sub-normal levels of vitamins in milk have been produced experimentally, the rations used to induce them are such as are known, if long used, to diminish the productivity of the cow, so that dairy farmers have no desire to use them. Hence in practice few cows are so fed, and those that are do not yield enough milk to have much influence on the quality of the market supply. The modern farmer feeds his milch-cows vitamin-rich rations the year round. Thus milks of sub-normal vitamin value are less common in the market, and commercial winter milk is more like summer milk, than the scientific literature might lead one to expect.

Physical properties of milk have also some nutritional significance: only two of these need be mentioned here. The fact that milk fat is present in an emulsified form makes it more readily assimilable than are most other food fats except those of eggs. The fact that milk coagulates in the stomach is, on the whole, distinctly advantageous to the digestive process, especially when the milk is sipped in the course of the eating of solid foods. But for some (not all) infants and invalids, there may be a slight advantage in the use of milk which forms curds of a more flocculent kind. Such "soft curd milk" is now produced commercially in two ways: (1) by selecting cows whose milk naturally forms curds somewhat "softer" than the average, and marketing the milk of such cows unmixed with that of others; or (2) by treating ordinary market milk with an artificial process which "softens" its curdling property, largely by removing a significant part of its calcium. It is the responsibility of the physician to decide in the individual case whether an infant or an invalid will gain any such advantage from the softening of the curd as to compensate for a reduction in the calcium intake.

Meats, Fish, Poultry, and Eggs

In view of the high dietary place given to meat by most people who can afford it, one who seeks thoroughly to assess the basis and wisdom of the traditional and economic place of meat in American and European food supplies cannot but be strongly impressed by the lack of comprehensive studies carried out by the newer methods of nutritional research. Several papers have been published in which present-day methods have been applied to the answering of particular questions, but we have seen no record of any study of the nutritional place of meat in the diet comparable in comprehensiveness with the investigations which have been made upon milk.

Official statistics* of per capita consumption of foods of the meat group in 1947, the latest year for which full data were available when this was written, are as follows:

Food	Pounds
Beef	69.1
Veal	10.7
Lamb and mutton	5.4
Pork	69.8
Fish (total)	10.8
Chicken	23.6
Turkey	4.5
Eggs	47.4

* Consumption of food in the United States, 1909–48, U. S. Dept. Agriculture, Misc. Publ. No. 691, p. 72 (1949).

Here the total meat—in the sense of beef and veal, lamb and mutton, and pork (including fat cuts but not lard)—was 155.0 pounds for the year; the total of these meats plus fish, 165.8 pounds; of meats, fish, and poultry, 193.9 pounds; and the total of meats, fish, poultry, and eggs, 241.3 pounds.

The 47.4 pounds of eggs may be counted as 25.3 dozens for the year, or an average of just over 6 eggs a week.

In general these statistics show that the high levels of consumption of both meats and eggs reached in the United States in wartime were being maintained in 1947.

Studies made by the United States Department of Agriculture in 1948–49* indicate that in the average family budgets of urban communities about one third of all income goes for food; and that of this about one fourth is spent for meat—24 per cent of the food money, to be exact—with an additional 10 per cent for fish, poultry, and eggs. "The part of the food dollar spent for meat was about the same at all income levels, but the part of the income spent for food varied widely with income—from 74 per cent for families of less than $1000 income to 17 per cent for families with incomes of $7500 and over."

Low-income families ate more meat, both absolutely and relatively, in 1948 than in 1942, while higher-income families ate about the same amounts of meat in these two years. This closer approach of the low-income people to the food habits of their higher-income fellow-citizens is probably more significant psychologically than physiologically, for even the 1942 low-income consumption of protein was already liberal, and the traditional bias toward high consumption of "animal protein" has lost its once-supposed nutritional basis with the discovery of vitamin B_{12}; which is as much a bacterial as an animal product, and is not protein.

When grain products, vegetables, fruits and milk have all been given their full places in the diet, the result is a food supply and dietary of such excellence that the extent to which meats, fats, and sweets are added is of relatively little consequence in normal nutrition.

* Bureau of Human Nutrition and Home Economics 1948–49 U. S. Dept. Agriculture, Commodity Summary No. 1, based on 1948 Food Consumption Surveys.

The appeal which meats, fats, and sweets make to the palate and the sense of satiety is enough more than amply strong in most people so that those of us who enjoy relatively comfortable purchasing power may well think in terms of moderating our consumer demand for these three types of food; in the interest of more equitable distribution. This can be physiologically and psychologically better for all concerned, through avoidance or over-weight and enhancement of a sense of social justice.

This last has (too often in the past) been "shrugged off" with the implication that dietaries differ as a matter of racial or social custom. Now that the importance of nutrition is more widely and keenly appreciated there is need for more frankness in facing the problem how far dietary differences are truly due to different social *choices* and how far they are forced by economic disparities. And in this connection we need fuller knowledge as to *long term* effects of differing levels of consumption of different foods.

Strange as it may seem in view of the large proportion of their food money which American consumers spend for meats, we still await the evidence of controlled laboratory researches in the feeding of experimental animals for entire life cycles.

Meats vary greatly in fatness, but all meats are rich either in fat or in protein, or both.

Tressler, Birdseye, and Murray (1932) have found that the tendering (tenderizing) of quick-frozen meat continues during cold storage. Tenderness of beef as it comes to cooking need not, therefore, involve the inherently expensive grain feeding of the meat animals. Much more economically may these be slaughtered as they come from good pastures and the meat allowed to attain added tenderness while waiting in the commercial or family refrigerator.

As may be seen from Table 29, the proteins of meat are somewhat similar to those of milk and of eggs in their amino acid make-up, and therefore in the efficiency with which they supplement the proteins of bread and cereals.

The different lean meats that have been studied are about equally good sources of riboflavin and apparently also of niacin, while in thiamine pork is richer than beef but perhaps also more variable.

On the other hand, meats contain relatively little of calcium, of

TABLE 29. *Amino Acid Data of Horn, Jones, and Blum: U.S.D.A. Misc. Publ. 696 (1950) Grams Obtained from 100 Grams of Protein in Each Case*

	Argi-nine	Histi-dine	Iso-leucine	Leucine	Lysine	Methio-nine	Phenyl-alanine	Threo-nine	Trypto-phan	Valine
Arachin	13.50	2.16	4.55	7.61	2.72	0.24	6.96	2.89	0.90	4.85
Casein	3.81	2.65	5.63	9.22	8.20	2.58	4.89	4.80	1.20	6.90
Conarachin	16.53	2.05	3.98	6.61	4.69	2.13	4.32	1.93	1.20	3.68
Glycinin	7.94	1.97	5.69	8.07	6.90	1.15	5.82	3.00	1.05	4.56
Lactalbumin	3.42	1.50	6.12	12.90	10.80	1.62	3.59	5.37	1.72	5.82
Ovalbumin	6.03	2.06	7.41	9.43	6.32	4.43	7.17	4.48	1.30	7.54
Ox muscle protein	7.87	1.98	6.50	9.37	10.00	2.75	4.58	5.80	1.30	5.85
Phaseolin (from beans)	5.97	2.24	6.69	10.50	7.20	1.12	8.04	4.16	0.50	6.00
Zein	1.95	0.76	5.03	21.10	0.21	1.41	7.30	2.62	0.03	3.98
Corn, whole, yellow	4.68	2.23	4.39	14.33	2.30	1.44	5.26	3.89	0.48	5.3
Egg, whole dried	8.50	2.30	8.73	12.55	7.88	2.74	7.31	5.91	1.71	6.99
Milk, dry skim	2.81	2.46	6.12	10.35	7.10	2.17	4.54	5.25	1.12	6.93
Oatmeal	7.31	2.20	4.40	7.76	2.96	1.04	4.58	3.60	1.04	5.22
Peanut flour	12.27	2.35	3.42	6.72	2.93	0.82	5.26	3.05	0.88	4.14
Soybean flour	7.79	2.38	4.98	7.49	7.16	0.99	4.76	4.55	1.12	4.90
Whole wheat	4.48	2.03	3.60	5.89	2.50	0.99	4.06	2.97	0.83	4.10
Yeast, dried brewers	4.70	1.62	4.93	6.76	7.28	1.10	3.72	5.28	0.94	5.28

vitamin A, or of vitamin C, so that in these respects they do not serve (as does a combination of milk and fruit) to make good the nutritional shortcomings of the breadstuffs and cereals.

Lean meat is a good source of phosphorus.

The evidence is conflicting as to the quantitative availability of the iron of meat in normal nutrition and in anemia.

The foregoing statements are made with muscle meats chiefly in mind, since the glandular organs can, in the nature of the case, constitute but a small fraction of the general meat supply. So far as it goes, liver (while varying greatly, depending upon how the animal was fed) is apt to contain, weight for weight, more vitamin A than muscle meats. Probably also liver will usually contain more vitamin C than muscle. The varying status of the latter has been discussed in Chapter XI. Waisman and Elvehjem accept Munsell's rating of the vitamin C value of beef muscle as zero, but credit beef liver with about 35 milligrams of vitamin C per 100 grams of fresh tissue. The extents of the diminutions of the different vitamin values in the cooking of different meats by various methods are being studied experimentally in several laboratories.

Notable among the data of Table 29 are: (*a*) the confirmation here of the earlier findings of higher lysine and tryptophane contents in casein and lactalbumin than in most other proteins; (*b*) interestingly, phaseolin, while of low tryptophan content, resembles casein, lactalbumin, and beef and (whole) egg protein, in having a relatively high content of lysine; (*c*) the general similarity of bean and beef protein in their respective amino acid contents.

In future such differences will doubtless be taken increasingly into account in the planning of diets.

Eggs

We do not know the origin of the folk-lore verse to which Hutchison gave currency, characterizing eggs as:

> Treasure houses wherein lie,
> Locked by Nature's alchemy,
> Flesh, and blood, and brain, and bone.

As rich sources of some nutrients of which we do not always get enough, eggs well deserve inclusion among the "protective" foods. But they do not (like fruits, vegetables, and milk) tend to safeguard the hygiene of the intestine and the reserve alkalinity of the blood and tissues; and for these and other reasons most careful students of nutrition tend to keep the egg in about its accustomed quantitative place in the typical American dietary, namely, 4 to 6 eggs per capita a week, while giving a growing place to fruits, vegetables, and milk. Some, however, recommend increasing egg consumption to an average of at least an egg a day per capita. The point of view of agriculture, including that of the subsistence homestead, tends to favor growth of the "poultry enterprise"; and the close interlinking of agricultural, home economic, and social security activities may perhaps be carrying advocacy of increased egg consumption a little further in the name of nutrition than the strictly scientific evidence yet extends as a basis for life-time advice. This is not to be taken as necessarily an argument against giving eggs a higher place in the dietary; but only as suggesting the desirability of getting further long-run experimental evidence before attempting to settle a life-time policy on this point. Much of value might be learned from full-life, successive-generation experiments with dietaries containing different liberal allowances of eggs, fed to laboratory animals whose nutritional chemistry (in respect to the factors of which eggs are important sources) is similar to our own.

In some respects eggs may be regarded as standing midway between meat and milk in nutritional characteristics. Like meats, they have been considerably studied as to particular points; but still need more comprehensive investigation by feeding at different levels throughout entire life cycles of successive generations.

Both the recent food consumption studies by Stiebeling and co-workers, and the earlier series of dietary studies already mentioned, show that eggs occupy strikingly different degrees of prominence in the dietary according to economic conditions. This is also true in other countries. There need be no doubt, we think, that the people whose poverty has kept their egg consumption below what we have called the "typical" American level of 4 or 5 eggs a week per person, will be benefited by having their dietaries brought up to this level.

Egg protein resembles meat and milk protein in nutritional efficiency, and egg-fat is easily digested because of its emulsified form. The mineral contents of eggs are much like those of lean meats.

Eggs are unique among staple foods in their relatively high vitamin D value (though of course a very small amount of a fish liver oil may contain as much vitamin D as does a whole egg). Eggs are also an important dietary source of vitamin A, thiamine, riboflavin and probably other members of the B group of vitamins; but quantitatively these values vary considerably with the feeding of the hen. The vitamin C content of eggs is negligible.

Table 29 brings together the amino acid make-up of typical proteins or natural protein mixtures of eggs, meat, milk, cereals, and legumes.

Fats (including Fatty Oils)

The problem of the proper place of commercial fats in the food supply presents several complications.

For one thing, the demand for fat is (quantitatively speaking) largely a matter of national habit. During 1914–1918 when a concerted effort was being made to ensure adequate food supplies to all the Allied peoples, it was found that a much higher per capita supply of fat was needed for efficiency and morale in the Occidental than in the Oriental countries. For the civilians as well as the soldiers of the European peoples, it was deemed important to provide at least 70 grams (two and one half ounces) of fat per capita per day, while the Oriental peoples felt no need of so much.

People of the Western World want liberal use of fats in cookery to give their foods the flavors, and perhaps even more particularly the textures, to which they have accustomed themselves; and also "fat sticks to the ribs" in the sense that a meal of a given calorie value does not so quickly leave the stomach if a liberal percentage of its calories is in the form of fat. And so, of course, the longer each meal stays in the stomach, the less likely is it that the muscular signals from an empty stomach ("the pangs of hunger") will be felt before the next meal. The problem of specifically essential fatty acids has been discussed in Chapter II.

Sugar and Other Commercial Sweets

In nature the sweetness of the nectar of a flower is quite clearly a bait to secure the visit of the bee and the distribution of the pollen by his agency. The sweetness of the flesh of a fruit guides animals to consume something that contains not only sugar but also significant amounts of mineral elements and vitamins; and in baiting the animal to eat the fruit it also serves the plant by securing distribution of its seeds.

The biological utility of artificially refined sugar is much more circumscribed. Nutritionally it is the extreme case of a one-sided food; for it furnishes calories and nothing else.

The repeated research findings of Bunting and others, that increasing prominence of sugar in the dietary means increasing proportion of tooth defects in children, should not be ignored.

It is probably true for the people as a whole, as was said in a discussion of the problem of sweets for children (published as a leaflet by the American Child Health Association and reprinted by the American Public Health Association in a report of its Committee on Nutritional Problems), "that in general the proper place of sugar in the food supplies and eating habits . . . is not in such concentrated forms as candy, nor in the indiscriminate and excessive sweetening of all kinds of foods, but rather as a preservative and flavor to facilitate the introduction into the . . . dietary of larger amounts of the fruit and the milk, the importance of which to . . . health has been increasingly emphasized with each year's progress in our knowledge of nutrition."

Within a relatively short time (from about 1825 to about 1925) sugar consumption has grown as we saw in Chapter II from about 10 pounds to about 100 pounds per capita per year in the United States, so that now most families take over a tenth, and many take probably as much as a fifth, of their total food calories in the form of sugar which furnishes practically no protein, mineral element, or vitamin. Obviously this must have the nutritional result of lowering the intakes of protein and of the mineral elements and vitamins by one-tenth to one-fifth from the levels at which they would otherwise be consumed. Is this desirable?

EXERCISES

1. Answer the question with which the above text ends, and explain your answer in from 500 to 1000 words.

2. Using such Governmental and sugar trade statistics as are available at the time of your writing, show whether there has been a significant increase or decrease in American per capita consumption of sugar since 1920–25.

3. How do recent advances of knowledge of the differences between the merely adequate and the optimal levels of intake affect your

judgment as to the use of so much "refined" food as was common in the first third of the twentieth century?

SUGGESTED READINGS

Boswell, V. R. 1949 Our vegetable travelers. *National Geographic Magazine* 96, 145–217.

Brenner, S., V. O. Wodlicka, and S. G. Dunlop 1949 Experimentation with dried yeast for use in army rations. *J. Am. Dietet. Assoc.* 25, 409–415.

Briant, A. M., V. E. MacKenzie, and F. Fenton 1946 Vitamin content of frozen peas, green beans and Lima beans, and market-fresh yams prepared in a Navy mess hall. *J. Am. Dietet. Assoc.* 22, 605–610.

British Medical Research Council 1945 Food yeast: A survey of its nutritive value. Med. Res. Counc. War Mem. No. 16 (16 pages); *Nutr. Abs. Rev.* 16, 174–175.

Brush, M. K., W. F. Hinman, and E. G. Halliday 1944 The nutritive value of canned foods. V. Distribution of water-soluble vitamins between solid and liquid portions of canned vegetables and fruits. *J. Nutrition* 28, 131–140.

Bureau of Agricultural Economics 1949 Consumption of food in the United States, 1909–48. *U. S. Dept. Agriculture, Misc. Publ.* No. 691.

Callison, E. C., J. E. Bear, and E. Orent-Keiles 1948 The effect of cooking on some nutrients in soy grits. *J. Am. Dietet. Assoc.* 24, 966–970.

Chang, I. C. L., and H. C. Murray 1949 Biological value of the protein and the mineral, vitamin, and amino acid content of soymilk and curd. *Cereal Chem.* 26, 297–306.

Clark, R. E., and F. O. Van Duyne 1949 Cooking losses, tenderness, palatability and thiamine and riboflavin content of beef as affected by roasting, pressure saucepan cooking, and broiling. *Food Research* 14, 221–230.

Clifcorn, L. E., et al. 1944 The nutritive value of canned foods. I–V. *J. Nutrition* 28, 101–140.

Cover, S., E. M. Dilsaver, and R. M. Hays 1949 Retention of B-vitamins in beef and veal after home cooking and storage. *Food Research* 14, 104–108.

Dawbarn, M. C. 1949 The effects of milling upon the nutritive value of wheaten flour and bread. *Nutr. Abs. Rev.* 18, 691–706.

Eheart, M. S., and M. L. Sholes 1948 Nutritive value of cooked, immature and mature cowpeas (blackeyed peas). *J. Am. Dietet. Assoc.* 24, 769–772.

FAIRBANKS, B. W.   1938   Improving the nutritive value of bread by the addition of dry milk solids. *Cereal Chemistry* **15**, 169–180; *Expt. Sta. Rec.* **80**, 131.

FLYNN, L. M., V. B. WILLIAMS, and A. G. HOGAN   1949   Cracked ice and preservation of stored fruits and vegetables. *Food Research* **14**, 231–240.

GARBER, M., M. M. MARQUETTE, and H. T. PARSONS   1949   The availability of vitamins from yeasts. V. *J. Nutrition* **38**, 225–236.

GEIGER, E.   1947   Experiments with delayed supplementation of incomplete amino acid mixtures. *J. Nutrition* **34**, 97–111.

GORDON, L. E., M. E. BOLLMAN, and M. E. LAMBERT   1949   Trimming losses in large-scale preparation of fresh vegetables. *J. Am. Dietet. Assoc.* **25**, 142–154.

GREWE, E.   1945   Use of peanut flour in baking. *Food Research* **10**, 28–41.

GUERRANT, N. B., O. B. FARDIG, M. G. VAVICH, and H. E. ELLENBERGER   1948   Nutritive value of canned food. Influence of temperature and time of storage on vitamin content. *Ind. Eng. Chem.* **40**, 2258–2263.

HANKINS, O. G., and P. E. HOWE   1946   Estimation of the composition of beef carcasses and cuts. *U. S. Dept. Agriculture, Tech. Bull.* No. 926.

HANNING, F., B. A. SCHICK, and H. J. SEIM   1949   Stability of riboflavin in eggs to cooking and to light. *Food Research* **14**, 203–208.

HARDING, P. L., J. R. WINSTON, and D. F. FISHER   1940   Seasonal changes in Florida oranges. *U. S. Dept. Agriculture, Tech. Bull.* No. 753.

HATHAWAY, I. L., and H. P. DAVIS   1945   Studies on the riboflavin content of cheese. *Nebraska Agr. Expt. Sta. Research Bull.* No. 137.

HAYDAK, M. H., L. S. PALMER, M. C. TANQUARY, and A. E. VIVINO   1942   Vitamin content of honeys. *J. Nutrition* **23**, 581–588.

HAYDEN, F. R., P. H. HEINZE, and B. L. WADE   1948   Vitamin content of snap beans grown in South Carolina. *Food Research* **13**, 143–161.

HINER, R. L., L. L. MADSEN, and O. G. HANKINS   1945   Histological characteristics, tenderness and drip losses of beef in relation to temperature of freezing. *Food Research* **10**, 1–13; *J. Home Econ.* **38**, 51–52.

HUGHES, O.   1940   *Introductory Foods.* (Macmillan).

IRWIN, M. H.   1939   Milk as a food throughout life. *Wisconsin Agr. Expt. Sta. Bull.* 447.

JACKSON, S. H., A. DOHERTY, and V. MALONE   1943   The recovery of the B vitamins in the milling of wheat. *Cereal Chem.* **20,** 551–559.

JENTSCH, M. S., and A. F. MORGAN 1949 Thiamine, riboflavin, and niacin content of walnuts. *Food Research* **14,** 40–53.

JONES, D. B., A. CALDWELL, and K. D. WIDNESS 1948 Comparative growth-promoting values of the proteins of cereal grains. *J. Nutrition* **35,** 639–649.

JUNQUEIRA, P. B., and B. S. SCHWEIGERT 1949 Effect of food supplements on growth, reproduction, and lactation. *J. Am. Dietet. Assoc.* **25,** 46–49.

KIK, M. C., and F. B. LANDINGHAM 1943 The influence of processing on the thiamine, riboflavin, and niacin content of rice. *Cereal Chem.* **20,** 569–572.

KIK, M. C., and R. R. WILLIAMS 1945 The nutritional improvement of white rice. *National Research Council Bull.* No. 112.

KLOSE, A. A., B. HILL, and H. L. FEVOLD 1948 Food value of soybean protein as related to processing. *Food Technol.* **2,** 201–206; *Chem. Abs.* **43,** 1494–1495.

KRAMER, A. 1945 Distribution of proximate and mineral nutrients in the drained and liquid portions of canned vegetables. *J. Am. Dietet. Assoc.* **21,** 354–356.

KUIKEN, K. A., and C. M. LYMAN 1949 Essential amino acid composition of soy bean meals prepared from 20 strains of soy beans. *J. Biol. Chem.* **177,** 29–36.

LANFORD, C. S. 1939 The effect of orange juice on calcium assimilation. *J. Biol. Chem.* **130,** 87–95.

LANFORD, C. S. 1942 Studies of liberal citrus intakes. *J. Nutrition* **23,** 409–416.

LONGENECKER, H. E. 1944 Fats in human nutrition. *J. Am. Dietet. Assoc.* **20,** 83–85.

MACK, P. B. 1949 Comparison of meat and legumes in a controlled feeding program. IV. *J. Am. Dietet. Assoc.* **25,** 848–857.

MANN, H. C. C. 1926 Diets for Boys During the School Age. (Brit.) Med. Res. Council, Spec. Report Series, No. 105. (London: His Majesty's Stationery Office.)

MCCOLLUM, E. V., and N. SIMMONDS 1929 *The Newer Knowledge of Nutrition,* 4th Ed., Chapters II–VII, IX, XXVII, XXX. (Macmillan.)

MCELROY, L. W., D. R. CLANDININ, W. LOBAY, and S. I. PETHYBRIDGE 1949 Nine essential amino acids in pure varieties of wheat, barley, and oats. *J. Nutrition* **37,** 329–336.

MCGUCKEN, F. C., and V. R. GODDARD 1948 Thiamine and riboflavin content of raw and cooked dried apricots. *J. Am. Dietet. Assoc.* **24,** 510–513.

MILLARES, R., and C. R. FELLERS   1948   Amino acid content of chicken. *J. Am. Dietet. Assoc.* **24**, 1057–1061.

MUNSELL, H. E., et al.   1949   Effect of large-scale methods of preparation on the vitamin content of foods. III. Cabbage. *J. Am. Dietet. Assoc.* **25**, 420–426.

MURRAY, H. C.   1948   Vitamin content of field-pea products: retention of thiamine and riboflavin on cooking. *Food Research* **13**, 397–399.

NOBLE, I., and J. GORDON   1949   Thiamine and riboflavin retention in bacon. *J. Am. Dietet. Assoc.* **25**, 130–133.

NOBLE, I., J. GORDON, and L. CATTERSON   1949   Thiamine and riboflavin retention in pork sausages. *J. Am. Dietet. Assoc.* **25**, 50–52; *J. Home Econ.* **41**, 279.

NUTRITION DIVISION   1949   Rice and rice diets. Food and Agriculture Organization of the United Nations, Washington, D. C.

OKEY, R.   1945   Cholesterol content of foods. *J. Am. Dietet. Assoc.* **21**, 341–344.

PAUL, P., B. LOWE, and B. R. McCLURG   1944   Changes in histological structure and palatability of beef during storage. *Food Research* **9**, 221–233; *J. Home Econ.* **37**, 113.

PHIPARD, E. F.   1947   What we eat, and why. *Yearbook of Agriculture*, 1943–47, pages 753–760.

PRESSLY, H.   1948   Influence of cooking on ascorbic acid content of collards. *Food Research* **13**, 491–496; *J. Home Econ.* **41**, 279.

REVIEW   1944   Carotene and ascorbic acid in peppers. *Nutrition Rev.* **2**, 12–13.

REVIEW   1949   Yeast for human and livestock feeding. *Nutrition Rev.* **7**, 86–88.

ROSE, M. S.   1940   *Feeding the Family*, 4th Ed. (Macmillan.)

ROSE, M. S., and E. McC. VAHLTEICH   1938   A review of investigations on the nutritive value of eggs. *J. Am. Dietet. Assoc.* **14**, 593–614.

SARETT, H. P., M. J. BENNETT, T. R. RIGGS, and V. H. CHELDELIN   1946   Thiamine, riboflavin, niacin, pantothenic acid, and ascorbic acid content of restaurant foods. *J. Nutrition* **31**, 755–763.

SCHROEDER, V. M., and D. L. HUSSEMANN   1948   Reconstituted dried whole milk as a beverage. *J. Home Econ.* **40**, 249–250.

SCHWEIGERT, B. S., B. T. GUTHNECK, H. R. KRAYBILL, and D. A. GREENWOOD   1949   The amino acid composition of pork and lamb cuts. *J. Biol. Chem.* **180**, 1077–1083.

SHELFT, B. B., R. M. GRISWOLD, E. TARLOWSKI, and E. G. HALLIDAY   1949   Nutritive value of canned foods: Effect of time and temperature of storage on vitamin content of commercially canned fruits and fruit juices (stored 18 and 24 months). *Ind. Eng. Chem.* **41**, 144–145.

SHERMAN, H. C. 1948 *Food Products,* 4th Ed. (Macmillan.)

SHERMAN, H. C., and C. PEARSON 1942 *Modern Bread from the Viewpoint of Nutrition.* (Macmillan.)

STANLEY, L., and J. A. CLINE 1950 *Foods: Their Selection and Preparation,* New Ed. (Ginn and Co.)

STARE, F. J., and D. M. HEGSTED 1944 The nutritive value of wheat germ, corn germ, and oat proteins. *Federation Proc.* **3**, 120–123.

STEWART, J. J., and A. L. EDWARDS 1948 *Foods: Production, Marketing, Consumption,* 2nd Ed. (Prentice-Hall, Inc.)

STIEBELING, H. K., and E. F. PHIPARD 1939 Diets of families of employed wage earners and clerical workers in cities. *U. S. Dept. Agriculture, Circular No. 507.*

SUTHERLAND, C. K., E. G. HALLIDAY, and W. F. HINMAN 1947 Vitamin retention and acceptability of fresh vegetables cooked by four household methods and by an institutional method. *Food Research* **12**, 496–509.

TRESSLER, D. K. 1945 Nutritive value of frozen foods. *J. Am. Dietet. Assoc.* **21**, 273–276.

TRESSLER, D. K., C. BIRDSEYE, and W. T. MURRAY 1932 Tenderness of meat. I. Determination of relative tenderness of chilled and quick-frozen beef. *Ind. Eng. Chem.* **24**, 242–245; *J. Home Econ.* **24**, 377–378.

TRESSLER, D. K., J. G. WOODRUFF, H. L. HANSON, G. E. VAIL, F. FENTON, and G. H. SULLIVAN 1948 About frozen foods and freezing them: A symposium. *J. Home Econ.* **40**, 233–240.

VAN DUYNE, F. O., J. T. CHASE, J. R. FANSKA, and J. I. SIMPSON 1947 Effect of certain home practices on reduced ascorbic acid content of peas, rhubarb, snap beans, soybeans, and spinach. *Food Research* **12**, 439–448; *J. Home Econ.* **40**, 277.

VAUGHN, W. T. 1940 An introduction to tropical foods. *J. Am. Dietet. Assoc.* **16**, 110–116.

WATT, B. K. 1950 Conserving food values. *J. Am. Dietet. Assoc.* **26**, 106, 108, 110.

WILDER, R. M., and R. R. WILLIAMS 1944 Enrichment of flour and bread: A history of the movement. *National Research Council Bull. No. 110.*

WOOD, A. 1949 The purchase of foods according to specifications. *J. Am. Dietet. Assoc.* **25**, 955–962.

XX

FOOD COSTS AND VALUES: NUTRITIONAL GUIDANCE IN FOOD ECONOMICS

Introductory

We have seen that, as Lord Astor put it, the newer scientific knowledge of nutrition makes the practical problem of food supply a question "not only of enough food, but enough of the *right kinds* of food."

And individual, family, and community food supplies doubtless have been, and still are, responsible for many of the relatively low levels of accomplishment for which in lack of this new knowledge an undue share of blame has in the past been laid upon heredity. However, it was estimated in the U. S. Department of Agriculture Yearbook for 1939, that probably 99 per cent of the people born in this country have heredity good enough to enable them to become productive workers and excellent citizens, but that half of them "do not get enough in the way of dairy products, fruits, and vegetables to enable them" to enjoy the full measure of health and vigor which is potential in their hereditary birthright. In the years since that estimate, the consumption of fruits, vegetables, and milk by low-income families has increased, but a further increase is both desirable and practicable.

The Economic Setting of the Problem of the Best Use of Foods

In the choice of one's food, or in purchasing the food for a family or other group, one usually must observe an economic limitation.

This fact has been implicitly recognized in the foregoing chapters and accompanying Exercises. The present chapter undertakes a somewhat more explicitly economic approach. Also, whereas previous chapters have been written primarily in terms of the individual consumer, this one is chiefly in terms of the family food budget: partly because the majority of readers will presumably spend most of their lives as members of family groups; and partly because in studies and writings on food economics the family is so frequently considered as the consuming unit. To comply with custom in this respect involves no failure of appreciation of the fact that in another aspect the food as it enters the home is still a raw material for processing by the homemaker.

Detailed advice upon the budgeting of incomes would lead beyond the scope of this book. Such problems are treated fully and from broad viewpoints in Andrews' *Economics of the Household* (Second Edition, 1935) and in Rose's *Feeding the Family* (Fourth Edition, 1940).

It is, however, part of the function of this chapter to emphasize the fundamentally important fact that science now finds it possible to do more for health, efficiency, and welfare through nutrition than was previously supposed or even seriously imagined; so that, with nutrition carrying a larger share of the responsibility for making life worth while, it is logical that an increased share of the cost of living should be budgeted for the cost of food.

And, even under difficult economic conditions, it is possible for this to be done, now that nutritional science furnishes clearer guidance to the better use of food.

Statistics show that such lines of expenditure as adornment (other than clothing) and amusement (other than by means of food, clothing, housing, and the automobile) run to very significant proportions even at the lower income levels. Hence the improvement of food economics under the guidance of the science of nutrition may be two-fold: (1) a better distribution of the food money; and (2) often also the allotment to food of a somewhat higher proportion of the total income, or of the total budget for the cost of living. And such a suggestion is not a proposal to diminish the few pleasures of the poor. Rather, it helps them to gain their greatest satisfactions.

For the satisfaction derived from such higher accomplishment as is made possible by higher health and efficiency exceeds the pleasure of mere consumption of goods; and in most families it is in turn exceeded by the contemplation of still higher health, efficiency, and accomplishment in and by the children who get the benefit of the newer knowledge of nutrition more completely and from an earlier age than did their parents.

Whatever the income, then, much depends upon the individual consumer's choice and use of food. For the full development of the subject with calculations and many actual meal plans for different types of people and for family groups, see Rose's *Feeding the Family* and *Laboratory Handbook for Dietetics,* the latter rewritten by Taylor and MacLeod (1949).

In the governmental study of family food consumption in the United States in 1942, ten per cent of the total expenditure for food was for fats. In the more intensive study (1948-49) of fat consumption by city families, only seven per cent of the total expenditure for food was reported as spent for fats. This difference was probably largely due to a more frequent inclusion of bacon and salt pork with fats in the survey made in 1942 than in that made in 1948. But it is also interesting to remember that all the families studied in 1948 lived in cities, where the markets offer a large range of fresh meats and fresh fruits to compete with butter for the consumer's food money throughout the year. Probably, too, the war-boom conditions of exceptionally full employment and high wages may have made more families feel able to buy butter liberally in 1942 than in 1948.

United States Food Consumption Surveys of 1948

At the time this is written in 1950, the Bureau of Human Nutrition and Home Economics of the U. S. Department of Agriculture is publishing a series of mimeographed reports upon the costs and nutritive values of presumably normal food supplies of American families classified and compared as to family composition, income, season of year, region of residence, and whether rural or urban.

Economy of Preservation and Distribution of Food

Preservation of a food in different forms may be important both economically and as diversifying the diet. Regions remote from fresh-milk markets can often ship canned and dried milk. Nutritionally equivalent amounts of different forms of milk are shown in Table 30.

TABLE 30. *Approximate Equivalents of One Quart of Fresh Whole Milk*

17 oz. (by weight) of evaporated milk
4 oz. dried whole milk
3 oz. dried skimmed milk + 1 oz. butter
5 oz. Cheddar type cheese
12 large dips (nearly 2 quarts) ice cream

This Table 30 is from Miscellaneous Publication No. 662, U. S. Department of Agriculture, December 1948, where the quantity given for each named milk product is stated to be "about equal in calcium to 1 quart of milk." A few explanatory facts will make this statement of approximate equivalents more explicit:

In the preparation of evaporated or dried milk there is no separation of constituents except removal of most of the water originally present in the whole fresh milk, and relatively slight diminution of some of the vitamin values.

Modern methods of removal of so much of the water from milk as to leave it in the form of powder (or flakes) of only about 2 per cent moisture content, may accomplish this with no measurable diminution of any of the nutrient factors of the milk.

In the preparation of evaporated milk the object is the same except that removal of water is not carried so far. The aim is a concentrated form of milk which can be restored to the composition of the original fresh whole milk. This ideal is very nearly realized, the known effects upon nutrients being only doubtfully measured diminutions of the thiamine and vitamin C (ascorbic acid) contents.

Pasteurization of milk probably lowers its vitamin C content about one-fifth. This is so near the limit of demonstrability, and our dependence upon milk for vitamin C is nowadays normally so slight that nutritionists commonly ignore it and make no distinction between raw and pasteurized milk in dietary calculations. Long-term feeding experiments with children in Great Britain and in the United States have revealed no nutritional difference between those given raw, and those given pasteurized milk.

Returning to the above-tabulated equivalencies between milk and some of its staple products, it may be noted that the comparison of milk with cheese or ice cream is somewhat less logical than with dried and evaporated milks, because in cheesemaking a part of the nutrients of the milk are lost in the whey, and in making ice cream the nutrients are diluted with sugar and other flavoring materials (and sometimes with fruit or nuts) and then there is also incorporated a considerable (and variable) proportion of air which increases the volume without appreciably changing the weight. This is why so many "dips" of ice cream are required to be equivalent to a quart of milk.

In the government tabulation of equivalencies, so striking a difference is attributed to the two chief forms of cheese (because the comparison is on the basis of calcium contents and in cheesemaking coagulation with rennet retains most of the milk-calcium in the cheese whereas, on souring, much the largest part of the milk-calcium is lost in the whey) that we omit cottage cheese from Table 30. If the comparison were made on the basis of protein or riboflavin (instead of calcium) content, it would be much more favorable to cottage cheese than it is. Calcium is, however, the more logical basis in the sense that our dietaries tend "automatically" to carry much larger margins of protein than of calcium.

Economic Problem of Food Supply

One way of putting the problem of the best use of food is to ask the question: Just what prominence is, or should be, given to each food (or type of food, or food-group) in the dietary of a given individual or family, or in a community or national food supply? What has been and is the custom of typical American families in this respect? Dietary studies designed to answer this question have been made in large numbers of American families, (though not at regular intervals) throughout the first half of the twentieth century. A series of 224 such studies widely distributed as to time, place, and economic levels yielded the average data shown in Table 31.

It is believed that these findings are fairly representative of the food habits of the people of the United States, in the last tenth of the 19th and the first third of the 20th centuries.

Correspondingly it is believed that a comparison of the data of Table 31 (first quarter of the twentieth century) with those of Table 28 (data of 1942) show the trend of the first generation of the people of the United States to whom was available the guidance of the earlier phases of the newer knowledge of nutrition.

With fuller knowledge, and more widespread and wholehearted educational effort, we may hope for further increase of prominence of fruits, vegetables, and milk in our national diet.

TABLE 31. *Average Percentage Distribution of Cost and Nutrients in 224 American Dietaries*

Type of Food	Relative Cost	Calories	Protein	Phosphorus	Calcium	Iron
Meat and fish	32.19	18.99	35.34	26.36	3.86	30.37
Eggs	5.47	1.77	4.64	4.02	3.64	6.25
Milk and cheese	10.59	8.08	11.56	20.61	55.76	5.11
Butter and other fats	9.55	10.32	0.31	0.32	0.73	0.33
Grain products	18.29	38.20	37.25	30.27	15.67	25.87
Sugar and molasses	4.57	10.06	0.14	0.20	1.81	1.80
Vegetables	10.55	9.05	9.55	15.58	14.87	26.42
Fruit	5.31	2.99	0.78	1.82	3.15	3.29
Nuts	0.15	0.14	0.11	0.13	0.07	0.09
Food adjuncts	3.33	0.40	0.32	0.69	0.44	0.47

The average food value per man per day of the dietaries summarized in Table 31 was calculated as follows:

Energy	3256.	Calories
Protein	106.	Grams
Phosphorus	1.63	Grams
Calcium	0.74	Gram
Iron	0.0179	Gram

Comparing our consumption of nutrients with the amounts required for normal nutrition (as summarized in previous chapters) it will be seen that the freely chosen dietaries contained in the average a more liberal surplus of protein, phosphorus, and iron than of calcium. Correspondingly, we find that the number of individual family dietaries deficient in calcium is high enough to cause serious concern, while the cases of deficiency of phosphorus or iron were considerably less frequent and there were few if any cases showing an actual deficiency of protein in otherwise adequate diets.

Based apparently upon a recommendation originally made by

Miss Lucy Gillett, the following simple food budget for city families has been widely quoted and found useful:

Divide your food money into fifths—
One fifth, more or less, for vegetables and fruit;
One fifth, or more, for milk, cream, ice cream, and cheese;
One fifth, or less, for meats, fish, poultry and eggs;
One fifth, more or less, for bread and cereals;
One fifth, or less, for fats, sugar, and other groceries and food adjuncts.

The suggestion that about a fifth of the total food money be spent for bread and cereals aims at making a dietary more economical than the American average. In practice, the proportion spent for bread and cereals may (and usually does) vary with the need for strict economy. It must usually be high in an extremely low-cost dietary and may be considerably lower where the level of expenditure is more liberal.

Whatever the level of expenditure, however, it seems wise to observe the two suggestions that:

(1) at least as much should be spent for milk (including cream and cheese if used) as for meats, poultry, and fish; and

(2) at least as much should be spent for fruits and vegetables as for meats, poultry, and fish.

These latter suggestions seem to have been found useful as a guide in both low-cost and liberal-cost food budgets and can obviously be applied in all cases in which even the simplest of records of expenditures are kept. They tend to make milk, vegetables, and fruits more prominent than in the average American dietary of the present or of the recent past, and we have several scientifically sound reasons for considering this a nutritional improvement.

From among the dietary records averaged in Table 31, 25 were taken at random and a calculation was made to see how their nutritive values would have been affected if, with no change in the amount of money spent or in the kinds of foods selected, the quantities of the different food groups had been simply readjusted in accordance with the two suggestions just given. It was found that such readjustment would leave the protein practically unchanged in amount while the calories and iron would be slightly increased and the calcium and phosphorus materially increased and brought into better quantitative relations with each other.

Furthermore, the dietaries thus adjusted would undoubtedly be improved in their vitamin A and C values, and in their riboflavin contents. And these three vitamins play such important parts in the building of the higher health that increased amounts of them in the diet mean an important gain in the constructive up-building of positive health and earning power.

That progress in this direction is already taking place, gradually but upon a large scale, is shown both by the United States Department of Agriculture's statistics of production, consumption, and railway transportation of different types of food, and by widespread studies of food habits.

The term *protective foods* was coined by McCollum and (as already noted) first applied only to milk and the green leaf vegetables, as being the two types of food rich in both the two factors, calcium and vitamin A value, which he had come to regard as most often deficient in the dietaries of American and European peoples.

The research findings of more recent years have extended this conception in two ways. We have come to realize that enrichment of the dietary in vitamin C and riboflavin, as well as in vitamin A and calcium, is usually beneficial; and this not merely for protection against actual deficiency, but also for the promotion or enhancement of vitality,—of "positive," or "buoyant," or better-than-average, health. Thus the idea has, perhaps, already outgrown the literal meaning of the word "protective"; but the term continues to do service with an enlarged and more constructive significance.

In this sense, and with the objective broadened to include the enrichment of the diet in the four factors,—calcium, riboflavin, and vitamins A and C,—we now apply the term protective foods to fruit, vegetables, and milk, with or without eggs.* Milk furnishes all four of the chemical factors just mentioned and is an outstanding source of three of them; while each of the other three types of food just mentioned is regarded as a good source of some two of the four factors. The richness of eggs in vitamin A and riboflavin fully entitles them to admission to this category according to this latter

* A widening of the term *protective foods* to include meat also has been proposed; but at the time of writing (1950) it is too early to judge whether this redefinition of the term will come into general use or not. Whole grain and "enriched" cereal products have also been "nominated" for inclusion in the "protective" group of foods. Perhaps the best plan is to discontinue the use of the term "protective" foods as being not sufficiently explicit to be satisfactory.

criterion, and the vitamin D and iron content of eggs and the high nutritive value of their proteins are all nutritional assets, especially for the growing child; but eggs do not, like fruits, vegetables, and milk, have the property of reducing intestinal putrefaction and promoting the development of a wholesome bacterial flora in the digestive tract. For this and some other reasons eggs are more cautiously emphasized, while of milk, fruit, and vegetables we now believe that (within reason) the larger the proportion of the needed calories taken in the forms of fruit, vegetables, and milk the better.

There has for some years been a steady and well-justified trend toward higher nutritional appreciation of the fruits and vegetables; and this trend continues. Hence it is an expression of the consensus of nutritional findings and opinion (and not merely, though also, of the judgment of the present writers) that we recommend for fruits and vegetables a still greater prominence in the dietary (or food budget) than is found in most previous books and bulletins.

Stiebeling's studies of food consumption at different economic levels show that as purchasing power rises from levels of severe poverty to those permitting more freedom in the choice of food, there is at first an increase in fruit and vegetable consumption fully proportionate to the increased per capita expenditure for food. But with still more comfortable levels of expenditure the extra food money does not go as largely to increased consumption of fruits and of succulent vegetables as would be desirable. In other words the consumer demand represented by the nation-wide data of about 1933–37 is responsive to, but not yet fully abreast of, the guidance of modern knowledge. Consumers still are too apt to think that about two pounds a day of fruits and vegetables is as much as they are justified in eating, whereas our present nutritional viewpoint is that certainly a third pound of per capita consumption of total fruits and vegetables (and very probably more) is an excellent investment.

Prominence of milk, fruits, and vegetables in the dietary ensures liberal intakes of calcium, riboflavin, and vitamins A and C; and, perhaps in somewhat less prominent but still important degree, of phosphorus, iron, thiamine, and niacin. If all white bread is *enriched* the intake of iron, thiamine, and niacin is further enhanced.

With all the breadstuffs and cereals enriched or whole-grain and with fruits, vegetables, and milk (including cheese, cream, and ice cream) given due prominence in the dietary, the newer knowledge of nutrition comes effectively into the service of the family food economy.

Stiebeling and Phipard (1939), in the general summary of their findings from the study of about 4000 family food-consumption records representing 43 cities or towns in eight major geographical regions of the United States during the period December 1934 to February 1937, point out that the *average* dietaries of this period (while already showing some effects of the teachings of the newer knowledge of nutrition) included only one-half to two-thirds as much milk and less than two-thirds as much of fruits and vegetables as did the dietaries which they graded as good, and add: "But even these *good* diets fell short of the allowances of these protective foods believed by many authorities to be optimal."

Most of these 4000 families spent between 25 and 40 per cent of their income for food. On the average, those having more money to spend for food increased their purchases of milk, butter, cream, eggs, meats, fruits, and succulent vegetables in greater degree than their purchases of grain products, sugars, and fats other than butter. Thus when total food expenditure was 200 per cent higher, that for fruits was 200 to 400 per cent higher but that for grain products and fats other than butter was only about 30 to 35 per cent higher.

Thus the newer knowledge of nutrition does not suggest any serious departure from the natural inclinations of present-day American consumers: rather it offers guidance and "implementation" for the realization of the fullest measure of satisfaction from a movement in the direction in which most consumers already wanted to go.

But for even a reasonable approach to best results the teaching of greater prominence of fruits, vegetables, and milk (including cheese, cream, and ice cream) in our dietaries and food supplies should be emphasized and practiced in higher degree than now.

Stiebeling and Phipard find that in every region studied families spending only small amounts of money for food use only small quantities of milk. And in the average of all the white families studied, while one-fourth to one-third of the food money was spent for meat, fish, poultry, and eggs, only one-fifth to one-fourth was spent for fruits and vegetables, and only one-eighth to one-sixth for milk and cheese. (The negro family food budgets showed still less appreciation of fruits, vegetables, and milk.)

Progress in the direction of giving higher place in the dietary to fruits, vegetables, and milk is (up until 1950, at any rate) more evident in the feeding of children than of grown people.

TABLE 32. *Rose's Recommendations (Adapted)*

	Percentage of Total Calories from Fruits, Vegetables, and Milk
For Children	
1– 2 years	70–85
2– 3 "	65–72
3– 4 "	62–69
4– 5 "	59–68
6– 7 "	54–60
8– 9 "	53–58
10–12 "	51–56
For High-School Boys and Girls	
at 2000 Calories	48–53
" 2500 "	42–45
For Healthy Adults on Low to Moderate Incomes	28–30
For a Family of 2 Adults and 3 Young Children on Low to Moderate Income	37–42

The data of Table 32 were adapted with the approval of the late Dr. Mary S. Rose from her teaching of "working plans for the construction of adequate diets."

Table 33 shows the "distribution standards" for children's dietaries recommended by Dr. Rose and Table 34 a differentiation according to economic level.

Table 34 shows corresponding distribution standards to guide the planning of minimum cost and moderate cost dietaries, respectively, for children of ages 5 to 16 years. The minimum-cost standard is based on the recommendations of the Committee on Economic Standards of the New York Nutrition Council. The moderate-cost standards are those used by Rose and Gray in judging the dietaries of child-caring institutions.

For family groups Stiebeling's "dietaries at four levels of cost" and supplementary suggestions will afford much additional guidance. An independent discussion based essentially upon them has also been published by Hambidge. (See suggested readings at the end of the chapter.)

TABLE 33. *Distribution of Calories in Diets of Children of 4 to 12 Years*

Per Cent of Total Calories from Each Class of Food

Age in Years	Foods from Cereal Grains	Milk	Vegetables and Fruits	Fats[a]	Sugars and Sweets	Eggs, Cheese, Meat, and Other Flesh Foods
4–5	23–25	45–50	14–18	5–8	2–5	5–6
5–6	23–25	45–50	14–18	5–8	2–5	5–6
6–7	20–25	40–45	14–15	10–12	3–4	4–5
8–9	20–25	38–42	15–16	12–13	4–6	5–6
10–12	20–25	34–38	17–18	13–14	6–8	7–8

[a] At least part of the fat to be butter or something known to furnish its equivalent of vitamin A.

TABLE 34. *Distribution of Calories in Diets of Minimum and of Moderate Cost for Children of Ages 5 to 16 Years*

Food Group	Minimum-Cost Diet Per Cent of Total Calories	Moderate-Cost Diet Per Cent of Total Calorie
I. Foods from cereal grains	37	24
II. Milk	22	32
III. Vegetables and fruits		
A. Dried legumes	3	1
B. Other vegetables and fruits	13	16
IV. Fats and oils	14	12
V. Sugars and sweets	5	7
VI. Meat, eggs, cheese	6	8

Omitting the emergency diet, Stiebeling and Ward's recommendations were as shown in Table 35.

McCollum's recommendation for milk consumption is one quart per capita per day. Inasmuch as new research findings, since 1933 when the recommendations of Stiebeling and Ward were published, tend strongly to raise the estimate of optimal intake of calcium and riboflavin, we believe that this is a sound reason for preferring 365 quarts rather than 305 quarts of milk per capita per year.

Also we believe that the trend of advance of nutritional knowledge since 1933 makes it logical to give an even more prominent place to fruits and vegetables in the dietary than is given in the Stiebeling and Ward recommendations.

We may repeat here the recommendation: (1) that at least half the total calories be taken in the form of fruit, vegetables, and milk (including cheese, cream, and ice cream); and (2) that at least half the cereals and breadstuffs consumed be in approximately whole-grain forms, with all white bread enriched.

TABLE. 35. *Yearly per Capita Consumption of Foods at Different Economic Levels as Recommended by Stiebeling and Ward*

Food		Adequate Diet at Minimum Cost	Adequate Diet at Moderate Cost	Liberal Diet
Milk[a]	quarts	260	305	305
Potatoes, sweetpotatoes	lbs.	165	165	155
Dried beans, peas, nuts	"	30	20	7
Tomatoes, citrus fruits	"	50	90	110
Leafy, green, and yellow vegetables	"	80	100	135
Dried fruits	"	20	25	20
Other fruits and vegetables	"	85	210	325
Flour, cereals	"	224	160	100
Fats[b]	"	49	52	52
Sugars	"	35	60	60
Meats, poultry, fish	"	60	100	165
Eggs	dozens	15	15	30

[a] Including such milk products as share its essential nutritional characteristics. The approximate equivalents are given in Table 30.

[b] In the data of this table, bacon and fat pork are included under Fats and not under Meats.

Food Budgets as Guided by Nutritional Knowledge

The Bureau of Human Nutrition and Home Economics has prepared, and the Department of Agriculture has issued as its Miscellaneous Publication No. 662, a booklet entitled, "Helping Families Plan Food Budgets."*

The following excerpts from it are appropriate to our present discussion.

* For sale by the Superintendent of Documents, U. S. Government Printing Office, Washington 25, D. C. Price, 15 cents.

Gauging a Family's Nutritional Needs

To measure the nutrients needed by a given family, account must be taken at all age levels of the size and activity of each member. The dietary allowances for children are based on average needs for the middle year in each age group. They are for children of normal activity and average weight and height. If, however, children vary considerably from average weight and height for their age, the quantities in the next higher or lower age group may be more suitable.

For adults, the recommended dietary allowances are based on the needs of a 154-pound man and a 123-pound woman, both of average height. Men and women considerably above or below the average in stature may have a higher or lower calorie requirement. Since many adults think of themselves as more active than they really are, the following illustrations of activity are given:

"Sedentary" persons do office work, clerking in a store, or housekeeping for a small family—the kind of work that calls for comparatively little muscular effort.

"Active" men do work like carpentering, ordinary farm labor, or factory work. *"Moderately active" women* do work such as waiting on tables or housekeeping for a moderate-sized family.

Men at "heavy work" spend 8 hours or more a day at such work as lumbering, ditch digging, or heavy farm labor. *"Very active" women* do work such as heavy housework at least 8 hours a day.

A person's activities apart from his job are also important. For example, a man who walks to and from work and spends several hours working in a garden or around the house may be in the active classification even though his job is considered sedentary.

The energy needs of many persons will fall midway between two of the classifications.

Master Food Plans

The nutrients for an adequate diet can be provided by many different combinations of food. Three master plans for meeting the requirements, two at low cost and one at moderate cost, are given in Tables 37, 38 and 39. In these plans the recommended dietary allowances* are translated into terms of food. Foods are classified in 11 groups and the quantities needed weekly are given for persons

---

* Given in full in Table 42, Appendix.

TABLE 36. *Food Groups and Approximate Number of Servings per Person, Low-cost and Moderate-cost Plans*

Food Groups[a]	Number of Servings per Person Low-cost Plan (Table 37)	Moderate-cost Plan (Table 38)
Leafy, green, and yellow vegetables	7 to 9 servings a week	10 to 12 servings a week
Citrus fruit, tomatoes	Children, 7 servings a week Pregnant and nursing women, 9 to 12 servings a week. Other adults, 6 or 7 servings a week.	Children, 8 to 9 servings a week. Pregnant and nursing women, 12 to 15 servings a week. Other adults, 7 to 9 servings a week.
Potatoes, sweetpotatoes	10 to 12 servings a week	7 to 9 servings a week.
Other vegetables and fruit	7 servings a week	10 to 12 servings a week.
Milk, cheese, ice cream (In terms of fluid milk)	Children, about 3½ cups of milk a day Pregnant women, a little more than 1 quart daily Nursing women, 1½ quarts a day. Other adults, 2½ to 3 cups a day.	Children, 3½ to 4 cups milk a day. Pregnant women, a little more than 1 quart daily. Nursing women, 1½ quarts a day. Other adults, 2½ to 3 cups a day.
Meat, poultry, fish	5 or 6 servings a week	7 or 8 servings a week.
Eggs	5 eggs a week	7 eggs a week.
Dry beans and peas, nuts	2 to 4 servings a week	1 to 2 servings a week.
Flour, cereal, baked goods (Whole-grain, enriched, restored)	Bread at every meal and also a cereal dish once a day.	At every meal.
Fats, oils	Throughout the week as desired. Butter or margarine daily.	Throughout the week as desired. Butter or margarine daily.
Sugar, sirup, preserves	Throughout the week as desired.	Throughout the week as desired.

[a] In addition to the foods in the 11 groups, fish-liver oil or some other source of vitamin D should be allowed for small children, pregnant and nursing women, also for older children and adults who have little opportunity for being in sunshine.

There are also certain miscellaneous food items to be considered in the total food plan. The miscellaneous group includes such items as coffee, tea, cocoa, chocolate; salt, pepper, other seasonings, and flavorings; baking powder and soda; prepared puddings and gelatin. No quantities are suggested for these items but allowance is made for their cost.

in each of 19 age, sex, and activity groups. From these, plans for families of different sizes and composition can easily be made.

These plans are flexible enough to fit various seasons, places, and family tastes, as well as to provide variety in meals from day to day and week to week. Tables 37 and 39 are for low cost and Table 38 for moderate cost.

Food Quantities in Terms of Servings

In planning menus based on food-group quantities, it is helpful to have the suggested pounds and quarts of foods translated into approximate numbers of servings. This is done in Table 36.

Selecting the Plan to Fit the Budget

Before families can decide whether to use the low-cost or the moderate-cost food plan, they will need to know about how much money is needed for each. They must also consider food cost in relation to their total budget. . . . Studies show that on the average, with a higher income, more dollars but a smaller percentage of income goes for food. With equal incomes, large families spend more for food per family but less per person than do small families. The actual cost to a family of the food in these plans depends on a number of things—current prices, the community in which the family lives, and whether the family buys in quantity, shops around for bargains, or produces some food at home. For families who must buy all of their food, the weekly cost of the foods in these plans is about as follows at September 1948 city food price levels:

Family Members	Low-cost Plan[a]	Moderate-cost Plan
Family of 2 persons (active man, sedentary woman)	$11 to $13	$15 to $17
Family of 4 persons (active man, moderately active woman, children 7–9 and 10–12 years)	18 to 20	25 to 27
Family of 4 persons with young children (active man, moderately active woman, and children 1–3 years and 4–6 years)	15 to 17	21 to 23
Family of 6 persons (active man, moderately active woman, boy 16–20 years, girl 13–15 years, and children 7–9 and 10–12 years)	28 to 31	39 to 42

[a] See also Table 39 for an additional low-cost plan.

TABLE 37. *Master Food Plan at Low Cost. Weekly Quantities of Food (as Purchased) for 19 Age, Sex, and Activity Groups*

Family Members	Leafy, Green, and Yellow Vegetables	Citrus Fruit, Tomatoes	Potatoes, Sweet-potatoes	Other Vegetables and Fruit	Milk[a]	Meat, Poultry, Fish	Eggs	Dry Beans and Peas, Nuts	Flour, Cereals[b]	Fats and Oils[c]	Sugar, Sirups, Preserves
	lb. oz.	lb. oz.	lb. oz.	lb. oz.	qt.	lb. oz.	No.	lb. oz.	lb. oz.	lb. oz.	lb. oz.
Children through 12 years:											
9–12 months	1— 8	1—12	0— 8	1— 0	6	0— 4	5	0— 1	0—10	0— 1	0— 1
1–3 years	1—12	1—12	1— 0	1— 0	5½	[d]0— 8	5	0— 1	1— 4	0— 1	0— 2
4–6 years	1—12	1—12	1— 8	1— 4	5½	1— 8	5	0— 2	1—12	0— 6	0— 6
7–9 years	2— 0	2— 0	2— 8	1— 8	5½	1— 8	5	0— 4	2— 4	0— 8	0—10
10–12 years	2— 4	2— 4	3— 0	1—12	6	1—12	5	0— 4	3— 4	0—12	0—12
Girls:											
13–15 years	2— 4	2— 4	3— 4	1—12	6½	[d]2— 0	5	0— 4	3— 8	0—12	0—12
16–20 years	2— 4	2— 4	3— 0	1—12	5	[d]2— 0	5	0— 4	3— 4	0—12	0—10
Boys:											
13–15 years	2— 8	2— 8	4— 0	2— 4	6½	2— 0	5	0— 8	4— 8	1— 0	0—14
16–20 years	2—12	2— 8	5— 0	2— 8	6½	2— 0	5	0— 8	5—12	1— 6	1— 0
Women:											
Sedentary	2— 4	2— 0	2— 4	1—12	5	2— 0	5	0— 4	2— 0	0—10	0—10
Moderately active	2— 4	2— 0	3— 0	1—12	5	2— 0	5	0— 4	3— 4	0—12	0—12
Very active	2— 8	2— 8	4— 0	2— 0	5	2— 0	5	0— 6	4— 8	1— 0	1— 0
Pregnant	3— 0	2—12	2— 8	2— 4	7½	[d]2— 4	7	0— 4	2— 8	0—10	0— 8
Nursing	3— 8	3—12	4— 0	2— 4	10½	[d]2— 8	7	0— 4	3— 0	0—10	0— 8
60 years or over[e]	2— 8	2— 4	2— 8	1—12	5	2— 0	4	0— 2	2— 4	0— 8	0— 8
Men:											
Sedentary	2— 4	2— 0	3— 0	1—12	5	2— 0	5	0— 4	3— 4	0—12	0—12
Physically active	2— 8	2— 8	4— 0	2— 0	5	2— 0	5	0— 6	4— 4	1— 0	1— 0
With heavy work	2— 8	2— 8	6— 0	2— 8	5	2— 0	5	0—10	7—12	1—14	1— 0
60 years or over[e]	2— 8	2— 4	3— 4	1—12	5	2— 0	4	0— 2	3— 4	0—10	0—10

[a] Or its equivalent in cheese, evaporated milk, or dry milk. (See Table 30.)
[b] Count 1½ pounds of bread as 1 pound of flour. Use as much of this as possible in the form of whole-grain, enriched, or restored products.
[c] For small children and pregnant and nursing women, cod-liver oil or some other source of vitamin D is also needed. For elderly persons and for persons who have no opportunity for exposure to clear sunshine, a small amount of vitamin D is also desirable.
[d] To meet iron allowance, 1 large or 2 small servings of liver or other organ meats should be served each week.
[e] The nutritive content of the weekly food quantities for a man and a woman 60 years or over were based on the National Research Council's recommended daily allowances for the sedentary man and woman.

TABLE 38. *Master Food Plan at Moderate Cost. Weekly Quantities of Food (as Purchased) for 19 Age, Sex, and Activity Groups*

Family Members	Leafy, Green, and Yellow Vegetables	Citrus Fruit, Tomatoes	Potatoes, Sweet-potatoes	Other Vegetables and Fruit	Milk[a]	Meat, Poultry, Fish	Eggs	Dry Beans and Peas, Nuts	Flour, Cereals[b]	Fats and Oils	Sugar, Syrups, Preserves
	lb. oz.	lb. oz.	lb. oz.	lb. oz.	qt.	lb. oz.	No.	lb. oz.	lb. oz.	lb. oz.	lb. oz.
Children through 12 years:											
9–12 months	1— 8	1—12	0— 8	1—12	6	0— 4	5	0— 1	0—10	0— 1	0— 1
1–3 years	2— 4	2— 0	1— 8	1—12	6	0— 4	6	0— 1	1— 4	0— 2	0— 2
4–6 years	2— 4	2— 4	1— 8	2— 4	6	a0—12	7	0— 1	1— 8	0— 6	0— 8
7–9 years	2— 8	2— 8	1—12	2— 8	6½	1— 4	7	0— 2	2— 0	0— 8	0—12
10–12 years	3— 0	2—12	2— 4	2— 8	7	1— 4	7	0— 2	2—12	0—12	0—14
Girls:											
13–15 years	3— 8	2—12	2— 8	3— 8	7	a2—12	7	0— 2	2—12	0—14	0—14
16–20 years	3— 8	2—12	2— 8	3— 8	6	a2—12	7	0— 2	2— 8	0—12	0—14
Boys:											
13–15 years	3— 8	3— 0	3— 8	3— 8	7	3— 0	7	0— 4	4— 0	1— 2	1— 2
16–20 years	4— 0	3— 8	4— 8	3— 8	7	3— 4	7	0— 6	5— 4	1— 6	1— 4
Women:											
Sedentary	3— 4	2— 8	1—12	3— 4	5	2— 8	7	0— 1	1—12	0—10	0—12
Moderately active	3— 8	2—12	2— 8	3—12	5	2—12	7	0— 2	2— 8	0—14	0—14
Very active	3—12	3— 0	3— 4	4— 0	5	3— 0	7	0— 2	3— 4	1— 0	1— 0
Pregnant	4— 0	3— 8	2— 4	4— 0	7½	d3— 0	7	0— 2	2— 4	1—10	0—10
Nursing	4— 0	4— 8	2— 0	4— 0	10½	d3— 0	7	0— 1	2— 8	0—12	0—12
60 years or over[e]	3— 8	2—12	2— 0	3— 0	5½	2— 8	6	0— 1	1—12	0— 8	0—10
Men:											
Sedentary	3— 8	2— 8	3— 4	3— 8	5	2—12	7	0— 2	2— 8	0—14	0—14
Physically active	3—12	3— 0	3— 4	4— 0	5	3— 0	7	0— 2	3—12	1— 2	1— 2
With heavy work	4— 0	3— 8	5— 0	4— 0	5	3— 8	7	0— 6	7— 0	2— 0	1— 4
60 years or over[e]	3— 8	2—12	2—12	3— 4	5½	2—12	6	0— 2	2— 8	0—12	0—12

[a] Or its equivalent in cheese, evaporated milk, or dry milk. (See Table 30.)
[b] Count 1½ pounds of bread as 1 pound of flour. Use as much of this as possible in the form of whole-grain, enriched, or restored products.
[c] For small children and pregnant and nursing women, cod-liver oil or some other source of vitamin D is also needed. For elderly persons and for persons who have no opportunity for exposure to clear sunshine, a small amount of vitamin D is also desirable.
[d] To meet iron allowance, 1 large or 2 small servings of liver or other organ meats should be served each week.
[e] The nutritive content of the weekly food quantities for a man and woman 60 years or over were based on the National Research Council's recommended daily allowances for the sedentary man and woman.

TABLE 39. *A Widely Applicable (Second Low Cost) Food Plan, from United States Department of Agriculture, Miscellaneous Publication No. 662, p. 16. Weekly Quantities of Food (as Purchased) for 19 Age, Sex, and Activity Groups*

Family Members	Leafy, Green, and Yellow Vegetables	Citrus Fruit, Tomatoes	Potatoes, Sweet-potatoes	Other Vegetables and Fruit	Milk[a]	Meat, Poultry, Fish	Eggs	Dry Beans and Peas, Nuts	Flour, Cereals[b]	Fats and Oils	Sugar, Sirups, Preserves
	lb. oz.	lb. oz.	lb. oz.	lb. oz.	qt.	lb. oz.	No.	lb. oz.	lb. oz.	lb. oz.	lb. oz.
Children through 12 years:											
9–12 months	1–8	1–12	0–8	1–0	6	0–0	5	0–1	0–10	0–1	0–0
1–3 years	1–8	1–4	1–8	0–8	5½	0–6	4	0–1	1–8	0–2	0–2
4–6 years	1–8	1–8	2–0	0–12	5½	0–8	3	0–4	2–4	0–6	0–4
7–9 years	1–12	1–8	3–0	0–12	5½	0–12	3	0–6	3–0	0–8	0–8
10–12 years	2–0	1–8	3–8	1–4	6	1–0	3	0–8	3–8	0–12	0–12
Girls:											
13–15 years	2–0	1–12	4–0	1–8	6½	1–0	4	0–8	3–12	0–12	0–12
16–20 years	2–0	1–12	3–8	1–8	4½	1–0	4	0–8	3–12	0–12	0–12
Boys:											
13–15 years	2–0	2–0	4–4	1–8	6½	1–4	4	0–12	4–12	1–2	0–14
16–20 years	2–4	2–0	5–8	1–8	6½	1–4	5	0–14	6–0	1–6	1–0
Women:											
Sedentary	2–0	1–8	3–0	1–4	5	1–0	4	0–4	3–0	0–8	0–8
Moderately active	2–0	1–8	3–8	1–8	4½	1–0	4	0–8	3–12	0–12	0–12
Very active	2–0	1–8	4–8	1–8	4½	1–4	4	0–12	4–12	1–0	0–14
Pregnant	2–12	2–0	3–0	1–8	7½	1–4	5	0–6	3–0	0–8	0–8
Nursing	3–0	3–12	4–4	1–8	10½	1–8	5	0–8	3–8	0–12	0–8
60 years or over	2–0	1–12	3–4	1–0	5	1–0	4	0–4	3–0	0–8	0–8
Men:											
Sedentary	2–0	1–8	3–8	1–8	4½	1–0	4	0–8	3–12	0–12	0–12
Physically active	2–0	1–8	4–8	1–8	4½	1–4	4	0–12	4–12	1–2	0–14
With heavy work	2–0	1–8	7–0	1–8	4½	1–4	5	1–0	7–12	1–14	1–4
60 years or over	2–0	1–12	4–0	1–4	5	1–0	4	0–6	3–12	0–10	0–10

[a] Or its equivalent in cheese, evaporated milk, or dry milk. (See Table 30.)
[b] Count 1½ pounds of bread as 1 pound of flour. Use as much of this as possible in the form of whole-grain, enriched, or restored products. The original publication has somewhat fuller footnotes.

EXERCISES

1. Taking the data of Table 28 as fairly typical of such American dietaries as are only beginning to be influenced by the newer knowledge of nutrition, what changes in the distribution of the food money among the different types of food would you now recommend?

2. If the allotment of the food money were readjusted so that as much was spent for milk and cheese, and also as much for fruits and vegetables, as for meats and fish, would you anticipate an increase or a decrease: (*a*) in the calcium content of the dietary; (*b*) in its ascorbic acid (vitamin C) content; (*c*) in its thiamine content; (*d*) in its riboflavin content; (*e*) in its vitamin A value; (*f*) in the excellence of its nutritional character as a whole?

3. As it is known that meat and fruit do quite directly "compete for the consumer's food money," what effect would you anticipate from the shifting (*a*) of one-third of the customary expenditure for meat and fish to fruit instead, (*b*) of one-third of the customary expenditure for fruit to meat instead?

4. Assuming such readjustment of the food budget as you under the guidance of the newer knowledge of nutrition consider it wise to make, would this call for any essential change in the set-up of menus or meal plans, or only for increases or decreases in the sizes of servings of certain foods?

5. Make meal plans set up in the general style in Rose's *Feeding the Family* and incorporating in full your present judgment as to the best relative amounts of the different types of food.

6. Compare your individual dietary or food consumption record, or that of a family whom you know, with the suggestions of Tables 36 to 39.

Does your dietary omit any one of the eleven "kinds" into which foods are grouped in those tables? If so, is the omission an advantage or a disadvantage nutritionally? Why?

7. Having in mind the fact that recent and current research shows some foods to be better investments than we have hitherto known, could you now improve your dietary nutritionally without seriously increasing its cost?

How much money per year could be made available for the further improvement of your dietary (or that of the family you have in mind) by a partial shifting of expenditure guided by your knowledge of nutrition?

SUGGESTED READINGS

ADDIS, L., L. H. GILLETT, and others   1938   Budget standards for family agencies in New York City. (The New York Budget Council, 105 East 22nd Street, New York City.)

ANDREWS, B. R. 1935 *Economics of the Household,* Revised Ed. (Macmillan.)

BOUDREAU, F. G. 1943 Social and economic implications of freedom from want of food. *Proc. Am. Philosophical Soc.* **87,** 126–132.

BUREAU OF HUMAN NUTRITION AND HOME ECONOMICS 1948 Helping families plan food budgets. *U. S. Dept. Agriculture, Misc. Publ. No. 662.*

BUREAU OF HUMAN NUTRITION AND HOME ECONOMICS 1949 Fats and oils consumed (by city families): Based on 1948 food consumption surveys. *Commodity Summary No. 2, U. S. Dept. Agriculture.*

CAVIN, J. P., M. C. BURK, et al. 1949 Consumption of food in the United States, 1909–48. *U. S. Dept. Agriculture, Misc. Publ. No. 691.*

CHINN, A., and G. M. GUSTAFSON 1941 The economy of combinations of dairy products in low-cost adequate diets. *J. Am. Dietet. Assoc.* **17,** 123–130.

GILLETT, L. H. 1933 Using home economics to make the most of what we have. *J. Home Econ.* **25,** 208–212.

GILLETT, L. H. 1936 Basis for estimating budgets with a human quality. *J. Home Econ.* **28,** 585–591.

GILLETT, L. H., and P. B. RICE 1931 *Influence of Education upon Food Selection.* (Published by the New York Association for Improving the Condition of the Poor, 105 East 22nd Street, New York City.)

GLEISER, F. W., and G. M. SEVERENCE 1938 Budgeting the student's food dollar in a cooperative residence hall system. *J. Am. Dietet. Assoc.* **14,** 692–696.

HAMBIDGE, G. 1934 *Your Meals and Your Money.* (McGraw-Hill.)

KREHL, W. A., and G. R. COWGILL 1948, 1950 Comparative cost and availability of canned, glassed, frozen and fresh fruits and vegetables. *J. Am. Dietet. Assoc.* **24,** 304–309; **26,** 168–172.

MAYNARD, L. A. 1946 The role and efficiency of animals in utilizing feed to produce human food. *J. Nutrition* **32,** 345–360.

MIGHELL, R. L., and R. P. CHRISTENSEN 1944 Measuring maximum contribution to food needs by producing areas. *J. Farm Econ.* **26,** 181–196.

NATIONAL FOOD ALLOTMENT PLAN 1944 S. 1331, 78th Congr., 1st Session.

ODLE, D. T., and M. M. KRAMER 1945 Nutritive value and cost distribution of food of Army students. *J. Am. Dietet. Assoc.* **21,** 285–286.

ORR, J. B. 1936 *Food, Health, and Income*. (London: Macmillan.)

PHIPARD, E. F., and H. K. STIEBELING 1949 Adequacy of American diets. *J. Am. Med. Assoc.* **139,** 579–585.

ROBERTS, L. J., R. BLAIR, and M. GREIDLER 1945 Results of providing a liberally adequate diet to children in an institution. *J. Pediat.* **27,** 393–409.

ROLLINS, M. A. 1948 A low-cost diet from commonly used foods. *J. Home Econ.* **40,** 311–312.

ROSE, M. S. 1940 *Feeding the Family*, 4th Ed. (Macmillan.)

SHERMAN, H. C. 1948 *Food Products*, 4th Ed. (Macmillan.)

STIEBELING, H. K. 1933 Food budgets for nutrition and production programs. *U. S. Dept. Agriculture, Misc. Publ. No. 183.*

STIEBELING, H. K. 1937 Food consumption of urban and village families at different levels of food expenditure. *J. Home Econ.* **29,** 6–10.

STIEBELING, H. K. 1939 Food habits, old and new. *U. S. Dept. Agriculture Yearbook,* "Food and Life," 124–130.

STIEBELING, H. K. 1941 Are we well fed? *U. S. Dept. Agriculture, Misc. Publ. No. 430.*

STIEBELING, H. K. 1948 How families use their incomes. *U. S. Dept. Agriculture, Misc. Publ. No. 653.*

STIEBELING, H. K., et al. 1941 Family food consumption and dietary levels: five regions. Urban and village series. *U. S. Dept. Agriculture, Misc. Publ. No. 452.*

STIEBELING, H. K., and F. CLARK 1939 Planning for good nutrition. *U. S. Dept. Agriculture Yearbook,* "Food and Life," 321–340.

STIEBELING, H. K., and C. M. COONS 1939 Present-day diets in the United States. *U. S. Dept. Agriculture Yearbook,* "Food and Life," 296–320.

STIEBELING, H. K., D. MONROE, C. M. COONS, E. F. PHIPARD, and F. CLARK 1941 Family food consumption and dietary levels: Five regions. Farm series. *U. S. Dept. Agriculture, Misc. Publ. No. 405.*

STIEBELING, H. K., and E. F. PHIPARD 1939 Diets of families of employed wage earners and clerical workers in cities. *U. S. Dept. Agriculture, Circ. 507.*

STIEBELING, H. K., and M. M. WARD 1933 Diets at four levels of nutritive content and cost. *U. S. Dept. Agriculture, Circ. 296.*

TAYLOR, C. M. 1942 *Food Values in Shares and Weights*. (Macmillan.)

TAYLOR, C. M., and G. MACLEOD 1949 *Rose's Laboratory Handbook for Dietetics*, 5th Ed. (Macmillan.)

UNITED STATES DEPARTMENT OF AGRICULTURE 1939 *Yearbook* (devoted essentially to nutrition). (Washington, D. C.: Government Printing Office.)

VAN SYCKLE, C. 1941 Home economics and the study of consumption. *J. Home Econ.* **33**, 82–86.

WHITACRE, J. 1942 An experience with low-cost diets. *J. Am. Dietet. Assoc.* **18**, 285–294.

XXI

HOW TO MAKE NUTRITIONAL KNOWLEDGE MORE EFFECTIVE

"Nutrition Policy"—Public and Personal

The ways of making nutritional knowledge more effective, than it has yet generally become, are sometimes grouped into three brackets as follows:

(1) Research and education in the functions of nutrients, the importance of nutrition to health and efficiency, and the wise use of food and of income;

(2) Direct economic action to promote the increased production and consumption of foods whose larger use is deemed to be nutritionally the more desirable;

(3) Improvement of the nutritional environment in which the people live by requiring certain widely used foods to be nutritionally enriched, restored, or fortified.

Following the general usage of nutritionists we here employ the phrase, *nutrition policy,* the word "policy" meaning, according to a modern dictionary,* primarily a definite course of action adopted as expedient or from other considerations.

That is, this chapter deals with definite courses of action looking to the ever increasingly effective use of nutritional knowledge, both as being expedient and for reasons which may be deemed higher than expediency alone. Thus some people may assert while others may deny that the United States has entered upon a policy of "school lunches" or of public support of one or another form of child feeding aiming to ensure that food adequate to the needs of

* *The American College Dictionary.* New York: Random House. 1948.

full health or of good nutritional status shall be brought within reach of all children of school age. But any such difference of opinion would (at this stage of the development of our civilization) probably apply only to the expediency of the particular project proposed. Nearly all would agree that for reasons of social justice if not also of expediency, each one of our United States should see that none of its children lacks food needed for full health.

Much can be said for each of the three general modes of attack upon the problem of the best use of food which have just been mentioned. Perhaps the thing which should be said first and with most emphasis is that these different approaches are all compatible with each other. Progress can and should be made in all these ways at once.

The science of nutrition is still a fertile field for research and one of the ways of making it more effective is to amplify it, and render it more precise in detail, by further research. Teaching nutrition, and using its guidance in food economics and in "the enrichment program," can all increase the effectiveness of the nutritional knowledge which we now have.

All three of these approaches to "the food problem" were used at the same time in the United Kingdom during the Second World War, and together they resulted in bringing the public health of England up to, and keeping it upon, a higher plane during the war than before, notwithstanding the wartime reductions of food imports and the diversion of medical service to the armed forces. Public education in foods and nutrition, nutritional guidance in the governmental control of food production and import, the legal requirement of nutritional enrichment of such a widely used food as white flour, and national control of the use of feed-stuffs and the distribution of milk, very nearly kept up the Calories of the food supply and actually increased its mineral and vitamin values with corresponding improvement of the public health.

Sir J. C. Drummond, as quoted in the *Journal of the American Dietetic Association,* has said that, since the outbreak of the Second World War, Great Britain has depended for nutritional security primarily upon potatoes, mixed vegetables, and bread made from flour containing a high percentage (usually 85 per cent) of the wheat grain.

According to the data of Montgomery and Cardell, the apparent yearly per capita consumption of sugar in the United States increased from 53 to 101 pounds, and of commercial fat from 13 to 44 pounds, between 1889 and 1927. And Ohlson, Nelson, and Swanson, using these data in their 1937 discussion, point out that this markedly increased consumption of commercial fat and sugar is largely responsible for the difficulty now experienced by home economics women in making dietaries according to "the pattern" or "the market" of today which shall be as high as is desirable in the many now recognized essentials without being too high in calories. Here the outstanding need is to recognize that the high levels of fat and sugar consumption which have crept into our dietaries during the past two generations are not to be regarded as permanent parts of our dietary pattern but as distortions which ought to be reduced rigorously to make room for more of the foods of high mineral and vitamin values.

Research and Education Policy, and Nutrition Service

It was especially to consider the broad aspects of nutrition policy that the League of Nations, under the challenge of the Delegation from Australia that something be done to "Marry agriculture and health," appointed a Mixed Committee representing nutrition, agriculture, and economics, under the chairmanship of Lord Astor, whose above mentioned declaration that, "It isn't sufficient that there be enough food; there must be enough of the *right kinds* of food," did much to give worldwide currency to this fundamental fact.

The British Medical Association took the initiative in organizing a conference on nutrition policy for Great Britain, which met in London, for the consideration of the wider aspects of nutrition, on April 27–29, 1939. Its key note recommendation was as follows: "The conference called by the British Medical Association and composed of representatives of medicine, agriculture at home and overseas, industry, and education, is deeply impressed with the importance of nutrition to the national welfare. It urges upon the Government the formulation of a long-term food policy in which the requirements of health, agriculture, and industry shall be considered in mutual relation. It is convinced that measures to secure the more ready availability, to all sections of the community, of foodstuffs which are held to be desirable on nutritional grounds should be accompanied by an education campaign to encourage their increased consumption."

In the United States the Federal and State Governments have made many contributions to nutritional research and education, but as yet have taken only somewhat tentative steps in the way of direct economic action to increase the production of the right kinds of foods for the best nutrition of the people. As the combined results of research and education reach larger numbers of people with increasing effectiveness, these people come consciously to *want* (for themselves and others) the higher health that the newer knowledge of nutrition offers. Hence it begins to be practicable for the allotment of funds to reward right use of the land, and to purchase surplus foods for distribution in whatever may appear the most equitable way or ways, but always guided more fully by nutritional considerations than was possible in the past.

Perhaps the underlying condition most needed in order to make nutritional knowledge more effective is a keener realization, a more constant consciousness, *a conviction,* of the fact that there is (or may be) a highly significant difference between the merely adequate and the optimal in nutrition. The attempt to bring about this realization is not a hopeless task, for important progress has been made already. This is shown, for instance, by our national statistics of production and consumption of fruits, vegetables, and milk; by comparative dietary studies at a 15-year interval in New York City; and by the editorial statement in the *Journal of the American Medical Association* that the difference between merely passable health and buoyant health is coming to be more appreciated.

Farmers now know that they cannot afford to keep animals of merely passable health. The level of productiveness that makes a farm animal profitable is dependent upon a state of nutrition more nearly optimal than that which is merely adequate to pass a veterinary inspection. Gove Hambidge remarks that many a farmer would be "ashamed to feed his livestock as casually as he feeds his family"; and suggests that it would be no more than intelligent for us (with the food-production possibilities which our country affords) to build a nation of people as sturdy as the animals in a good farmyard.

The preceding paragraphs do not imply that nutrition is solely responsible for the difference between merely passable health on the one hand and positive or buoyant health on the other. Physical education plays several parts; and heredity is a large factor in superiority both in the human family and among its domestic animals. The present point of emphasis is that *both heredity and training become more productive* when supported by the superior nutritional condition and internal environment to which our newer knowledge can serve as a guide. More can now be accomplished through nutrition than we previously were wont to suppose.

In the exceedingly modest terms in which Sir Frederick Gowland Hopkins put it, "Nurture can assist Nature to a larger extent than Science has hitherto thought."

Thus a very important first step in making nutritional knowledge more effective is to train oneself, and to help others, to an adequate realization of its potentiality.

The researches of Dove at the Maine Agricultural Experiment Station indicate that the *innately superior* farm animal may owe this superiority to an hereditary endowment which guides "instinctively" to better-than-average eating habits. Then, if the other animals of the herd are fed according to his example, their level of attainment and productivity is improved. (This seems a valuable suggestion for human improvement; but one to be used with very conscientious care, lest it be perverted by citing unrepresentative cases!)

Nutrition Policy is Made Effective by Both Economic and Educational Methods

How each of us may use nutritional knowledge as effectively as possible in our own lives, and extend its benefits to the lives of as many other people as possible, is both an economic and an educational problem.

It is economic in the sense that most of us would follow the guidance of the newer knowledge of nutrition somewhat more readily, fully, and effectively if we had more money to spend for food; and in the sense of the wider view which shows that malnutrition is much more prevalent among the poor than among the well-to-do. As incomes rise above the poverty level, nutritional conditions automatically improve. With more money to spend for food, people in general buy themselves nutritionally better food supplies than those to which the majority now feel themselves confined by the limitations of their purchasing power.

Yet at the same time, there is also an educational problem; for careful studies show clearly, as has recently been especially emphasized by Stiebeling, that a very large proportion of families can learn to have nutritionally much better dietaries than they now do, even at their present levels of expenditure for food.

Recognizing that both economic and educational problems are involved, many people are now of the opinion that the primary and fundamental need is *nutritional consciousness* or *nutrition policy;* and that when a right policy in regard to nutrition is consciously adopted, both educational and more directly economic methods will be found or made effective for its promotion.

Much has already been done by the U. S. Department of Agriculture and the State colleges and extension services in agriculture and home economics; and by state and local nutritionists and nutrition committees. And in recent years, the Red Cross has also done much for public education in nutrition.

Nearly every state department of health now provides a nutrition service in some form. A recent summary of these is as follows:

State nutrition services. A report of the U. S. Children's Bureau showed that during the fiscal year ending June 30, 1947 the States were exercising wide individual initiative in their ways of making nutritional knowledge increasingly effective in the maternal and child health activities under the Social Security Act. Plans for this work in forty-two States included 99 nutritionists, of whom nine were designated as directors, 41 as consultants, and 49 as nutritionists. One state employed a physician as director of nutrition service. In 33 States the nutrition unit is administratively placed in the Division of Maternal and Child Health, and in four additional States the nutritional personnel were listed with the maternal and child health personnel; while in five States the nutrition service was in a separate unit responsible to the State health officer. Nutrition service was under the local health administration in three States; under Health Education in two States; and under the Division of Preventive Medicine in one State. At least eight States were planning further training for one or more of their nutritional personnel.

The independently incorporated Nutrition Foundation states its program as follows:—

"The Nutrition Foundation is primarily concerned with advancing the science of nutrition. It will seek this end by activities such as these:

"Research projects which have an immediate bearing upon the war emergency, both for the armed forces and for the civilian population,

"Research work which has a long-range value in providing basic information and guidance in the science of nutrition,

"Research studies in nutrition which have a direct bearing upon public health,

"Assistance in bridging the gaps between research findings and the channels through which such information may become effective."

The enrichment program offers a means of spreading the benefit of *one part* of the newer knowledge of nutrition with a promptness comparable to some sanitary reforms instead of by the slow process of educating every individual or family concerned. When specialists in sanitary science and the necessary administrative officers are convinced of the importance of some sanitary measure to the public health, often the reform can be put into effect by legislation, or administrative action, or the two together, so that every citizen then lives in a better sanitary environment whether or not he has been educated to the significance of the reform. Similarly it now seems that we as a people have (or had) been living in a bad nutritional environment in that the bread almost universally used had been artificially impoverished of most of its thiamine through the over-refinement of white flour, and that now the leaders of thought in the nutrition field can by united effort have the thiamine restored to the bread supply so that all the people will get the benefit promptly. To us this seems sound so far as it goes. Realizing that what is projected is only a partial restoration, it yet seems well worth while; and that it may well be supported by all interested in nutrition.

Nutrition Education

Underlying all these and many other activities for the extension of nutritional knowledge is, of course, the regular teaching of nutrition in schools and colleges, and the extension of such teaching into social welfare agencies of many kinds and into the technical training for the medical, nursing, and public health professions.

The fact that better nutrition of the people is both an economic and an educational problem is further shown in the findings of Stiebeling and Phipard (1939).* When, having estimated individually the nutrient contents of a very large number of family dietaries, they grouped them as nutritionally "good," "fair," or "poor," it became quite clear (as indicated earlier in this chapter) that in general more money spent for food means a larger proportion of good dietaries; but also that with the same amount spent for food some families get nutritionally good dietaries while some of their neighbors do not. For example, among East South Central city families with an expenditure (at 1939 price levels) of $2.50 a person a week for food, 32 per cent bought diets nutritionally "good," 31 per cent bought diets nutritionally "fair," and 37 per cent (at the same level of expenditure!) bought diets nutritionally "poor."

Even with the help of the enrichment program, it remains true that to a greater extent than in most economic and hygienic reforms, improvement in nutrition must be attained by the educational building up of new or improved habits of conscious choice in the individual citizen, the cumulative effect of which is recognized as consumer demand.

Thus the purchase of a dozen oranges or an extra quart of milk may confidently be expected to have a two-fold influence: (1) in the building of a higher level of nutritional wellbeing and resultant health and efficiency in the family or individual consumer; and (2) in the upbuilding of the agricultural industries which produce these articles of food.

Our everyday choices of food are probably among the most frequent and certainly among the most influential of the conscious choices that we make.

What serves us best is to accept wholeheartedly the guidance of the newer knowledge of nutrition, and to make a steady habit of acting upon this scientific guidance just as fully as circumstances permit. If to give to fruits, vegetables, and milk as large a place in the dietary as present nutritional knowledge shows desirable should involve turning over a new leaf in one's daily food practice, then let it be turned once for all: not grudgingly and hesitantly, not in a spirit of fussiness; but definitely and with cheerful thanks that science has shown us a way in which choices that we make every day can have unexpectedly far-reaching beneficial effects.

Such adoption of the newer knowledge leaves wide latitude for individual preference and for due consideration of economic con-

* Full reference among Suggested Readings, Chapter XX.

ditions in the choice among fruits and vegetables; and also for choice among the different forms of milk (fresh, canned, and dried) and such of its products as sufficiently possess its nutritional characteristics,—fermented milk, cheese, cream, and ice cream.

As explained in a previous chapter, we interpret findings now available as indicating that for the best results as much as half of the needed food calories should be taken in the form of fruit, vegetables, and milk in some form or forms. For those who do not find it feasible to plan their food in terms of calories, much the same result will usually be obtained if at least half the expenditure for food is for fruits, vegetables, milk, cheese, cream, and ice cream. To provide more fully for thiamine (vitamin B_1), and iron, we have recommended also that of such amounts of breadstuffs or cereals as one may choose to eat, at least half should be in the approximately "whole grain" forms; and we now add, "Let all white bread be enriched."

Note that this application of the newer knowledge of nutrition leaves half the food (whether in terms of calories or of cost) to the free choice of the individual. So there is ample room to "eat what you want while eating what you should." Yet for those who wish guidance in all of their expenditures for food, there is the Department of Agriculture publication, "Helping Families Plan Food Budgets," upon which we have drawn freely in Chapter XX.

One who has studied carefully the new scientific knowledge can get its benefit without necessarily renouncing any particular article or type of food. If on some days it is impracticable to make as modern a selection of food as is here recommended, one can even-up on some subsequent day or days. A moderate amount of such practice as the exercises suggested at the ends of the previous chapters will afford, taken thoughtfully, should enable one to acquire a sense of proportion in regard to foods and dietaries which will give the needed guidance without constant weighing, measuring, or calculation.

Recorded observations extending over a consecutive period of four years, leave the definite impression that one may eat among other people, accepting the food choices made by others to the full extent that business and social customs call for, not making oneself conspicuous or self-conscious, but so balancing in the meals which are under one's control (and in the choices which even conventional meals allow) that half of the total food calories will be taken in the form of fruits, vegetables, and milk, in accordance with the suggestion already made and discussed.

Freedom in the Choice of Food

An important factor in making nutritional knowledge fully effective is a realization that, as already explained in part, a wide freedom of choice of food is entirely compatible with the gaining of the benefits which the newer chemistry of nutrition offers.

Freeing of the mind from needless inhibitions in one's choices among foods helps one to a more effective use of scientific guidance in nutrition; and it is also worthwhile from the viewpoint of the pleasures of the palate. For, as an editorial writer has pointed out, beside the meeting of nutritional needs, "eating has an immense vogue as an amusement."

Religious inhibitions in the use of food do not fall within the scope of this book to discuss further than to say that the newer knowledge of food values makes it easier to provide full nutritional equivalents for any particular article of food which may be interdicted.

Sanitary considerations may also be given all due weight without significantly hampering our food choices. Until recently, discussions of food and health have dwelt largely upon ways in which food may conceivably do injury. Public pressures for "pure food" legislation, and the resulting Federal and State laws, have been activated chiefly by fears of injury and fraud; and as embodied in statute have dealt mainly in prohibitions of adulteration and misbranding. If with these laws in operation too many people still harass themselves and hamper their use of nutritional knowledge by exaggerated fears of unsanitary qualities in food, it is because they do not yet fully realize that during the past thirty years,—partly through the permanent accomplishments of the "pure food movement" and partly through the advances of nutritional knowledge,—*the center of gravity of the problem of the relations of food to health and social welfare has shifted from sanitation to nutrition.*

This is not to say that all the sanitary problems of the food supply have been entirely solved. It is to say that sanitary practices and nutritional knowledge now stand at such points that the consumer who thinks of his food choices chiefly in terms of his fears is sadly behind the times; and that it is far wiser to think of our foods *primarily* in terms of what they can do *constructively* in the building of higher health. Inasmuch as the constructive health values of a scientific choice of foods have been considerably emphasized throughout this book we must assume that the reader will bear them in mind when we now mention the considerations which may occasionally tend to divert our food consciousness back into its old unhappy channels. Obviously, consumers may sometimes have occasion to assert themselves, either directly or through their local health officers, in regard to proper standards of municipal housekeeping cleanliness in the retail handling of foods. Thirty to forty years ago there was need of greater cleanliness in slaughterhouses and on dairy farms; during the intervening years the conditions formerly complained of have been very generally corrected.

In America at least, the sanitary conditions surrounding the production and handling of milk have been so greatly improved and are now so carefully and constantly safeguarded by the health authorities of most communities that the consumer need no longer feel any special anxiety regarding the safety of the market milk supply.

Under the United States meat inspection law, Federal inspection of animals for slaughter and of the sanitary conditions of handling meat, governs the operations of establishments which engage in interstate commerce in meats or meat products. This inspection is quite thorough in most respects; but the Federal authorities have not found it feasible to include the microscopic examinations which would be necessary to exclude pork which is infested with trichinae. Nor have any local health officers, so far as we know. The consumer's protection from trichinosis depends, therefore, on individual insistence upon very thorough cooking of the flesh of swine in whatever form it is eaten. (Current reports of frequency of trichinosis indicate that this precaution is not yet as fully appreciated as it should be.)

Meat of local origin, which has not been subject to Federal inspection, must, of course, depend upon local standards for its sanitary safeguards.

In former years, there was much controversy as to what preservative substances might be added to foods and under what conditions. The question (or group of questions,—for each preservative should of course be judged individually after investigation on its own merits) was studied in considerable detail by the United

States Department of Agriculture, both in its laboratories in Washington and through consultants working in their own laboratories in several universities; and the rulings based on the findings of these investigations have been followed for a generation in the enforcement of the food laws without giving rise to any serious difference of legal or scientific opinion. Hence the question of preservatives may presumably be regarded as having been settled in the sense that it need no longer be carried as anxiety in the mind of the consumer, or bias one's choice of food.

Spray residues on fruits and vegetables constitute, however, a somewhat analogous problem which is not yet (1950) settled in the same sense. Until less-toxic sprays or more thorough methods of commercial washing to remove spray residues are introduced, it may be wise for the consumer either to reject the entire skin of sprayed fruits and vegetables or to scrub very thoroughly in washing such foods before eating, and also to remove by means of a knife all parts which cannot be effectively reached in scrubbing. Spray residues thus constitute a part of a larger problem as to whether any of the supposed improvers used in food technology leave anything in the food which may be deleterious when consumed almost daily over a lifetime.

The Government seems now (1950) to be taking more seriously any sanitary hazards of present-day food supply as may conceivably be of such nature as to interfere seriously with the choice of foods for their nutritive values.

Food allergies, which render the people afflicted with them abnormally sensitive to foods which are perfectly wholesome to normal people, may seriously handicap food choices in relatively rare cases. The services of a physician who specializes in allergy may be required to determine whether a person who thinks he "cannot eat" some important article or type of food is suffering from a real allergy or only from an aversion.

In the vast majority of cases (in peacetime, at least) the dominant limitation upon the choice of food is lack of money to buy as much as all members of the family would like to eat of the foods of their choice. Here, education in the newer aspects of the nutritive values can do much to assist the individual or the family to get the maximum of satisfaction for the food expenditure, as we have sought to explain in the preceding chapter and the earlier pages of this one.

Further Consideration of Consumer Demand and the Consequent Adjustment of Food Production

There need be no fear about the ability of our farms to supply the extra fruit, vegetables, and milk that will be called for as more and more consumers shift the emphasis of their food choice in the direction which our newer knowledge of nutrition indicates.

We are informed by experts of the United States Department of Agriculture that the farmers of this country could readily increase many-fold their present production of practically any fruit or vegetable for which there is sufficient growth of consumer demand. Land and labor formerly devoted too exclusively to the growing of cotton, and for which diversification is now universally recognized as needed on grounds of business economics in any case, may well be devoted, in part or in rotation, to the growing of small fruits, melons, and fresh vegetables (often referred to in agricultural and economic terms as "truck crops"). Here there is an enormous potential resource for the meeting of a growing market demand for fruits and vegetables; and the growth of such consumer demand will be favorable to the farmer in two ways, by relieving him from financial dependence upon a single cash crop and by greatly improving the home-grown food supply of the farm family.

Moreover, according to the findings of Dr. O. E. Baker (long of the United States Department of Agriculture), fruit occupies only from 1 to 2 per cent, and vegetables only about 4 per cent of the crop acreage in this country, so that production of both could be doubled or trebled without affecting the returns from other crops to any serious degree.

Some regions and some breeds of cattle are adapted to the production of meat and others to the production of milk. This country has enough of the former to ensure an abundant meat supply in any case; but it is also true that there are enormous areas of our most productive farm lands which can and do produce both meat and milk, and shift their emphasis toward the one or the other "according to the market," *i.e.*, to the consumer demand.

There are also other regions in which the most profitable agricultural alternatives are meat on the one hand and some fruit or vegetable on the other; *e.g.*, apples in the Northwest; and lettuce in Colorado, where they still speak of the partially converted cattlemen "who want to sow their lettuce-seed from the saddle."

The Federal agricultural experts have also made careful estimates of the relative amounts of human food produced by a given acreage of farm land, with separate consideration of plowed land and pasture land when animal production is involved. To enter fully into this important study of our present and potential food production resources would lead beyond the scope of this book.* It suffices for our present purpose to say that fruits, vegetables, and milk are more advantageous crops for the farmer to produce (even if they require more attention) than are their usual alternatives, so that the increasing emphasis upon these foods can not only be amply met by our farmers but will also be distinctly helpful to the normal evolution of American agriculture.

Whatever part political policy or statesmanship may play, the science of nutrition will increasingly serve human progress through an ever better informed and more intelligent consumer demand in the daily choice and use of food.

This daily use of our science,—alike to "illuminate the mind" and to "ameliorate man's estate,"—is an opportunity and a responsibility in which each of us has a share.

EXERCISE

Write your own supplement to the foregoing discussion of how to make nutritional knowledge more effective.

SUGGESTED READINGS

AMERICAN MEDICAL ASSOCIATION 1945 Policies of the Council on Foods and Nutrition regarding nutritive quality of foods. *J. Am. Med. Assoc.* **129**, 348–349.

ANDERSON, R. K., and H. R. SANDSTEAD 1947 Nutritional appraisal and demonstration program of the U. S. Public Health Service. *J. Am. Dietet. Assoc.* **23**, 101–107.

AYKROYD, W. R. 1948 Food and nutrition—certain international aspects and developments. *J. Am. Dietet. Assoc.* **24**, 1–4.

BANE, L. 1941 Milestones and guideposts in agriculture and home economics. *J. Home Econ.* **33**, 148–151.

BLACK, J. D., and M. E. KIEFER 1948 *Future Food and Agriculture Policy.* (McGraw-Hill.)

* One of the present writers has discussed more fully the food problems just mentioned in two other books: Sherman's *Food Products,* 4th Ed. (Macmillan), and Sherman's *Foods: Their Values and Management* (Columbia University Press).

Bosley, B. 1947 A practical approach to nutrition education for children. *J. Am. Dietet. Assoc.* **23**, 304–309.

Boudreau, F. G. 1939 International and national aspects of the campaign for better nutrition. *J. Am. Dietet. Assoc.* **15**, 885–893.

Boudreau, F. G., and H. D. Kruse 1939 Malnutrition: A challenge and an opportunity. *Am. J. Public Health* **29**, 427–433.

Bourquin, A. 1947 Community nutrition institute at Syracuse University. *J. Am. Dietet. Assoc.* **23**, 940.

Bovee, D. L., and J. Downes 1941 The influence of nutrition education in families of the Mulberry area of New York City. *Milbank Memorial Fund Quart.* **19**, 121–146.

Bureau of Human Nutrition and Home Economics 1948 Helping families plan food budgets. *U. S. Dept. Agriculture, Misc. Publ. No. 662.*

Bureau of Human Nutrition and Home Economics 1950 Family fare: food management and recipes. *U. S. Dept. Agriculture, Home and Garden Bull. No. 1.*

Burke, B. S. 1944 Nutrition during pregnancy: a review. *J. Am. Dietet. Assoc.* **20**, 735–741.

Burke, B. S. 1945 Nutrition and its relationship to the complications of pregnancy and the survival of the infant. *Am. J. Public Health* **35**, 334–340.

Burke, B. S. 1945*b* Nutrition—its place in our prenatal care programs. *Milbank Memorial Fund Quart.* **23**, 54–65.

Christensen, R. P. 1948 Efficient use of food resources in the United States. *U. S. Dept. Agriculture, Tech. Bull. No. 963.*

Clark, F., B. Friend, and M. C. Burk 1947 Nutritive value of the per capita food supply 1909–45. *U. S. Dept. Agriculture, Misc. Publ. No. 616.*

Clements, F. W. 1945 The organization of nutrition activities in Australia. *Nutrition Rev.* **3**, 161–162.

Dodd, N. E. 1948 What are FAO's functions? *J. Am. Dietet. Assoc.* **24**, 973.

Donelson, E. G., *et al.* 1945 Nutritional status of midwestern college women. *J. Am. Dietet. Assoc.* **21**, 145–147; *Nutr. Abs. Rev.* **15**, 341–342.

Ebbs, J. H., and W. J. Moyle 1942 The importance of nutrition in the prenatal clinic. *J. Am. Dietet. Assoc.* **18**, 12–15.

Edited by J. S. Simmons 1949 *Public Health in the World Today.* (Harvard University Press.)

Editorial 1936 Food requirements in the modern state. *Nature* **138**, 379–380.

Editorial 1942 Nutrition education via press and radio. *J. Am. Dietet. Assoc.* **18**, 236–237.

ELIOT, M. M., and M. M. HESELTINE   1947   Nutrition in maternal and child health programs. *Nutrition Rev.* **5**, 33–35.

ELLIOTT, F. F.   1944   Redirecting world agricultural production and trade toward better nutrition. *J. Farm Econ.* **26**, 10–30.

ELVEHJEM, C. A.   1946   Future studies in nutrition. *Nutrition Rev.* **4**, 1–6.

EPPRIGHT, E. S.   1947   Factors influencing food acceptance. *J. Am. Dietet. Assoc.* **23**, 579–587.

Food and Agriculture Organization of the United Nations   1948   The State of Food and Agriculture. A Survey of World Conditions and Prospects, Washington, D. C., U. S. A.

GETTING, V. A.   1947   A modern nutrition program in a state health department. *Milbank Memorial Fund Quart.* **25**, 256–260.

GILLETT, L. H.   1946   *Nutrition in Public Health.* (Saunders.)

GOLD, N. L., A. C. HOFFMAN, and F. V. WAUGH   1940   Economic analysis of the food stamp plan (98 pages). A special report, Bur. Agr. Econ. and Surplus Marketing Admin., U. S. Dept. Agriculture.

GOODHART, R. S.   1948   Nutrition programs for industrial workers. *Nutrition Rev.* **6**, 289–291.

GRAY, C. A.   1942   Nutrition education in an industrial community. *J. Am. Dietet. Assoc.* **18**, 740–741.

GREGORY, R.   1937   Nutritional science and its social aspects. *Nutr. Abs. Rev.* **7**, 1–5.

HARDY, M. C., A. SPOHN, G. AUSTIN, S. McGIFFERT, E. MOHR, and A. B. PETERSON   1943   Nutritional and dietary inadequacies among city children from different socio-economic groups. *J. Am. Dietet. Assoc.* **19**, 173–181; *Nutr. Abs. Rev.* **13**, 95–96.

HAWLEY, E. E.   1942   How one city tackled the nutrition problem. *J. Am. Dietet. Assoc.* **18**, 295–297.

HESELTINE, M. M.   1937   Home Economics in social welfare and public health. *J. Home Econ.* **29**, 683–686.

HESELTINE, M. M.   1948   The health and welfare of the world's children. *J. Am. Dietet. Assoc.* **24**, 91–93.

HOLLINGSWORTH, D. F.   1947   Nutritional policies in Great Britain, 1939–46. *J. Am. Dietet. Assoc.* **23**, 96–100.

IRWIN, M. H.   1942   Training in good food habits. *J. Am. Dietet. Assoc.* **18**, 237–239.

JEANS, P. C., and W. M. MARRIOTT   1947   *Infant Nutrition,* 4th Ed. (St. Louis: C. V. Mosby Co.)

JOLLIFFE, N.   1942   Nutritional failures: Their causes and prevention. *Milbank Memorial Fund Quart.* **20**, 103–125.

JOLLIFFE, N., J. S. McLESTER, and H. C. SHERMAN   1942   The prevalence of malnutrition. *J. Am. Med. Assoc.* **118**, 944–950.

Koch, E. 1945 Chicago's nutrition problem. *J. Am. Dietet. Assoc.* **21**, 214–217.

Kruse, H. D. 1942 A concept of the deficiency states. *Milbank Memorial Fund Quart.* **20**, 245–261.

Kruse, H. D., O. A. Bessey, N. Jolliffe, J. S. McLester, F. F. Tisdall, and R. M. Wilder 1943 Inadequate diets and nutritional deficiencies in the United States: Their prevalence and significance. *National Research Council Bull. No. 109.*

Lamb, M. W., and C. M. McPherson 1948 Trends in dietary practices of college women. *J. Home Econ.* **40**, 19–21.

Leighton, G., and P. L. McKinlay 1930 Milk consumption and the growth of school children: Report of an investigation in Lanarkshire schools. (Department of Health for Scotland.) (Edinburgh: His Majesty's Stationery Office.)

Lewis, M. N. 1949 The dietitian's role in the education of medical students. *J. Am. Dietet. Assoc.* **25**, 588–590.

Lockwood, E. A. 1949 Nutrition education. *Nutrition Rev.* **7**, 129–131.

Mack, P. B., J. M. Smith, C. H. Logan, and A. T. O'Brien 1942 Mass studies in human nutrition: Nutritional status of children in a college community. *J. Am. Dietet. Assoc.* **18**, 69–78.

McCollum, E. V., et al. 1939 *The Newer Knowledge of Nutrition,* 5th Ed. (Macmillan.)

McCormick, M. G. 1939 The educational possibilities of the school lunch. *J. Home Econ.* **31**, 226–228.

McLester, J. S. 1939 Borderline states of nutritive failure. *J. Am. Med. Assoc.* **112**, 2110–2114.

Ministry of Health, London 1946 On the state of the public health during six years of war. (London: His Majesty's Stationery Office.) (iv + 280 pages) *Nutr. Abs. Rev.* **17**, 556.

Mitchell, H. S. 1942 Our own nutrition problems. *J. Am. Dietet. Assoc.* **18**, 9–11.

Moser, A. M. 1942 A rural school experiment with noon lunches. *J. Home Econ.* **34**, 22–24.

Mudge, G. G. 1945 Teaching nutrition to public health nurses. *J. Am. Dietet. Assoc.* **21**, 634–636.

Murlin, J. R. 1942 Nutritional problems in relation to the nation's health. *Federation Proc.* **1**, 209–213.

O'Brien, H. R. 1947 The World Health Organization and global nutrition. *J. Am. Dietet. Assoc.* **23**, 85–89.

Ohlson, M. A., P. M. Nelson, and P. P. Swanson 1937 Cooperative research among colleges. *J. Home Econ.* **29**, 108–113.

Orr, J. B. 1941 Nutrition and human welfare. *Nutr. Abs. Rev.* **11**, 3–11.

PARRAN, T. 1946 Nutrition in the public health programs. *Nutrition Rev.* **4,** 129–130.

PETT, L. B., and M. J. ANGUS 1949 Follow-up of nutrition surveys. *J. Am. Dietet. Assoc.* **25,** 405–408.

PIQUET, H. S. 1945 Since Hot Springs. *J. Home Econ.* **37,** 84–88.

PYKE, M. 1947 Principles of nutritional rehabilitation. *J. Am. Dietet. Assoc.* **23,** 90–95.

QUAST, F. 1939 The university cafeteria as a means of improving the dietary of students. *J. Am. Dietet. Assoc.* **15,** 101–104.

REVIEW 1946 The United Nations Food and Agriculture Organization. *Nutrition Rev.* **4,** 8–11.

REVIEW 1946*b* Some effects of nutrition education by the public health nurse. *Nutrition Rev.* **4,** 19–21.

REVIEW 1949 Effect of school feeding programs on nutritional status. *Nutrition Rev.* **7,** 101–103.

REVIEW 1949*b* Improvement of nutrient value of food by plant breeding, guided by chemical control. *Nutrition Rev.* **7,** 186–187.

ROBERTS, L. J. 1935 *Nutrition Work with Children,* Rev. Ed. (University of Chicago Press.)

ROBERTS, L. J. 1944 Improvement of the nutritional status of American people. *J. Home Econ.* **36,** 401–404.

ROSE, M. S. 1932 *Teaching Nutrition to Boys and Girls.* (Macmillan.)

ROSE, M. S. 1935 University teaching of nutrition and dietetics in the United States. *Nutr. Abs. Rev.* **4,** 439–446.

ROSE, M. S. 1939 Nutrition and the health of the school child. *J. Am. Dietet. Assoc.* **15,** 63–85.

ROSE, M. S. 1940 *Feeding the Family,* 4th Ed. (Macmillan.)

ROWNTREE, J. I. 1938 The teaching of nutrition. *J. Home Econ.* **30,** 156–160.

SEBRELL, W. H. 1943 Nutrition in preventive medicine. *J. Am. Med. Assoc.* **123,** 280–287, 342–351.

SEBRELL, W. H. 1945 Nutrition and public health. *J. Am. Dietet. Assoc.* **21,** 18–21.

SEBRELL, W. H. 1948 We need more nutritionists. *Nutrition Rev.* **6,** 97–99.

SHANK, R. E. 1949 Nutrition in preventive medicine. *Nutrition Rev.* **7,** 1–3.

SMITH, C. A. 1949 Effect of maternal nutrition upon pregnancy and the newborn. *J. Am. Dietet. Assoc.* **25,** 665–668.

STAMM, E. K., and D. G. WIEHL 1942 The school lunch as a method for improving diets of high school students. *Milbank Memorial Fund Quart.* **20,** 83–96.

STARE, F. J. 1947 Medical and public education in nutrition. *Nutrition Rev.* **5**, 1–4.

STIEBELING, H. K. 1941 The National Research Council's Committee on Food Habits. *J. Home Econ.* **33**, 541–543.

STIEBELING, H. K. 1941b Do we want better nutrition? *J. Home Econ.* **33**, 570.

STIEBELING, H. K. 1942 Food consumption studies and dietary recommendations. *Federation Proc.* **1**, 327–330.

STIEBELING, H. K. 1949 A long range view of nutrition. *J. Home Econ.* **41**, 1–4.

STIEBELING, H. K., and F. CLARK 1939 Planning for good nutrition. *U. S. Dept. Agriculture Yearbook,* "Food and Life," 321–340.

STIEBELING, H. K., M. FARIOLETTI, F. V. WAUGH, and J. P. CAVIN 1939 Better nutrition as a national goal. *U. S. Dept. Agriculture Yearbook,* "Food and Life," 380–402.

TISDALL, F. F. 1945 The role of nutrition in preventive medicine. *Milbank Memorial Fund Quart.* **23**, 39–53.

TISSUE, K. A. 1940 Diet and resistance in tuberculosis. *J. Am. Dietet. Assoc.* **16**, 313–324.

TODD, T. W. 1938 Objective ratings of the constitution of the growing child based on examination of physical development and mental expansion. *Am. J. Diseases Children* **55**, 149–159.

TODHUNTER, E. N. 1948 Child feeding problems and the school lunch program. *J. Am. Dietet. Assoc.* **24**, 422–430.

TRULSON, M., D. M. HEGSTED, and F. J. STARE 1949 New York State Nutrition Survey. I. A nutrition survey of public school children. *J. Am. Dietet. Assoc.* **25**, 595–605.

WHITE, R. L. 1939 Training for community nutrition work. *J. Home Econ.* **31**, 221–225.

WILDER, R. M. 1945 Misinterpretation and misuse of the recommended dietary allowances. *Science* **101**, 285–288.

WILKINS, W. 1947 New types of activity for nutrition services in public health. *Milbank Memorial Fund Quart.* **25**, 247–255.

WILLIAMS, R. R. 1948 Cereal grains and the world food shortage. *J. Am. Dietet. Assoc.* **24**, 5–8.

WILSON, M. L. (Editor) 1942 *Proceedings of the National Nutrition Conference, Washington, May 1941.* (Government Printing Office.)

WRIGHT, M. D. 1941 The Oslo meal: Its acceptability among industrial workers. *J. Roy. Inst. Pub. Health and Hyg.* **3**, 3–8; *J. Home Econ.* **33**, 202.

Appendix A

FATTY ACIDS

With few if any exceptions the fatty acids of natural fats contain even numbers of carbon atoms; for both their building-up and breaking down processes go on mainly, if not entirely, by steps which add or remove a two-carbon "link" at a time.

Also these fatty acids belong, so far as known, to one or another of five series: the saturated series, of which stearic acid is an example, in which the molecule has no "double bond"; the series which includes oleic acid, which is unsaturated to the extent of one double bond in the molecule, and three further-unsaturated series with, respectively, two, three, and four double bonds in the molecule.

All statements regarding the *occurrence* of fatty acids in fats are to be understood as meaning that the acid occurs as *glyceride* (triglyceride), perhaps accompanied by a trace of the same acid in a free state.

Saturated Fatty Acids

The saturated fatty acids constitute an homologous series of the type formula $C_nH_{2n}O_2$. The nutritionally important members of this series are:

Butyric acid, $CH_3(CH_2)_2COOH$ (or more simply written $C_4H_8O_2$), occurring chiefly in butter fat of which it constitutes about 5 to 6 per cent;

Caproic acid, $C_6H_{12}O_2$, occurring in milk fats and coconut oil;[*]

Caprylic acid, $C_8H_{16}O_2$, which also occurs in milk fats and coconut oil;

Capric acid, $C_{10}H_{20}O_2$, occurring in the fats of milk (butter), of the coconut, and of the spice bush;

Lauric acid, $C_{12}H_{24}O_2$, which occurs in butter, coconut and palm oils, and in higher proportion in the fat of the spice bush;

---

[*] As the melting point of coconut fat lies between ordinary temperate and tropical temperatures, this commodity is an oil as shipped from the Tropics which produce it while it is a soft solid when it appears in such markets as London and New York.

Myristic acid, $C_{14}H_{28}O_2$, which also occurs in the fats just named, and in small proportions in many plant and animal fats;

Palmitic acid, $C_{16}H_{32}O_2$, which occurs widely and abundantly in both animal and vegetable fats;

Stearic acid, $C_{18}H_{36}O_2$, which also is widely distributed in both plant and animal fats, more abundantly in the hard fats of both groups. (While *stearin* as a scientific term is the name for the individual chemical substance, glyceryl tristearate, the triglyceride of stearic acid alone; the harder portion of a fat as pressed industrially may in commerce be called its stearin, *e.g.*, "beef stearin," "cottonseed stearin," etc.); and

Arachidic acid, $C_{20}H_{40}O_2$, which takes its name from peanut oil, has also been found in several other food fats.

Unsaturated Fatty Acids

The best known fatty acids of the series $C_nH_{2n-2}O_2$ are:

Oleic acid, $C_{18}H_{34}O_2$, which occurs in nearly all fats and fatty oils; and

Erucic acid, $C_{22}H_{42}O_2$, long known as occurring in the seed fats of the cruciferous plants such as commercial rapeseed and mustardseed oils, and more recently found to occur also in marine animal oils.

Acids of the series $C_nH_{2n-4}O_2$, $C_nH_{2n-6}O_2$, and $C_nH_{2n-8}O_2$ are illustrated respectively by *linoleic acid*, $C_{18}H_{32}O_2$; *linolenic acid*, $C_{18}H_{30}O_2$; and *arachidonic acid*, $C_{20}H_{32}O_2$. These are the best known members of their respective series; but probably many others exist in nature. It is also quite probable that these well-established names may sometimes be applied inadvertently to unidentified isomers as well as to the individual substances originally isolated and named.

In the earlier chemical investigations of natural fats small amounts of these highly unsaturated fatty acids were doubtless often overlooked. Now that their apparent nutritional importance is stimulating reinvestigation they are being found more widely distributed than previously reported, and new members are being added to this group.

Appendix B

DIGESTIVE ENZYMES

The Chief Digestive Enzymes and Their Actions

	Enzymes	Secreted by	Action
Act on Carbohydrates	Ptyalin (salivary amylase)	Salivary glands	Converts starch to maltose
	Amylopsin (pancreatic amylase)	Pancreas	Converts starch to maltose
	Invertase (Sucrase)	Intestinal mucosa	Converts sucrose to glucose and fructose
	Maltase	Intestinal mucosa	Converts maltose to glucose
	Lactase	Intestinal mucosa	Converts lactose to glucose and galactose
Act on Fats	Lipases	Gastric mucosa and pancreas	Split fats to fatty acids and glycerol
Act on Proteins	Pepsin	Gastric mucosa	Splits proteins to proteoses and peptones
	"Trypsin" (actually a group of enzymes)	Pancreas	Splits proteins to proteoses, peptones, polypeptides, and amino acids
	"Erepsin" (actually a group of enzymes)	Intestinal mucosa	Splits peptones to amino acids and ammonia

Appendix C

COMPOSITION AND NUTRITIVE VALUES OF FOODS

In the tabulations which follow, the nutrients are stated per 100 grams of the edible food material (also sometimes written per 100 g. of the edible portion, E.P.).

Table 40 shows the approximate dimensions of a 100 g. portion of nearly every food included; then the grams (percentage by weight) of protein, fat, and carbohydrate; then in parallel columns the numbers of Calories as computed (*a*) by the "Atwater" and (*b*) by the "more specific" factors (Chapter IV).

Table 41 shows, for nearly every food included therein: (*a*) the milligrams of calcium, phosphorus, iron, ascorbic acid (vitamin C), thiamine (vitamin B_1), riboflavin, and niacin; then (*b*) the International Units of vitamin A: each per 100 g. of the edible material.

The chief source of the data in these tables is *Agriculture Handbook No. 8* published by the U. S. Department of Agriculture in June 1950. A few foods not included in the Department's table are included in one or both of Tables 40 and 41. In a few additional cases of individual nutrient values we have substituted a question mark for what seemed to be a dubious reported figure.

Supplementary data less well suited to comparison of energy factors than those in Table 40 but still useful for many purposes of dietary computation are here included in Table 40A.

TABLE 40. *Protein, Fat, and Carbohydrate Content and Energy Value of Foods: Expressed per 100 Grams of the Edible Material*

Food	Approximate Measure	Protein	Fat	Carbo-hydrate	Atwater Factors	Specific Factors
		grams	grams	grams	Calories	Calories
Almonds	¾ c.	18.6	54.1	19.6	640	597
Apple, raw	1 small, 2″ diam.	0.3	0.4	14.9	64	58
Apple pie	3″ sector, 9″ diam.	2.1	9.5	39.5	266	246
Apricots, dried	½ c. packed	5.2	0.4	66.9	278	262
fresh	2–3 average	1.0	0.1	12.9	56	51
Asparagus	8–12 stalks, 5″ long	2.2	0.2	3.9	26	21
Avocado	½, 4″ long	1.7	26.4	5.1	265	245
Bacon	10 slices, 1½″ × 4½″ × ⅛″	9.1	65.0	1.1	626	630
Banana(s)	1, 6½″ long	1.2	0.2	23.0	99	88
Barley, pearled	½ c.	8.2	1.0	78.8	357	349
Beans, baked, pork and molasses	½ c.	5.8	3.0	19.2	125	125
dry	½ c.	21.4	1.6	61.6	346	338
Lima, dry	⅔ c.	20.7	1.3	61.6	341	333
Lima, fresh	⅝ c.	7.5	0.8	23.5	131	128
snap or string	¾ c., 1″ pieces	2.4	0.2	7.7	42	35
Beef, dried or chipped	7 thin slices, 4″ × 5″	34.3	6.3	0.2	194	203
round, lean		(19.5)*	11.1	0.0	178	182
Beet(s)	½ c., diced	1.6	0.1	9.6	45	42
Beet greens	½ c., cooked	2.0	0.3	5.6	33	27

394

Biscuit, baking powder	5½ small biscuits	8.2	10.6	52.2	337	342
Blackberries	¾ c.	1.2	1.0	12.2	62	57
Blueberries	¾ c.	0.6	0.6	15.1	68	61
Bread, Boston brown	2 slices, 3″ diam., ⅞″ thick	4.8	2.1	46.0	222	219
raisin	4–5 slices	7.1	3.1	57.8	288	284
white, enriched†	4–5 slices	8.5	3.2	51.8	270	275
whole wheat	4–5 slices	9.3	2.6	49.0	257	240
Broccoli	⅞ c., cooked	3.3	0.2	5.5	37	29
Brussels sprouts	7 sprouts, 1½″ diam.	4.4	0.5	8.9	58	47
Butter	½ c. scant; or 10 sq., 1¼″ × 1¼″ × ¼″	0.6	81.0	0.4	733	716
Buttermilk, cultured	½ c. scant	3.5	0.1	5.1	35	36
Cabbage	1½ c. chopped, raw	1.4	0.2	5.3	29	24
Cantaloupe	¼ melon, 5″ diam.	0.6	0.2	4.6	23	20
Carrots	¾ c. ½″ cubes	1.2	0.3	9.3	45	42
Cashew nuts	¾ c.	18.5	48.2	27.0	616	578
Cauliflower	1 c., chopped	2.4	0.2	4.9	31	25
Celery	4 medium stalks	1.3	0.2	3.7	22	18
Chard	⅓ c. cooked	1.4	0.2	4.4	25	21
Cheese, Cheddar type		25.0	32.2	2.1	398	398
cottage, skim milk	5½ tbsp.	19.5	0.5	2.0	91	95
cream		9.0	37.0	2.0	377	371
Parmesan	1¼ c. grated	36.0	26.0	2.9	390	393
Swiss		27.5	28.0	1.7	369	370

* Figures in parenthesis, imputed value.
† With 4% non-fat milk solids.

TABLE 40. *Protein, Fat, and Carbohydrate Content and Energy Value of Foods; Expressed per 100 Grams of the Edible Material (Continued)*

Food	Approximate Measure	Protein	Fat	Carbo-hydrate	Atwater Factors	Specific Factors
		grams	grams	grams	Calories	Calories
Cherries, fresh	⅔ c.	1.1	0.5	14.8	68	61
Chicken, broiler	½ med. broiler	20.2	7.2	0.0	155	151
Cod, fresh		16.5	0.4	0.0	70	74
Collards	½ c. cooked	3.9	0.6	7.2	50	40
Corn, sweet, fresh		3.7	1.2	20.5	108	92
Cornmeal, degermed, uncooked	⅔ c.	7.9	1.2	78.4	356	363
Crackers, Graham		8.0	10.0	74.3	419	393
soda, plain		9.6	9.6	72.7	416	420
Cranberries	1 c.	0.4	0.7	11.3	53	48
Cream, thin, 20%	⅜ c.	2.9	20.0	4.0	208	204
Cucumbers	14 slices, ⅛" thick, 2" diam.	0.7	0.1	2.7	14	12
Dandelion greens		2.7	0.7	8.8	52	44
Eggplant	1 c. diced	1.1	0.2	5.5	28	24
Eggs, fresh, whole	2 medium	12.8	11.5	0.7	158	162
white	3½ whites	10.8	0.0	0.8	46	50
yolk	6½ yolks	16.3	31.9	0.7	355	361
Endive (Escarole)		1.6	0.2	4.0	24	20
Farina, uncooked	⅝ c.	10.9	0.8	77.4	360	370
Figs, raw	3 1½" diam.	1.4	0.4	19.6	88	79

Fig bars		4.2	4.8	75.8	363	350
Flour, white, enriched	7/8 c., sifted	10.5	1.0	76.1	355	364
whole wheat	3/4 c.	13.3	2.0	71.0	356	333
(from hard wheats)						
Grapefruit	1/2, 4″ diam.	0.5	0.2	10.1	44	40
Grape(s)	20 good-sized (1/2 c.)	1.4	1.4	14.9	74	70
Grapejuice, comm'l.	1/2 c. scant	0.4	0.0	18.2	75	67
Haddock		18.2	0.1	0.0	74	79
Halibut		18.6	5.2	0.0	121	126
Ham, smoked, med. fat		16.9	35.0	(0.3)	384	389
Heart, beef		16.9	3.7	0.7	104	108
Honey	1/4 c.	0.3	0.0	79.5	319	294
Ice cream, comm'l., plain	1/2 c.	4.0	12.5	20.6	212	207
Kale	1/2 c., cooked	3.9	0.6	7.2	50	40
Kidney, beef	1/2 c., cubed	15.0	8.1	0.9	136	141
Lamb, leg, med. fat		18.0	17.5	0.0	230	235
Lard	1/2 c.	0.0	100.0	0.0	900	902
Lemon		0.9	0.6	8.7	44	32
juice	1/2 c.	0.4	0.2	7.7	34	24
Lettuce	6 large leaves	1.2	0.2	2.9	18	15
Macaroni, uncooked	1 c., or 10 sticks 9″ long	12.8	1.4	76.5	370	377
Margarine	1/2 c. scant; or 10 sq., 1 1/4″ × 1 1/4″ × 1/4″	0.6	81.0	0.4	733	720
Milk, fluid, whole	3/8 c.	3.5	3.9	4.9	69	68
non-fat (skim)	1/2 c.	3.5	0.1	5.1	35	36

TABLE 40. Protein, Fat, and Carbohydrate Content and Energy Value of Foods: Expressed per 100 Grams of the Edible Material (Continued)

Food	Approximate Measure	Protein	Fat	Carbo-hydrate	Energy Value Atwater Factors	Energy Value Specific Factors
		grams	grams	grams	Calories	Calories
Milk (*Continued*)						
condensed (sweetened)	⅓ c.	8.1	8.4	54.8	327	320
evaporated	½ c.	7.0	7.9	9.9	139	138
skimmed, dried		35.6	1.0	52.0	359	362
whole, dried	1 c.	25.8	26.7	38.0	496	492
Mustard greens	⅝ c., cooked	2.3	0.3	4.0	28	22
Oatmeal, oats	1⅓ c.	14.2	7.4	68.2	396	390
cooked	1½ c.	2.3	1.2	11.0	64	63
Okra	10–12 pods	1.8	0.2	7.4	39	32
Olives, green		1.5	13.5	4.0	143	132
Onions, mature	3, 1½″ diam.	1.4	0.2	10.3	49	45
Orange(s)	1 small, 2½″ diam.	0.9	0.2	11.2	50	45
Parsnips	½ c. cubes	1.5	0.5	18.2	83	78
Peaches	1 medium	0.5	0.1	12.0	51	46
canned	1 large half plus 1½ tbsp. juice	0.4	0.1	18.2	75	68
dried		3.0	0.6	69.4	295	265
Peanuts, roasted	¾ c., shelled	26.9	44.2	23.6	597	559
Peanut butter	6 tbsp.	26.1	47.8	21.0	619	576
Pears, fresh	1 large	0.7	0.4	15.8	70	63

Peas, fresh green	3/4 c., shelled	6.7	0.4	17.7	101	98
mature, split	1/2 c.	24.5	1.0	61.7	354	344
Pecans	3/4 c.	9.4	73.0	13.0	747	696
Peppers, green	1 pepper, 3–4" long	1.2	0.2	5.7	29	25
Pineapple, canned	2 slices, 3 tbsp. juice	0.4	0.1	21.1	87	78
fresh	1/2 c., diced	0.4	0.2	13.7	58	52
Plums	3, 1½" diam.	0.7	0.2	12.9	56	50
Pork, loin, chops, med. fat	1 med. chop, ½" thick	16.4	25.0	0.0	291	296
Potatoes	3/4 c., riced; 1, 2½" diam.	2.0	0.1	19.1	85	83
Prunes, dried	12 medium	2.3	0.6	71.0	299	268
Radishes	10 red button	1.2	0.1	4.2	22	20
Raisins	3/4 c.	2.3	0.5	71.2	298	268
Rice, brown		7.5	1.7	77.7	356	360
white, uncooked	1/2 c.	7.6	0.3	79.4	351	362
Rutabagas	2/3 c., ½" cubes	1.1	0.1	8.9	41	38
Salmon, canned		20.2	9.6	0.0	167	173
Sardines, canned in oil, drained solids		25.7	11.0	1.2	207	214
Sauerkraut, solids	2/3 c.	1.4	0.3	4.4	26	22
Scallops	15–20	14.8	0.1	3.4	74	78
Shredded wheat	3½ biscuits	10.1	2.5	80.1	384	360
Spinach	½ c., cooked	2.3	0.3	3.2	25	20
Squash, summer	½ c., cooked and mashed	0.6	0.1	3.9	19	16
winter	½ c., cooked and mashed	1.5	0.3	8.8	44	38
Strawberries	½ to 2/3 c.	0.8	0.5	8.3	41	37

399

TABLE 40. *Protein, Fat, and Carbohydrate Content and Energy Value of Foods: Expressed per 100 Grams of the Edible Material (Continued)*

Food	Approximate Measure	Protein	Fat	Carbo-hydrate	Atwater Factors	Specific Factors
		grams	grams	grams	Calories	Calories
Sugar, brown, dark	½ c.	0.0	0.0	95.5	382	370
white	½ c.	0.0	0.0	99.5	398	385
Sweetpotato		1.8	0.7	27.9	125	123
Tangerines	2, 2″ diam.	0.8	0.3	10.9	50	44
Tapioca, dry	½ c.	0.6	0.2	86.4	350	360
Tomatoes	1, 2½″ diam.	1.0	0.3	4.0	23	20
Tuna, canned, drained solids		29.0	8.2	0.0	190	198
Turkey		20.1	20.2	0.0	262	268
Turnip(s)	¾ c., 1″ cubes	1.1	0.2	7.1	35	32
Turnip greens	½ c., cooked	2.9	0.4	5.4	37	30
Veal cutlet		19.5	9.0	0.0	159	164
Vegetable soup, canned, condensed	⅜ c.	3.3	1.4	11.5	72	65
Walnuts, English	1⅙ c., chopped	15.0	64.4	15.6	702	654
Watercress		1.7	0.3	3.3	23	18
Watermelon	1 slice, 2½″ × 2½″ × 1″	0.5	0.2	6.9	31	28
White sauce	⅓ c., generous	4.0	12.5	8.8	164	162
Yeast, baker's comp.		(10.6)	0.4	13.0	(98)	86
brewer's dried		(36.9)	1.6	37.4	(312)	(273)

400

TABLE 40A. *(Supplement to Table 40.) Data from U. S. Department of Agriculture and 2nd Edition of This Book*

Food	Approximate Measure	Protein	Fat	Carbo-hydrate	Energy Value Atwater Factors	Energy Value Specific Factors
		grams	grams	grams	Calories	Calories
Apple, baked[1]	½ large apple	0.4	0.5	36.0	150[2]	
Apple sauce[1]	⅜ c.	0.2	0.8	37.2	157[2]	
Artichoke, French	½, 3″ diam., 4″ long	3.4	0.5	12.0	66	
Beans, baked with pork and tomato sauce	½ c.	5.8	2.1	18.4		113
Beef, corned, canned, medium fat		25.3	12.0	0.0		216
Bluefish, raw		20.5	4.0	0.0		124
Bologna	1 piece, 2⅞″ diam., 1 1/16″ thick	14.8	15.9	3.6		221
Brazil nuts		14.4	65.9	11.0		646
Bread, rye	3⅓ slices, 3½″ × 4″ × ½″	9.1	1.2	52.4		244
whole wheat, raisin	4–5 slices	7.3	3.1	53.2	269	
Buns	3–4 average	9.4	7.2	59.1	339	
Cheese, Roquefort	3″ sector, 1″ thick, 6½″ diam.	21.4	32.3	0.0	376	
Chestnuts		6.2	5.4	42.1	242	
Chocolate wafers	8, 2″ diam.	4.9	21.0	71.4	494	
Coconut, dried, sweetened		3.6	39.1	53.2		556
Coleslaw	1¼ c.	1.3	6.1	7.7		86
Corn, canned	⅜ c.	2.0	0.5	16.1		67

TABLE 40A. (Supplement to Table 40.) Data from U. S. Department of Agriculture and 2nd Edition of This Book. (Continued)

					Energy Value	
					Atwater·	Specific
Food	Approximate Measure	Protein	Fat	Carbo-hydrate	Factors	Factors
		grams	grams	grams	Calories	Calories
Cornflakes	3 c.	8.1	0.4	85.0		385
Corn syrup	¼ c.	0.0	0.0	85.0	340	
Crabmeat	⅔ c.	16.9	2.9	1.3		104
Cream (thick whipping)	⅜ c.	2.3	35.0	3.2		330
Currants, dried		2.4	1.7	74.2	322	
fresh		1.2	0.2	13.6		55
Custard pie	2″ sector, 9″ diam.	5.2	8.7	26.3		204
Dates (comm'l., dried)	14 average	2.2	0.6	75.4		284
Filberts	½ c.	15.6	65.3	13.0	702	
Flounder, "sole"		14.9	0.5	0.0		68
Herring, smoked, kippered		22.2	12.9	0.0		211
Kohlrabi	½ to ¾ c., diced	2.1	0.1	6.7	36	30
Macaroons	8 average	6.5	15.2	65.2		424
Mayonnaise	½ c.	1.5	78.0	3.0		708
Mince pie	3″ sector, 9″ diam.	2.5	6.9	45.6		252
Molasses, cane,						
first extraction	⅓ c.	2.4	—	69.3	287	
Olive oil	½ c.	0.0	100.0	0.0	900	
Oysters, meat only	4 large, or ½ c. solids	9.8	2.1	5.6		84

TABLE 40A. (Supplement to Table 40.) Data from U. S. Department of Agriculture and 2nd Edition of This Book (Continued)

Food	Approximate Measure	Protein	Fat	Carbo-hydrate	Energy Value Atwater Factors	Specific Factors
		grams	grams	grams	Calories	Calories
Raspberries, red	¾ c.	1.2	0.4	13.8		57
Shad	Cross section, 3½″ on back	18.7	9.8	0.0		168
Shad roe		20.9	3.8	2.6	128	
Soybean flour, flakes, grits, medium fat		42.5	6.5	37.2		264
Squash pie	2″ sector, 9″ diam.	4.4	8.4	21.7	180	

[1] Sweetened.
[2] About half the calories are here due to sweetening.

TABLE 41. *Approximate Averages of Certain Mineral and Vitamin Values in Typical Foods: Expressed per 100 Grams of the Edible Material*

Food	Calcium	Phosphorus	Iron	Ascorbic Acid (Vitamin C)	Thiamine (Vitamin B_1)	Riboflavin	Niacin	Vitamin A Value
	mgm.	mgm.	mgm.	mgm.	mgm.	mgm.	mgm.	I.U.
Almonds	254	475	4.4	trace	0.25	0.67	4.6	0
Apples	6	10	0.3	5	.04	.03	.2	90
pie	7	24	0.4	1	.03	.02	.2	160
Apricots, dried	86	119	4.9	12	.01	.16	3.3	7430
fresh	16	23	.5	7	.03	.05	.8	2790
Asparagus	21	62	.9	33	.16	.19	1.4	1000
Avocado	10	38	.6	16	.06	.13	1.1	290
Bacon	13	108	.8	0	.38	.12	1.9	(0)*
Bananas	8	28	.6	10	.04	.05	.7	430
Beans, baked	56	113	2.1	2†	.05	.04	.5	30
dried	163	437	6.9	2	.67	.23	2.2	?
Lima, dried	68	381	7.5	2	.48	.18	2.0	0
Lima, green	63	158	2.3	32	.21	.11	1.4	280
snap	65	44	1.1	19	.08	.11	.5	630
Beef, corned, canned	20	106	4.3	0	.02	.24	3.4	(0)
dried	20	404	5.1	0	.07	.32	3.8	(0)
lean muscle (round)	11	180	2.9	0	.08	.17	4.7	(0)
"roasting meat"‡	11	204	2.8	0	.12	.15	5.1	(0)

404

Beet greens	§	45	3.2	34	.08	.18	.4	6700
Beets	27	43	1.0	.10	.02	.05	.4	20
Blackberries	32	32	0.9	21	.04	.04	.4	200
Blueberries	16	13	.8	16	(.02)	(.02)	(.3)	280
Bluefish	23	243	.6	—	(.12)	(.09)	1.9	—
Bologna	(9)	(112)	2.2				2.7	(0)
Bran, various sources	113	893	16.8	0	.18	.19	21	100
Bread, Boston brown	185	158	2.5	0	.6	.4	1.4	140
white, enriched¶	79	92	1.8	0	.08	.12	2.2	0
white, raisin, enriched	80	104	1.8	?	.24	.15	2.2	0
whole wheat	96	263	2.2	0	.24	.15	3.0	0
Broccoli	130	76	1.3	118	.30	.13	1.1	3500
Brussels sprouts	34	78	1.3	94	.10	.21	0.7	400
Butter	20	16	0.0	0	.08	.16	.1	3300‖
Buttermilk, cultured from skim milk	(118)	93	.1	1	trace	.01	.1	(trace)
Cabbage	46	31	.5	50	.04	.18	.3	80
Cantaloupe	17	16	.4	33	.06	.05	.5	3420**

* Figure in parenthesis, imputed value.
† Ascorbic acid attributable to tomato sauce frequently used.
? Indicates that the data are scanty or contradictory.
‡ Average values for composition of all cuts in a boned and trimmed carcass of commercial grade generally used for (a) chopped meat, (b) roasting and broiling, (c) stewing and boiling.
§ 118 mgm.; may not be available because of presence of oxalic acid.
¶ Made with 4% non-fat milk solids.
‖ Year-round average.
** Based on deeply colored varieties.

TABLE 41. *Approximate Averages of Certain Mineral and Vitamin Values in Typical Foods: Expressed per 100 Grams of the Edible Material (Continued)*

Food	Calcium	Phos-phorus	Iron	Ascorbic Acid (Vitamin C)	Thiamine (Vitamin B_1)	Ribo-flavin	Niacin	Vitamin A Value
	mgm.	mgm.	mgm.	mgm.	mgm.	mgm.	mgm.	I.U.
Carrots	39	37	.8	6	.06	.06	.5	12,000
Cashew nuts	46	428	5.0	—	0.63	.19	2.1	—
Cauliflower	22	72	1.1	69	.11	.10	.6	90
Celery	50	40	.5	7	.05	.04	.4	0
Chard	*	36	2.5	38	.06	.07	.4	2800
Cheese, Cheddar type‡	725	495	1.0	(0)	.02	.42	trace	1400
cottage, from skim milk‡	96	189	.3	(0)	.02	.31	(.1)	(20)
Parmesan‡	1160	823	.4	0	.02	.73	.2	1060
Swiss‡	925	563	.9	?	.01	(.4)	(.1)	1450
Cherries, canned	11	12	(.3)	6	.03	.02	.2	720
fresh	18	20	.4	8	.05	.06	.4	620
Chestnuts	34	90	.8	—	.22	+	+	—
Chicken, broiler	14	200	1.5	—	.08	.16	10.2	(0)
roasters	14	200	1.5	—	.08	.16	8.0	trace
Chocolate, unsweetened	†	446	(4.4)	(0)	.05	.24	1.1	60
Coconut, dry, shredded	43	191	3.6	(0)	trace	trace	trace	0
fresh	21	98	2.0	2	.10	.01	.2	0
Coconut custard pie	125	116	1.2	—	.05	.16	.3	230

406

Cod	10	194	0.4	2	.06	2.2	—
Collards	249	58	1.6	100	.11	(2.0)	6870
Corn, canned, solids and liquid	4	51	.5	5	.03	.9	200§
Corn, sweet, white or yellow, fresh	9	120	.5	12	.15	1.7	390§
Cornflakes	11	58	1.3	0	.04	1.6	(0)
Cornmeal, degermed, uncooked	6	99	1.1	(0)	.14	1.0	300¶
Crackers, Graham	20	203	1.9	0	.30	1.5	(0)
soda, plain	20	96	1.1	(0)	.06	1.1	(0)
Cranberries	14	11	0.6	12	(.03)	0.1	40
Cranberry sauce, canned	(8)	(7)	(.3)	2	(.02)	(.1)	(30)
Cream, thin, 20% fat	97	77	0.1	1	.03	.1	830
thick, 35% fat	78	61	0.1	1	.02	.1	1440
Cucumbers	10	21	.3	8	.03	.2	0‖
Currants, fresh red	36	33	.9	36	.04	—	120
Dandelion greens	187	70	3.1	36	.19	(.8)	13650
Dates, dried	72	60	2.1	0	.09	2.2	60

* 105 mgm.; may not be available because of presence of oxalic acid.
† A plus mark (+) means present but not measured as to quantity; ++ and +++ indicate more.
† 95 mgm.; may not be available because of presence of oxalic acid.
‡ Reported differences of calcium content and vitamin values among kinds of cheese being probably largely accidental, it is well to emphasize instead, two general facts: (1) The rennet-made cheeses such as Brick, Brie, Camembert, Edam, Emmenthal or Swiss, Parmesan, Pineapple, Roquefort and Stilton have, like Cheddar, about one per cent of calcium; while those which like Cottage are coagulated by acidification have only about one-eighth as much.
§ Based on yellow corn; white corn contains only a trace.
¶ Based on yellow cornmeal; white cornmeal contains only a trace.
‖ Based on pared cucumbers; unpared contains about 260 I.U. vitamin A per 100 grams.

TABLE 41. *Approximate Averages of Certain Mineral and Vitamin Values in Typical Foods: Expressed per 100 Grams of the Edible Material (Continued)*

Food	Calcium	Phosphorus	Iron	Ascorbic Acid (Vitamin C)	Thiamine (Vitamin B₁)	Riboflavin	Niacin	Vitamin A Value
	mgm.	mgm.	mgm.	mgm.	mgm.	mgm.	mgm.	I.U.
Eggplant	15	37	.4	5	.04	.05	.6	30
Eggs, whole, fresh	54	210	2.7	0	.10	.29	.1	1140
white	6	17	.2	0	0	.26	(.1)	(0)
yolk	147	586	7.2	0	.27	.35	trace	3210
Endive	79	56	1.7	11	.07	.12	.4	3000
Farina, uncooked	28	112	1.0*	(0)	.06*	.06*	.8*	(0)
Figs	54	32	0.6	2	.06	.05	.5	80
Flour, white, enriched whole wheat (from hard wheats)	16	87	2.9	(0)	.44	.26	3.5	(0)
	41	372	3.3	(0)	.55	.12	4.3	(0)
Frankforters	8	100	1.5	0	.18	.19	2.8	(0)
Gooseberries	22	28	.5	33	—	—	—	290
Grapefruit	22	18	.2	40	.04	.02	.2	trace
juice, canned, unsw.	8	13	.3	35	.03	.02	.2	trace
Grape(s)	17	21	.6	4	.06	.04	.2	80
juice	10	10	.3	trace	.04	.05	(.2)	—
Haddock	23	197	.7	—	.05	.08	2.4	—
Halibut	13	211	.7	—	.07	.06	9.2	440

408

Ham, fresh	9	168	2.3	0	.74	.18	4.0	(0)
smoked	10	136	2.5	0	.70	.19	4.0	(0)
Hazelnuts	287	354	4.1	—	.4	—	—	?
Heart, beef	9	203	4.6	6	.58	.89	7.8	30
Herring, kippered	66	254	(1.4)	—	trace	.28	(2.9)	—
Hominy	11	70	1.0	0	.15	.05	(.9)	(0)
Honey	5	16	.9	4	trace	.04	.2	(0)
Huckleberries, see Blueberries								
Ice cream, plain	123	99	.1	1	.04	.19	.1	520
Kale	225	62	2.2	115	.10	.26	2.0	7540†
Kidney, beef	9	221	7.9	13	.37	2.55	6.4	1150
Kohlrabi	46	50	.6	61	.06	.05	.2	trace
Lamb, chop (rib)	9	138	2.2	0	.13	.18	4.3	(0)
leg of	10	213	2.7	0	.16	.22	5.2	(0)
Leeks	58	56	.8	15	.1	.07	.5	50
Lemons	40	22	.6	50	.04	trace	.1	0
juice	14	11	.1	50	.04	trace	.1	0
Lentils, dry	59	423	7.4	5	.56	.24	2.2	570
Lettuce, headed	22	25	.5	8	.04	.08	.2	540
loose leafed	62	20	1.1	18	.04	.08	.2	1620
Liver, beef	7	358	6.6	31	.26	3.33	13.7	?
Lobster	61	184	0.6	—	(.13)	.06	(1.9)	—
Loganberries	35	19	1.2	24	(.03)	(.07)	(.3)	(200)
Macaroni, uncooked	22	165	1.5*	0	.09*	.06*	2.0*	(0)

* More if enriched.
† Other investigators have given much higher results for the vitamin value of kale.

TABLE 41. *Approximate Averages of Certain Mineral and Vitamin Values in Typical Foods: Expressed per 100 Grams of the Edible Material (Continued)*

Food	Calcium	Phosphorus	Iron	Ascorbic Acid (Vitamin C)	Thiamine (Vitamin B_1)	Riboflavin	Niacin	Vitamin A Value
	mgm.	mgm.	mgm.	mgm.	mgm.	mgm.	mgm.	I.U.
Mackerel	5	239	1.0	—	.15	.35	8.4	(450)
Mangoes	9	13	.2	41	.06	.06	.9	6350
Margarine	20	16	.0	(0)	(0)	(0)	(0)	3300*
Mayonnaise†	19	60	1.0	0	.04	.04	(0)	210
Milk, condensed, sweetened	273	228	.2	1	.05	.39	.2	(430)
evaporated, unsweetened	243	195	.2	1	.05	.36	.2	400
malted, dry	287	379	2.1	(0)	.33	.54	—	1020
skimmed, dry	1300	1030	.6	7	.35	1.96	1.1	(40)
skimmed, fresh	123	97	.1	1	.04	.18	.1	trace
whole, dried	949	728	.6	6	.30	1.46	.7	1400
whole, fresh	118	93	.1	1	.04	.17	.1	(160)
Molasses, cane, first extraction	165	45	4.3	—	.07	.06	.2	—
Mustard greens	220	38	2.9	102	.09	.20	.8	6460
Mutton, see Lamb								
Nectarines	5	22	0.5	?	?	?	?	1500
Oatmeal, dry	53	405	4.5	(0)	.60	.14	1.0	(0)
Okra	82	62	.7	30	.08	.07	1.1	740

Oleomargarine, see Margarine							
Olives, green	87	17	1.6	—	trace	—	300
ripe, Mission	87	17	1.6	—	trace	—	60
Onions, mature	32	44	.5	9	.03	.04	50
young green	135	24	.9	24	(.03)	(.04)	(50)
Oranges	33	23	.4	49	.08	.03	(190)
juice	19	16	.2	49	.08	.03	(190)
Oysters, meat only	94	143	5.6	—	.15	.20	(320)
Parsnips	57	80	.7	18	.08	.12	0
Peaches, dried (sulfured)	44	126	6.9	19	.01	.20	3250
fresh	8	22	.6	8	.02	.05	880
Peanut(s), roasted	74	393	1.9	(0)	.30	.13	0
Peanut butter	74	393	1.9	(0)	.12	.13	0
Pears, fresh	13	16	.3	4	.02	.04	20
Peas, canned	25	67	1.8	8	.11	.06	540
dried, split	33	268	5.1	2	.77	.28	370
fresh, green	22	122	1.9	26	.34	.16	680
Pecans	74	324	2.4	2	.72	.11	50
Peppers, green	11	25	.4	120	.04	.07	630
Pineapple, canned	29	7	.6	9	.07	.02	80
fresh	16	11	.3	24	.08	.02	130
juice, canned	15	8	.5	9	.05	.02	80

* Based on the average vitamin A content of fortified margarine. "Most of the margarines manufactured for use in the United States have 15,000 I.U. of vitamin A added per pound. The minimum Federal specifications for fortified margarine require the addition of 9,000 I.U. of vitamin A per pound." U. S. Dept. Agriculture.
† Minerals and vitamins are calculated from a recipe.

TABLE 41. *Approximate Averages of Certain Mineral and Vitamin Values in Typical Foods: Expressed per 100 Grams of the Edible Material (Continued)*

Food	Calcium	Phos-phorus	Iron	Ascorbic Acid (Vitamin C)	Thiamine (Vitamin B_1)	Ribo-flavin	Niacin	Vitamin A Value
	mgm.	mgm.	mgm.	mgm.	mgm.	mgm.	mgm.	I.U.
Plums, fresh	17	20	.5	5	.06	.04	.5	350
Pork, loin	10	186	2.5	0	.80	.19	4.3	(0)
sausage	6	100	1.6	0	.43	.17	2.3	(0)
Potatoes	11	56	.7	17*	.11	.04	1.2	20
Prunes, dried, unsulfured	54	85	3.9	3	.10	.16	1.7	1890
Pumpkin, fresh	21	44	.8	8	(.05)	(.08)	(.6)	(3400)
canned	(20)	(36)	(.7)	—	.02	.06	.5	3400
Radishes	37	31	1.0	24	.03	.02	.3	30
Raisins	78	129	3.3	trace	.15	.08	.5	50
Raspberries, red	40	37	.9	24	.02	(.07)	(.3)	130
Rhubarb	†	25	.5	9	.01	—	.1	30
Rice, brown	39	303	2.0	(0)	.32	.05	4.6	(0)
converted	24	136	.8	(0)	.20	.03	3.8	(0)
white	24	136	.8	(0)	.07	.03	1.6	(0)
Rutabaga	55	41	.4	36	.07	.08	.9	330
Salmon, canned, pink	187	286	.8	(0)	.03	.18	8.0	70‡
Sardines, canned in oil, drained solids	386	586	2.7	(0)	.02	.17	4.8	220

412

Sauerkraut, canned	36	18	(.5)	16	.03	.06	.1	30
Scallops	26	208	1.8	—	(.04)	.10	1.4	0
Shad	—	260	.5	—	(.15)	.24	(8.4)	—
Shad roe	23	242	1.2	—	.25	+	—	2500
Shredded wheat	47	360	3.5	0	.22	.12	4.4	(0)
Shrimp, canned	115	263	3.1	(0)	.01	.03	2.2	60
Soybean flour, flakes, grits, medium fat	244	610	13.0	(0)	.82	.34	2.6	110
Spinach	§	55	3.0	59	.11	.20	.6	?
Squash, summer white fleshed	15	15	.4	17	.05	.09	.8	260
winter, yellow fleshed	19	28	.6	8	.05	.12	.5	4950
Strawberries	28	27	.8	60	.03	.07	.3	60
Sugar, brown	76¶	37¶	2.6	(0)	(0)	(0)	(0)	(0)
white	—	—	—	(0)	(0)	(0)	(0)	(0)
Sweetpotatoes	30	49	.7	22	.09	.05	.6	7700‖
Tangerines	(33)	(23)	(.4)	31	.07	(.03)	(.2)	(420)
Tapioca	12	12	(1.0)	(0)	(0)	(0)	(0)	(0)
Tomatoes, canned	(11)	(27)	(.6)	16	.06	.03	.7	1050
catsup	12	18	.8	11	.09	.07	2.2	(1880)
fresh	11	27	.6	23	.06	.04	.5	1100

* Year round average. Recently dug potatoes contain about 24 mg. of ascorbic acid per 100 gm. The value is only half as high after 3 months of storage and about one-third as high when potatoes have been stored as long as six months.
† 51 mgm.; may not be available because of presence of oxalic acid.
‡ Based on pink salmon. Canned red salmon may have a value several times higher.
§ 81 mgm. Presumably not available because of presence of oxalic acid.
¶ Based on dark brown sugar; lower values for light brown sugar.
‖ If pale varieties only were used, value would be very much lower.

413

TABLE 41. *Approximate Averages of Certain Mineral and Vitamin Values in Typical Foods: Expressed per 100 Grams of the Edible Material.* (Continued)

Food	Calcium	Phos-phorus	Iron	Ascorbic Acid (Vitamin C)	Thiamine (Vitamin B_1)	Ribo-flavin	Niacin	Vitamin A Value
	mgm.	mgm.	mgm.	mgm.	mgm.	mgm.	mgm.	I.U.
Tomato juice	(7)	(15)	(.4)	16	.05	.03	.8	1050
Tuna fish, canned, drained solids	(8)	(351)	1.4	(0)	.05	.12	12.8	80
Turkey, medium fat	23	320	3.8	(0)	.09	.14	8.0	trace
Turnips	40	34	.5	28	.05	.07	.5	trace
Turnip greens	259	50	2.4	136	.09	.46	.8	9540
Veal, cutlet,* leg of*	11	200	2.9	0	.14	.26	6.5	(0)
	14	229	2.6	0	.15	.38	6.3	(0)
Vegetable soup, canned	18	26	.5	2	.02	.03	.4	?
Walnuts, English	83	380	2.1	3	.48	.13	1.2	30
Watercress	195	46	2.0	77	.08	.16	.8	4720
Watermelon	7	12	.2	6	.05	.05	.2	590
Wheat germ	84	1096	8.1	(0)	2.05	.80	4.6	(0)
Yeast, compressed baker's	25	605	4.9	(0)	.45	2.07	28.2	(0)
dried, brewer's	106	1893	18.2	(0)	9.69	5.45	36.2	(0)

* From Columbia University data through second edition of this book.

Appendix D

RECOMMENDED DIETARY ALLOWANCES

Table 42, with its accompanying footnotes and "Further recommendations," is reproduced from Number 129 of the Reprint and Circular Series of the National Research Council, 2101 Constitution Avenue, Washington, 25, D. C.

In the original publication may also be found a review of some of the evidence on which are based the expert judgments represented in the recommendations. It is pointed out that, "The Board recognizes a responsibility to explain as clearly as it can (even at the cost of some near-repetition) just how the levels of nutrient intake which it *recommends* are related to the lesser quantities which are essential to avoid manifest nutritional deficiencies. Studies on man, as well as more complete experience with animals, clearly indicate substantial improvements in growth and function when the intakes of certain nutrients are increased above the level which is just sufficient to prevent obvious deficiency symptoms. The level above which lesions or symptoms are not commonly observed is merely one point on a long curve relating intake to function. The allowance of a margin of intake above the critical level for each nutrient is, therefore, designed to permit additional benefits as well as to cover individual variations. No fixed formula for computing the margin between "minimal requirements" and "recommended allowances" would be equally logical for all nutrients or for all population groups. There is now much evidence from long-term animal experimentation that, aside from individual variations of need, the margins between optimal intake and minimal requirements are wider for some nutrients than for others. In the judgment of the Board substantially lower levels than those given in the accompanying table would not be expected to give equally good results with large numbers of people through long periods of time."

TABLE 42. Recommended Daily Dietary Allowances[1]
Revised 1948
Food and Nutrition Board, National Research Council

	Calories[2]	Protein, gm.	Calcium, gm.	Iron, mg.	Vitamin A,[3] I.U.	Thiamine,[4] mg.	Riboflavin,[4] mg.	Niacin (Nicotinic Acid),[4] mg.	Ascorbic Acid, mg.	Vitamin D, I.U.
Man (154 lb., 70 kg.)										
Sedentary	2400	70	1.0	12[5]	5000	1.2	1.8	12	75	[6]
Physically active	3000	70	1.0	12[5]	5000	1.5	1.8	15	75	[6]
With heavy work	4500	70	1.0	12[5]	5000	1.8	1.8	18	75	[6]
Woman (123 lb., 56 kg.)										
Sedentary	2000	60	1.0	12	5000	1.0	1.5	10	70	[6]
Moderately active	2400	60	1.0	12	5000	1.2	1.5	12	70	[6]
Very active	3000	60	1.0	12	5000	1.5	1.5	15	70	[6]
Pregnancy (latter half)	2400[7]	85	1.5	15	6000	1.5	2.5	15	100	400
Lactation	3000	100	2.0	15	8000	1.5	3.0	15	150	400
Children up to 12 years[8]										
Under 1 yr.[9]	110/2.2 lb. (1 kg.)	3.5/2.2 lb. (1 kg.)	1.0	6	1500	0.4	0.6	4	30	400
1–3 yrs. (27 lb., 12 kg.)	1200	40	1.0	7	2000	0.6	0.9	6	35	400
4–6 yrs. (42 lb., 19 kg.)	1600	50	1.0	8	2500	0.8	1.2	8	50	400
7–9 yrs. (58 lb., 26 kg.)	2000	60	1.0	10	3500	1.0	1.5	10	60	400
10–12 yrs. (78 lb., 35 kg.)	2500	70	1.2	12	4500	1.2	1.8	12	75	400

Children over 12 yrs.[8]								
Girls, 13–15 yrs. (108 lb., 49 kg.)	2600	80	1.3	15	5000	1.3	2.0	13	80	400
16–20 yrs. (122 lb., 55 kg.)	2400	75	1.0	15	5000	1.2	1.8	12	80	400
Boys, 13–15 yrs. (108 lb., 49 kg.)	3200	85	1.4	15	5000	1.5	2.0	15	90	400
16–20 yrs. (141 lb., 64 kg.)	3800	100	1.4	15	6000	1.7	2.5	17	100	400

[1] Objectives toward which to aim in planning practical dietaries: The recommended allowances can be attained with a good variety of common foods which will also provide other minerals and vitamins for which requirements are less well known.

[2] Calorie allowances must be adjusted up or down to meet specific needs. The calorie values in the table are therefore not applicable to all individuals but rather represent group averages. The proper calorie allowance is that which over an extended period will maintain body weight or rate of growth at the level most conducive to well-being.

[3] The allowance depends on the relative amounts of vitamin A and carotene. The allowances of the table are based on the premise that approximately two-thirds of the vitamin A value of the average diet in this country is contributed by carotene and that carotene has half or less than half the value of vitamin A.

[4] For adults (except pregnant and lactating women) receiving diets supplying 2000 calories or less, such as reducing diets, the allowances of thiamine and niacin may be 1 mg. and 10 mg. respectively. The fact that figures are given for different calorie levels for thiamine and niacin does not imply that we can estimate the requirement of these factors within 500 calories, but they are added merely for simplicity of calculation. In the present revision, riboflavin allowances are based on body weight rather than caloric levels. Other members of the B complex also are required, though no values can be given. Foods supplying adequate thiamine, riboflavin, and niacin will tend to supply sufficient of the remaining B vitamins.

[5] There is evidence that the male adult needs relatively little iron. The need will usually be provided for if the diet is satisfactory in other respects.

[6] The need for supplemental vitamin D by vigorous adults leading a normal life seems to be minimum. For persons working at night and for nuns and others whose habits shield them from the sunlight, as well as for elderly persons, the ingestion of small amounts of vitamin D is desirable.

[7] During the latter part of pregnancy the calorie allowance should increase to approximately 20 percent above the preceding level. The value of 2400 calories represents the allowance for pregnant, sedentary women.

[8] Allowances for children are based on the needs for the middle year in each group (as 2, 5, 8, etc.) and are for moderate activity and for average weight at the middle year of the age group.

[9] Needs for infants increase from month to month with size and activity. The amounts given are for approximately 6 to 8 months. The dietary requirements for some of the nutrients such as protein and calcium are less if derived largely from human milk.

Further Recommendations of the National Research Council:

Fat. There is available little information concerning the human requirement for fat. Fat allowances must be based at present more on food habits than on physiological requirements. While a requirement for certain unsaturated fatty acids (the linoleic and arachidonic acids of natural fats) has been amply demonstrated with experimental animals, the human need for these fatty acids is not known. In spite of the paucity of information on this subject there are several factors which make it desirable (1) that fat be included in the diet to the extent of at least 20 to 25 per cent of the total calories and (2) that the fat intake include essential unsaturated fatty acids to the extent of at least 1 per cent of the total calories. At higher levels of energy expenditure, e.g., for a very active person consuming 4500 calories and for children and for adolescent persons, it is desirable that 30 to 35 per cent of the total calories be derived from fat. Since foodstuffs such as meat, milk, cheese, nuts, etc., contribute fat to the diet, it is necessary to use separated or "visible" fats such as butter, oleomargarine, lard, or shortenings to supply only one-third to one-half the amounts indicated.

Water. A suitable allowance of water for adults is 2.5 liters daily in most instances. An ordinary standard for diverse persons is one milliliter for each calorie of food. Most of this quantity is contained in prepared foods. At work or in hot weather, requirements may reach 5 to 13 liters daily. Water should be allowed *ad libitum,* since sensations of thirst usually serve as adequate guides to intake except for infants and sick persons.

Salt. The needs for salt and for water are closely interrelated. A liberal allowance of sodium chloride for the adult is 5 grams daily, except for some persons who sweat profusely. The average normal intake of salt is 10 to 15 grams daily, an amount which meets the salt requirements for a water intake up to 4 liters daily. When sweating is excessive, one additional gram of salt should be consumed for each liter of water in excess of 4 liters daily. With heavy work or in hot climates 20 to 30 grams daily may be consumed with meals and in drinking water. Even then, most persons do not need more salt than usually occurs in prepared foods. It has been shown that after acclimatization persons produce sweat that contains only about 0.5 gram to the liter in contrast with a content of 2 to 3 grams for sweat of the unacclimatized person. Consequently after acclimatization, need for increase of salt beyond that of ordinary food disappears.

Iodine. The requirement for iodine is small, probably about 0.002 to 0.004 mg. daily for each kilogram of body weight, or a total of 0.15 to 0.30 mg. daily for the adult. This need is met by the regular use of iodized salt; its use is especially important in *adolescence* and *pregnancy*.

Phosphorus. Available evidence indicates that the phosphorus allowances should be at least equal to those for calcium in the diets of children and of women during the latter part of pregnancy and during lactation. In the case of other adults the phosphorus allowances should be approximately. 1.5 times those for calcium. In general it is safe to assume that if the calcium and protein needs are met through common foods, the phosphorus requirement also will be covered, because the common foods richest in calcium and protein are also the best sources of phosphorus.

Copper. The requirement for copper for adults is about 1 to 2 mg. daily. Infants and children require approximately 0.05 mg. for each kilogram of body weight. The requirement for copper is approximately one-tenth that for iron. A good diet normally will supply sufficient copper.

Vitamin K. The requirement for vitamin K usually is satisfied by any good diet except for the infant in utero and for the first few days after birth. Supplemental vitamin K is recommended during the last month of pregnancy. When it has not been given in this manner, it is recommended for the mother preceding delivery or for the baby immediately after birth.

Appendix E

GLOSSARY*

absorption: taking up of water or materials in solution.
acetone substances: a group of substances often formed in the metabolism of fat (sometimes called "acetone bodies").
achylia: lack of hydrochloric acid and pepsin in the gastric juice.
achlorhydria: lack of hydrochloric acid in gastric juice.
acidophile: easily stained by acid dyes.
acidosis: any condition in which the body's alkaline reserve is depleted; may result from abnormal loss of alkaline salts from the body or (more commonly) from abnormal accumulation of acids. Term often used in restricted sense as synonymous with ketosis, defined below.
acrodynia: a disease of the skin.
adermin: term sometimes used for pyridoxine.
adipose: fatty.
adrenal (suprarenal) glands: a pair of endocrine glands, one being situated above each kidney.
adrenaline (epinephrine): a hormone secreted by the adrenal glands.
aerobic: acting in the presence of, and through the influence of, oxygen.
alanine: one of the digestion products of proteins.
alkaline reserve: the amount of potentially alkaline material available in the body to neutralize acids. Term often used in restricted sense as synonymous with the bicarbonate of the blood.
alkaline tide: increased alkalinity of the body generally and decreased acidity of the urine after a meal.
alkalosis: increased alkalinity in the body.
allergy: a condition of unusual or exaggerated specific susceptibility to a substance which is harmless in similar amounts for most individuals.
alveolar process: bony ridge containing tooth socket.
alveoli: membranous air sacs in the lungs.
anaerobic: in absence of oxygen.
anaphylaxis: sensitization; allergy.
aneurin: term sometimes used for thiamine.
anorexia: lack or loss of appetite for food.

---

* Students please note that the Index should also be consulted, for many of these and other terms are explained in the text.

antigen: a foreign agent which causes the production of an "antibody."

antineuritic: preventing neuritis.

antitoxin: specific agent against a toxin.

appetite: the inclination or desire to eat; distinguished from hunger as the drive to eat.

arginine: one of the digestion products of proteins.

aspartic acid: one of the digestion products of proteins.

atherosclerosis: one form of thickening of the walls of arteries.

atrophy: a wasting in size.

bacteriostatic: preventing or arresting the growth of bacteria.

base: a substance which combines with acids to form salts.

basophile: easily stained by basic dyes.

betaine: a nitrogenous base occurring in many natural foods, of nutritional interest as a source of "labile methyl" groupings.

bile: fluid secreted by the liver and poured into the intestines.

bradycardia: abnormal slowness of the heart-beat.

bronchioles: minute branches of the bronchial tubes.

buffer: a substance which tends to prevent or minimize a change in the reaction of a solution.

calciferol: vitamin D_2; a form of antirachitic vitamin produced by irradiation of ergosterol.

calcification: the process by which tissue becomes hardened by a deposit of calcium salts within its substance; deposition of a calcium compound.

calorigenic: heat-generating.

calorimeter: an instrument for measuring the heat change in any system; such as the bomb calorimeter which is used to determine the energy value of foods through measurement of the heat liberated during their oxidation; and the types of apparatus illustrated and discussed in Chapter IV by which is measured the heat production of the body.

carcinoma: a malignant tumor or cancer.

carcinogenic: cancer-producing.

carotenes: yellow pigments having the formula $C_{40}H_{56}$ of which three modifications are known, alpha-, beta-, and gamma-carotene, respectively, each serving nutritionally as a precursor of vitamin A.

casein: the principal protein of milk.

cephalin: a constituent of the brain; a substituted fat which contains phosphorus and nitrogen.

cerebrosides (galactolipids): constituents of brain and nerve substance which contain nitrogenous, fatty, and carbohydrate radicles.

cerebrospinal: pertaining to the brain and spinal cord.
chlorophyll: the green pigment of plants.
cholesterol: the principal sterol of animal origin.
choline: a nitrogenous base (containing "labile methyl" groupings), which is a constituent of the phospholipid lecithin and of other body substances.
chorea (St. Vitus's dance): a convulsive nervous disease, with involuntary and irregular jerking movements.
chyme: the partially digested material which the stomach passes on to the intestine.
cirrhosis: a disease characterized by excessive formation of connective tissue followed by contraction.
citrus: a genus of trees, including citron, grapefruit, lemon, lime, and orange.
conjunctivitis: inflammation of the membranes which line the eyelids and cover the eyeball.
connective tissue: a tissue holding together and in place other, usually more active, tissues, as, for example, muscle fibers or the cells of glands.
constitution: an important but not well defined concept, perhaps usually understood as meaning that inherited potentiality of health which one can impair but cannot enhance. Recent work in nutrition is enabling us to take a less fatalistic and more constructively scientific attitude toward the individual health-potentiality which is partly an inheritance and partly the result of nutritional conditioning both before and after birth.
cysteine: the reduction product of cystine, which very readily becomes reoxidized to cystine.
cystine: one of the digestion products of proteins.
cytopenia: deficiency in the cellular elements of the blood.

deaminization: the process by which the amino group, $-NH_2$, is split out of a molecule, as deaminization of amino acids in metabolism.
dentition: teething.
dermatitis: inflammation of the skin.
digestive hydrolysis: see hydrolysis.
diuresis: increased secretion of urine.

electrolyte: a substance which in aqueous solution breaks down into electrically charged particles known as ions.
endocrine: secreting internally or into the blood stream; as endocrine glands, or glands of internal secretion.
endogenous: originating within the organism.

environment: while usually suggesting surroundings, includes, by scientific definition, nutrition and any or all other *environmental factors,* that is, everything that conditions the life-process except the hereditary or genetic factors. See also Internal environment.
enzyme: consult the Index for explanation in the text.
epithelium: the covering of the skin and mucous membranes.
epinephrine (adrenaline): a hormone secreted by the adrenal glands.
ergosterol: a sterol found abundantly in fungi such as ergot and yeast and in very small amounts among the sterols of higher plants; on exposure to ultraviolet light of suitable wavelength it is converted into vitamin D_2.
etiology: cause, or study of causes.
exogenous: originating outside the organism.
"extrinsic principle": a factor from without, found effective in pernicious anemia.

fibroblast: a connective tissue cell.
flavin: yellow-green fluorescent water-soluble pigment. The flavin of greatest interest in nutrition is riboflavin (vitamin G, lactoflavin, lactochrome).

gastric: pertaining to the stomach.
geriatrics: pertaining to aging, or to the aged.
glutamic (glutaminic) acid: one of the digestion products of proteins.
glutathione: a substance containing glutamic acid, cysteine, and glycine which is found in active plant and animal tissues and is believed to play an important part in the oxidation and reduction reactions of the cells.
glycine (glycocoll): one of the digestion products of proteins.

hemeralopia: night blindness; condition in which a person sees more poorly at night or in a dim light than his normal vision would seem to warrant.
hemoglobin: the red protein found in the red blood cells; contains iron and is capable of uniting loosely with oxygen.
hemorrhage: (1) a loss of blood; (2) any portion of blood which has escaped the blood vessels.
histidine: one of the digestion products of proteins.
hormone: consult the Index for explanation in the text.
hydrolysis: a chemical change in which, with the introduction of the elements of water, a larger molecule is split into a smaller one or more.
hydrolyze: see hydrolysis.
hydroxyglutamic acid: one of the digestion products of proteins.

hydroxyproline: one of the digestion products of proteins.
hypertrophy: excessive growth of an organ or tissue.
hypochromic: characterized by deficiency of pigment, specifically of hemoglobin.
hypoprothrombinemia: subnormal blood level of prothrombin.

idiopathy: abnormality which is "self-originating" in the sense that it is not referable to any evident cause.
imbalance: lack of balance.
insulin: the active substance of the internal secretion of the pancreas.
intercellular: between the cells.
intermediary metabolism: the transfers and chemical changes undergone by nutrients after digestion and absorption.
internal environment: the resultant-condition within the living body of all factors other than those which are directly hereditary. While most that has hitherto been written regarding the internal environment emphasizes its relative constancy, we are now learning that it is very importantly influenced by nutrition.
intravenous: into a vein.
"intrinsic principle": a substance from within, effective in pernicious anemia.
in vitro: (literally "in glass") in a test-tube or other laboratory apparatus as contrasted with
in vivo: in the living organism.
ion: electrically charged atom or group of atoms such as is formed when an electrolyte is dissolved in water.
irritability: the ability to respond to a stimulus.
isoleucine: one of the digestion products of proteins.
isomers: chemically different substances having the same empirical formula.

keratin: a very insoluble protein which forms the base of epidermis, hair, and of all horny tissues.
keratomalacia: softening of the cornea.
ketosis: a condition in which, due to the failure of the body to complete the oxidation of fatty acids, there is an abnormal accumulation of socalled "ketone bodies" (acetone, hydroxybutric acid, and acetoacetic acid).

"labile methyl": a methyl ($-CH_3$) grouping which in metabolism may be transferred as a unit from one compound to another, as from methionine to choline.
lactalbumin: one of the proteins of milk.

lactic acid: a three-carbon organic acid ($CH_3CHOHCOOH$) formed as an intermediary in carbohydrate metabolism.
lecithin: a substance having the molecular structure of a fat in which one of the fatty acid radicles is replaced by phosphoric acid carrying choline (a nitrogenous base).
leucine: one of the digestion products of proteins.
longevity: length of life.
lymphatic: a vessel which carries lymph.
lysine: one of the digestion products of proteins.

macroscopic: seen with the naked eye.
matrix: the intercellular portion of a tissue.
metaplasia: change of one kind of tissue into another.
methionine: one of the digestion products of proteins.
methyl: (methyl radicle, —CH_3) a grouping which may transfer as a unit in chemical reactions.
microcytic: characterized by abnormally small red blood cells.
mitosis: cell division.

neurasthenia: nervous exhaustion, extreme abnormal fatigability.
neutrality: the state of being neither acid nor alkaline.
norleucine: one of the digestion products of proteins.

optimal (adj.), **optimum** (noun): the best.
organic: containing the element carbon; however, carbon dioxide, carbonic acid, and the carbonates and bicarbonates are not ordinarily regarded as organic.
"original chromosomal endowment": the set of chromosomes with which the individual is endowed at conception.
osmotic pressure: a physico-chemical property shown by substances in solution. It is most clearly manifest in the phenomenon of osmosis, which occurs when the solution is separated from pure water (or from a solution containing less of the dissolved substance) by a socalled semipermeable membrane, through which can pass water but not the substances in solution. Under these conditions, water passes through the membrane into the (more concentrated) solution.
oxidation: a chemical process involving the addition of the element oxygen to a compound, or the removal of the element hydrogen from the compound, or a chemically analogous change.
oxidation potential: a measure of the property of inducing oxidative changes.

parathyroid: group of small glands situated near the thyroid gland, and which secrete a hormone regulating calcium metabolism.

parenteral: not through the digestive tract.

parkinsonism: a nervous disease, characterized by muscular rigidity, rhythmic tremor, abolition of automatic associated movements.

pediatrics: pertaining to children or to development during childhood.

peripheral: relating to the portions of the body near the surface or in or near the extremities.

petechiae: tiny hemorrhage-spots, as in the skin.

pharmacodynamic: related to the effects of medicine, as contrasted with those of food.

phenylalanine: one of the digestion products of proteins.

phosphate: salt of phosphoric acid, H_3PO_4. Salts of the type BH_2PO_4 in which only one hydrogen has been replaced by reaction with base are called *mono-* or *primary* or *acid* phosphates; salts of the type B_2HPO_4 are called *di-* or *secondary* or *basic*.

phospholipids (phospholipins, phosphatids): substituted fats containing nitrogen and phosphorus.

polyneuritis (multiple neuritis): inflammation of many nerves at once.

precursor: a substance which is converted into another. For example, the carotenes are precursors of vitamin A, as explained in the text.

proline: one of the digestion products of proteins.

protein balance: the relationship found by comparing the amounts of nitrogen entering and leaving the body.

prothrombin: a precursor of blood-clot.

protoplasm: the essential substance of both the cell body and nucleus of cells of animals and plants, regarded as the only form of matter in which the phenomena of life are manifested.

provitamin: a substance which may be converted into a vitamin; thus, the carotenes are provitamins A, ergosterol is a provitamin D.

purpura: a disease characterized by purple patches on skin and mucous membranes due to subcutaneous bleeding.

pyruvic acid: a three-carbon organic acid ($CH_3COCOOH$) formed as an intermediary in carbohydrate metabolism.

radicle: a characteristic constituent part of a substance; as the amino-acid radicles in proteins.

reduction: a chemical process involving the addition of the element hydrogen to a compound, or the removal of the element oxygen from the compound, or a chemically analogous change.

rennin: the milk-curdling enzyme of the gastric juice.

resolved: (hydrolyzed, as in digestion).

ribose: a simple sugar containing five carbon atoms.

salt: the product of the reaction of an acid with a base.

senility: the state of showing the characteristics of old age.
serine: one of the digestion products of proteins.
sterols: a chemically related group of fat-soluble substances of very complex molecular structure; the provitamins D are important members of this group of substances.
stomatitis: inflammation of the mouth.
subcutaneous: beneath the skin.
synergistic: acting together with another agent.
synthesis: building up from simpler substances, or an artificial as distinguished from a natural formation.
synthesize: see Synthesis.

tachycardia: excessive rapidity of heart-beat.
tetany: a disease characterized by sudden, violent, involuntary contraction of the muscles of the extremities.
thermolabile: liable to be destroyed by heat.
threonine: one of the digestion products of proteins.
tonus (tone): a sustained state of partial activity such as exists in muscles at all times.
Trichinae: nematode parasites, one of which, *T. spiralis,* is frequently found in a cyst in hog muscle. Human beings also may become infested with these parasites (the resulting disease being known as **trichinosis**) by eating under-cooked pork from hogs so affected.
tryptophane: one of the digestion products of proteins.
tyrosine: one of the digestion products of proteins.

ultraviolet rays: rays of light of slightly shorter wave-length than visible light.
urea: the principal nitrogenous end-product of the metabolism of proteins in the body.

valine: one of the digestion products of proteins.
vascularization: the process of becoming "full of" (blood) vessels. It may be entirely normal as in the ends of the long bones; or clearly a departure from normal as when the whites of one's eyes become "bloodshot"; or there may be a doubtful zone between normal and abnormal vascularization as in the cornea where a degree of vascularization previously considered a normal variation is now considered a sign of riboflavin deficiency.

xerophthalmia: a dry and lustreless condition of the eyeball.
xerosis: lack of adequate moisture in a tissue.

SUBJECT INDEX*

Ability to resist disease, as affected by nutrition, 3–8, 123–126, 176, 177–178, 179–181, 213, 218–222, 224–225, 227, 233–235, 254, 255–259, 262–263, 265
Absorption, 28, 34, 35, 38–39, 40–44, 283
Abundance of dietary vitamin A value, as affecting frequency and duration of infection, 262–263
  as influencing length of life, 264, 265
Accomplishment, higher, made possible by better health and longer life through nutritional guidance in the use of food, 1–9, 125–128, 177–178, 219–222, 256, 264–265, 347–348
Acetic acid, 115
Acid(s), *see also* under their individual names
  acetic, 115
  amino, 24, 43–44, 85–96, 98–100, 103, 162, 336, 337, 339, 391
  arachidonic, 21, 390, 418
  ascorbic, 172–192; *see* Vitamin C
  categories of, 114
  citric, 14, 114, 115
  fatty, 21, 389–390
  fixed, 113, 116
  folic, 147, 242–243
  hippuric, 115
  lactic, 114, 115
  linoleic, 21, 390, 418
  linolenic, 21, 390
  malic, 114, 115
  nicotinic, *see* Niacin
  of gastric juice, 35–36
  organic, 114–115; *see also* under name of each
  oxalic, 115, 134–135, 405, 407, 413
  pantothenic, 148, 243, 249

  pteroylglutamic acid, 147, 242–243
  quinic, 115
  tartaric, 114, 115
Acid(s) concerned in acid-base balance (four categories), 114
Acid(s), how excreted from the body, 113, 114
Acid-base balance, 114, 115–119
"Acid forming" elements, 117, 118
Acidity, as reducing destruction of thiamine, 210–212
  as reducing destruction of vitamin C, 184–186
Acidosis, 116
Acrodynia, 240
Action, economic, to increase the production and consumption of those foods whose larger use is nutritionally desirable, 369, 373
  governmental, to increase the production of "the right kinds of food" for the best nutrition of the people, 372
  specific dynamic, of the foodstuffs, 59, 60
Activity, relations of, to nutritional needs, 47–50, 58–62, 70, 416–417
Adequate *vs.* optimal diet, 3–7, 124–133, 178–181, 219–222, 264–265, 372
Adipose (tissue), 74, 259
Adjustment of food production to consumer demand, 381–382
Administration of Federal Food Law, 16
Adrenaline, 86
Adult life expectancy, 125; *see also* Length of life
Age and physique at college entrance, 1
Age as affecting food needs, 79–82, 416–417

* Students may well consult the Glossary also.

SUBJECT INDEX

Aging, 125–130, 178–181, 222, 264–265
Alanine, 86
Alertness as influenced by the vitamin A value of the food, 252–253
Alkaline reserve, 117
Alkalinity, effect on loss of vitamin C, 184–185
  effect on loss of thiamine, 210–212
Alkalinity, reserve of, 117
Allergies, 380
Allowances, of calcium, 123–126, 130–131, 133, 416–417
  of energy (calories), 69–72, 77–82, 416–417
  of iron, 148–151, 416–417
  of niacin, 231–233, 416–417
  of protein, 96–101, 416–417
  of riboflavin, 219–224, 416–417
  of thiamine, 206–207, 416–417
  of vitamin A value, 265–266, 416–417
  of vitamin C (ascorbic acid), 178–182, 416–417
Allowances, Recommended Dietary, 8–9, 69, 77–79, 82, 98, 100–101, 123–126, 130, 133, 148–151, 168–169, 180, 207, 223, 233, 266, 289, 415–419
Allowances of National Research Council aimed to cover needs of 99 percent of the normal population, 124
Almonds, 394, 404
Alternatives for meat, 321–331, 334–339
Ameloblasts, 309
American Medical Association Council on Foods (and Nutrition), 50, 287–288
Amino acids, 43–45, 85–99, 148, 162, 336, 391
  absorption and metabolism, 43–45
  in food proteins, 336
  in thyroxine, 162
  minimum and recommended intakes of essential, 99
  nutritionally essential, 24, 85, 89–96, 98–99, 336
  shortage, as a factor in some anemias, 148
Amylase(s), 30
Amylopsin (pancreatic amylase), 391

Analogy of the body with an internal combustion motor and not with a heat engine, 50, 51
Analyses of experimental animals in nutrition research, 126–129
Analysis of foods, 25
"Anchorage" factor in rickets, 276
Anemia(s), 143–148, 240
  calcium shortage sometimes a factor in, 149
  hemorrhagic, 144–146
  hyperchromic, 143
  hypochromic, 143, 147, 148
  idiopathic, 147–148
  iron-deficiency, 143, 147
  macrocytic, 146
  nutritional, 143, 145, 148
  of vitamin B_6 deficiency, 240
  pernicious, 146–147
    extrinsic and intrinsic factors, 146–147
    limiting factor in, 146
  three types of, 144–148
Aneurin, *see* Thiamine
Animals as instruments of research in the problems of human nutrition, 1–5, 87
"Animal starch," *see* Glycogen
Antihemorrhagic vitamin (vitamin K), 296–297, 419
Anti-pernicious anemia substance, 146, 147, 241–242
Antirachitic factor, 275–295; *see also* Vitamin(s) D
Antiscorbutics, *see* Vitamin C (ascorbic acid)
Antrum, 35
Apparatus, digestive, 31–39, 41
Appetite, 32, 73, 203–204
Apple(s), 18, 64, 76, 118, 135, 153, 186, 191, 192, 208, 268, 394, 404
Apple, baked, 401
Apple, favorable to calcium assimilation, 136
Apple pie, 394, 404
Apple sauce, 401
Approaches to a policy for solution of the food problem, 369–382
Apricots, 394, 404
Arachidic acid, 390
Arachidonic acid, 21, 390, 418
Arachin, amino acid data, 336

SUBJECT INDEX 431

Arginine, 86, 91, 336
  in different proteins, 336
Ariboflavinosis, 221–222
Artichoke, 401
Articles of food, 5
Ascorbic acid (vitamin C), 172–197
  contents of typical foods, 191, 404–414
  losses on cooking, 186
  Recommended Dietary Allowances, 416–417
  see also Vitamin C
Ash of foods, 14, 25; *see also* Mineral elements
Asparagus, 186, 189, 231, 268, 394, 404
Aspartic acid, 86
Aspects of digestion, 28–43
Atrophy of epithelial cells in vitamin A deficiency, 258
Attachment of jaw as favorable to thorough chewing of food, 33
Attitudes toward acceptance of the guidance of the science of nutrition in our daily food habits, 369–382
Atwater bomb calorimeter, 63
Atwater-Rosa-Benedict respiration calorimeter, 51–53
Automobile engine analogy of body, 50–51
Avocado, 394, 404

Bacon, 394, 404
Bacteria, and caries, 303, 304, 310
  folic acid synthesis by, 243
  niacin-forming, 235
  vitamin B_{12} formation by, 241
  vitamin K formation by, 296
Balance, acid-base, 114, 115–119
  calcium, 136
  protein, 90–91, 96–98
Bananas, 18, 118, 153, 208, 229, 268, 394, 404
Band, transverse, of stomach, 35
Barley, as food, 319
  pearled, 394
Basal energy metabolism, 54, 56, 57, 73, 82
  metabolic rate, 54, 56, 57, 73, 82
  metabolism, 54, 56, 57, 73, 82

"Base forming" elements, 117, 118
Bean(s), baked, 268, 394, 401, 404
  dried, 10, 153, 208, 209, 321–323, 394, 404
  economy of, 318, 321–323
  green snap or string, 208, 231, 269, 325, 394, 404
  Lima, 394, 404
    dried, 208
  pea or navy, dried, 208, 209
  protein, 336, 337
Beef, 118, 135, 146, 152–154, 394, 404
  consumption of, 333
  corned, 401, 404
  dried or chipped, 394, 404
Beef muscle, 208, 228, 229, 336
Beet(s), 394, 405
Beet greens, 115, 134, 135, 136, 394, 405
Beet sugar, *see* Sucrose
Benefit to digestion from use of raw fruit or celery at end of meal, 34
Benefits added by increased liberality of calcium in diet, 124–128
  of milk, 4–6, 329–330
  of riboflavin, 219–221, 225, 227
  of vitamin A, 264–265
Beriberi, 198–201
  eradication from Japanese navy, 198–200
  in Bilibid prison, Manila, 201
Beta-lactose, 17
Bile, 32, 38
  duct, 32
    disease in relation to vitamin K, 296
  in digestion and absorption of fat, 41
  salts, 296
Bilirubin, 142
Biosynthesis of niacin, 235
Biotin, 113, 243–244
Biscuit, baking powder, 395
Bitot spots in vitamin A deficiency, 257
Blackberries, 395, 405
"Blacktongue," 232
"Bladder stones" in vitamin A deficiency, 259
Blindness resulting from vitamin A deficiency, 257
Blood, 127–128, 141–148, 152, 178–180

Blood (Continued)
  calcium content of, 127–128
  color index, 143
  iron content of, 141
  loss of from body, 143, 144–146, 147–148, 150
  vitamin C level in, 178–180
Blood donors, 150
Blueberries, 395, 405
Bluefish, 401, 405
Body, elementary composition of, 108
Body-fat, distribution, 74
  functions, 75
Body fuel, see Energy
Body heat conserved by body fat, 75
Body temperature, regulation of, 61–62, 75
Body weight and its control, 50, 67–82
  increase of, 74
  reduction of, 50, 73–74
  standard tables, 75, 80
  wellbeing as influenced by, 74, 76–77
Bologna, 401, 405
Bomb calorimeter, 63
Bone marrow, 142–143, 275
"Bone salt," 109, 127–128, 275–276
Bones, 109, 275–280, 282–285, 286; see also Calcium and Rickets
Bow-legs and knock-knees in rickets, 277
Boys, dietary recommendations for, 79, 101, 133, 151, 180, 266, 356, 357, 362–364, 415–417; see also Dietary recommendations
  nutrition experiment with, 328–329
Bradycardia, 205–206
Brain work, effect on energy metabolism, 67–68
Braising, 231
Bran, 155, 405
Brazil nut, 94, 401
Bread, 10, 64, 118, 135, 208, 209, 212, 314, 319–321, 352, 354, 360, 362–364, 395, 401, 405
  Boston brown, 395, 405
  calcium content of, as influenced by increased use of milk in bread-making, 319–321
  flour, and wheat compared as to calcium and phosphorus contents, 135

  fortification with vitamins, 209, 319, 320
  improvement by use of vitamin-rich yeast, 209, 320
  raisin, 395, 405
  rye, 401
  white, enriched, 395, 405
  whole wheat, 395, 405
  whole wheat, raisin, 401
Breadstuffs, 230, 319–321, 360, 362–364
Bridging the gaps between nutrition research and its everyday application, 374–382
Broccoli, 135, 186, 229, 231, 269, 395, 405
  for home gardens, 325
Broiling, 231
Brussels sprouts, 395, 405
Budd's postulation and King's identification of the antiscorbutic substance, 173–174
Budget(s), food, 346–365
Building from good health to better, 4–7, 9, 128–133, 179–181, 203–205, 218–222, 259–265
"Building stones," 31; see also Amino acids
Buns, 401
Buoyant health, 4, 5, 347–348, 372–373; see also Adequate vs. optimal
Bureau of Human Nutrition and Home Economics, 9
Butter, 10, 20, 64, 81, 230, 252, 257, 267, 268, 317, 318, 328, 329, 360, 389, 395, 405
  as one of ten to twelve food groups, 317, 318
Buttermilk, 115
  cultured from skimmed milk, 395, 405
Butyric acid, 20, 389

Cabbage, 10, 136, 164, 183, 186, 188, 191, 208, 229, 231, 269, 325, 395, 405
  calcium of, well utilized, 136
  from goitrous vs. non-goitrous regions, 164
  nutritive value, 325

SUBJECT INDEX

Calciferol, 281; *see* Vitamin D₂
Calcification, 276–277, 279, 281–283, 301–302, 306–308; *see also* Rickets
Calcium, 5, 108, 109, 112, 113, 115, 117, 121, 123–138, 176, 275–277, 282, 288, 306, 315, 318, 320, 321, 324, 325, 329, 330–333
  absorption of, 115, 283
  amount required in normal nutrition, 123–126
  content of average American dietary, 351
    of dietary as influenced by milk consumption, 328–332
    of body, influenced by age and by food, 132
    in relation to age, growth, and food, 131–133
    of foods, 134–138, 404–414
  deficiency of, 121–137
  effects of different levels of intake, 125–133
  extent and significance of the margin of optimal over minimal-adequate intake, 123–133
  in growth and development, 128–133
  mobilization, 276, 282–285
  need accentuated by the fact that we are born calcium-poor, 128–133
  of body, 99 per cent or more in the bones and teeth, 127
  of some foods not available because of oxalic acid, 135–136
  Recommended Dietary Allowances, 416–417
  requirements for minimal adequacy and for best lifetime results, 123–128
  retention during growth, 128–133, 275–285
  relation to teeth, 306, 315
  shortage of, sometimes a factor in anemia, 149
  utilization of, as affected by oxalic acid of food, 135–136
    as affected by vitamin D, 276–285
    variability, individual, 123–124
Calcium and phosphorus, contents of typical foods, 134–138, 404–414

Calorie(s), allowances for pregnancy and lactation, and in childhood, 79-81
  definition and expression, 47, 48
  desirable proportions from different types of foods, 356, 357, 358
  distribution in diets of children, 356, 357
  needed per day according to occupation (total energy requirements of normal adults), 67–82
  proportion taken as sugar, 16
  per gram of foodstuffs, 62
  Recommended Dietary Allowances, 416–417
  recommended percentage from fruits, vegetables, and milk, 356, 358
  values of foods as computed by "more specific factors," 65; *see also* Appendix C, 393–403
  see also Energy
Calorimeter, bomb, for measuring energy values of foods, 62, 63
  respiration, for measuring energy output of the body, 51–54
Calorimetry, direct and indirect compared, 52
Cane sugar, *see* Sucrose
Cantaloupe, 118, 191, 395, 405
Capacity, lifetime, for expenditure of energy, 49
Capric acid, 389
Caproic acid, 389
Caprylic acid, 389
Carbohydrate(s), 14, 15–19, 25, 32, 39–40, 45, 62, 391, 394–403
  contents of foods, 394–403
  from food concentrated in the liver, 39–40
  conversion of, into fat, 44
  descriptive introduction to, 14, 15–19
  determination in food analysis, 25
  energy value of, 62
  fate in the body, 28, 30, 39–40, 44, 62, 391
Carbon, 107, 108
Cardiac region of stomach, 35
Caries, 301–315
  factors in, 304
  Marshall's classification of causes, 303

Caries (Continued)
  imperfect structure of teeth and, 302, 310, 312
  relation to fluorine, 311–313
    to sugar intake, 310–311, 314
    to vitamin D and sunshine, 307–308
    to water supply, 306, 311–313
Carotene(s), 251, 255, 267, 268–269
Carrots, 118, 153, 164, 186, 208, 229, 268, 325, 395, 406
  from goitrous vs. non-goitrous regions, 164
  nutritive value, 325
Cartilage in growth of bone, 275, 282
Casein, 88, 90, 92, 93, 94, 95, 336, 337
  amino acid data, 336
Cashew nuts, 395, 406
Catalases, 141
Catalysts (catalytic agents), 29–30; see also Enzymes
Cauliflower, 186, 231, 269, 395, 406
Causes of tooth defects, 302–304; see also Caries, Teeth
Celery, 34, 189, 191, 311, 395, 406
  advantage of, to end a meal, 34, 189, 191, 311
Cellulose, 19
"Center of gravity of the problem of the relations of food to health and welfare has shifted from sanitation to nutrition," 378
Cereal(s), 10, 19, 64, 81, 94, 155, 317, 318, 319–321, 351, 352, 357, 358, 360, 362–364
Characteristics of the chief types of food, 317–341
Chard, 115, 134, 395, 406
Checking-card of U. S. Department of Agriculture Extension Service, 10–11
Cheese, 10, 64, 76, 81, 135, 228, 230, 234, 328, 330, 349, 350, 351, 352, 357, 360, 395, 401, 406, 407
  Brick, 407
  Brie, 407
  calcium and phosphorus contents of Cheddar and cottage types, 135, 406
  Camembert, 407
  Cheddar type, 395, 406, 407
  Cottage, skim milk, 395, 406, 407
  cream, 395
  Edam, 407
  Emmenthal, 407
  Parmesan, 395, 406, 407
  pineapple, 407
  Roquefort, 401, 407
  Stilton type, 407
  Swiss, 395, 406, 407
Cheeses, contrast in calcium content between rennet-made and acid-made types, 407
Cheilosis, 221
"Chemical control" through hormones, 161
Chemical messenger, 36, 86
"Chemical regulation" of body temperature, 61
Chenopodiaceae, 134
Cherries, canned, 406
  fresh, 396, 406
Chestnuts, 401, 406
Chewing, 33
Chicken, 208
  broiler, 396, 406
  consumption of, 333
  roaster, 406
Children, dietary recommendations for, 100–101, 133, 180, 266, 356, 357, 362–364, 415–419; see also Allowances, Dietary recommendations
  energy needs of, 79–81
  iron in the nutrition of, 151
  planning of dietaries for, 356, 357, 361, 362–364
  see also Growth, and under Requirements and Allowances for individual elements, factors, or nutrients
Chloride(s) (chlorine), 108, 110, 111, 116, 117; see also Salt
Chlorine (chloride ion), 108, 112–113
Chocolate, unsweetened, 406
Chocolate wafers, 401
Choices of kinds and amounts of foods among the most frequent and influential of the choices we make, 370–373, 375–382
Cholesterol, 281
Choline, 244–245, 250
Chromatin, 141
Chyme, 36, 37
Cirrhosis, 245

SUBJECT INDEX 435

Citric acid and citrates, 14, 114
Citrin, 245, 250
Citrus (fruits), 10, 174, 183, 187, 190, 230, 317, 318, 326, 358; *see also* Grapefruit, Lemon, Orange
Citrus fruits-and-tomatoes as one of ten to twelve food groups, 317–318
Classification, of anemias, 143
  of defects of teeth, 302, 303
  of foods into ten to twelve food groups, 317
  of the functions of mineral elements, 109
Clotting of blood, 113, 296–297
Coagulation, of blood as related to vitamin K, 296–297
  of milk in the stomach, 332–333
Coagulation-vitamin (vitamin K), 296–297
Cobalt, 108, 113, 142, 242
Coconut, dried, sweetened, 401, 406
  fresh, 406
Coconut custard pie, 406
Cod, 396, 407
Codliver oil, 10, 255, 257, 278, 279, 286, 314
Coleslaw, 401
Collaboration of the National Research Council and the Federal Food and Drug Administration in the Enrichment Program, 320
Collards, 234, 325, 396, 407
  calcium well utilized, 136
Color-index of blood, 143, 144, 147
Committee on Food and Nutrition, 8
Commodity relationships in foods, 318
Comparisons of losses in cooking, 186, 231, 269
Comparison of nutrients in average American dietary with amounts required for normal nutrition, 350, 351
Compatibility of different approaches to the problem of enough of the right kinds of food, 370
Competition of bones and muscles for the phosphorus brought by the blood, 284
"Complete" proteins, 87–93, 94–96
Compositae, 135
Composition, elementary, of the body, 108
  of foods, 393–414; *see also* under name of each
Conarachin, amino acid data, 336
Conjunctivitis, 256–258
Concept of "a nation of people as sturdy as the animals in a good farmyard," 372
Conservation of vitamin C values of foods in cooking, 182–187
Consistency of fats, 20–21
Constituents of foods, general, 5, 13–15
Constructive potentialities in diet, 264–265
Consumer demand and the consequent adjustment of food production, 381–382
Consumption of foods of various types, 358
Consumption of sugar, 17, 351, 357, 358
  place in food budget, 360, 362–364
Contents of stomach during digestion, 34–38
Contractility, 112
Contractions of stomach wall, 36
Control of body weight, 72–79
Control of food production and import in the United Kingdom during the Second World War, 370
Controls in animal experimentation, 254–255
Conviction as an important factor in making nutritional knowledge effective, 372
Cooking losses, of thiamine, riboflavin, and niacin, 231
  of vitamin A, 269
  of vitamin C (ascorbic acid), 186
Copper, 108, 110, 142, 145, 147, 154, 155, 419
  effect on destruction of vitamin C, 183
  in foods, 151–156
Corn, 16, 18, 19, 87–89, 95, 319, 369, 401, 407
  as food, 319
  canned, 401, 407
  sweet, fresh, 396, 407
Corn protein, amino acid data, 336

Corn sugar, *see* Glucose
Corn syrup, 402
Cornflakes, 402, 407
Cornmeal, degermed, uncooked, 396, 407
Corrosion of teeth, 302
Cost of food, 346–364
  of different types of food in typical American dietaries, 318, 351
Course of the food through the digestive tract, 31–39
Crabmeat, 402
Crackers, Graham, 396, 407
  soda, 396, 407
Cranberries, 115, 396, 407
  favorable to calcium assimilation, 136
Cranberry sauce, canned, 407
Craving for common salt, 113
Cream, 230, 328, 352, 354
  thick, whipping, 402, 407
  thin, 396, 407
Crop, corn, 19
Cruciferae, 135, 390
Cryptoxanthin, 251
Cucumbers, 396, 407
Curd, 14, 332–333; *see also* Casein
Curdling of milk, 14
Cure of myxedema by thyroxine, 167
Currants, dried, 402
  fresh, 402, 407
Custard pie, 402
Cystine, 86, 92, 93
Cytochromes, 141

Daily Dietary Allowances, 415–419; *see also* Allowances, Recommended Dietary
Dandelion greens, 135, 268, 396, 407
Dates, commercial, dried, 402, 407
Deaminization of amino acids, 43, 44
Degrees of health, 5–7, 125–126, 179–181, 203–205, 221–222, 252–253, 347–348, 372–373
Demands of consumers as influencing food production, 381–382
Dentifrices, 303
Dentine, 301, 302, 309

Dependence of the United Kingdom, during the Second World War, "for nutritional security, upon potatoes, mixed vegetables, and bread made from flour containing a high percentage of the wheat grain," 370
Depletion of bodily stores of nutrients, 253, 259–260
Dermatitis, 231–232, 240, 243, 256
Destruction in cooking processes, of niacin, 231
  of riboflavin, 231
  of thiamine, 210–212, 231
  of vitamin A, 269
  of vitamin C (ascorbic acid), 183, 184, 185, 186
Determination of proteins, fats, and carbohydrates in foods, 25
Development, bodily and mental, 1, 128–133; *see also* Growth
Dextrin(s), 19
Dextrose, *see* Glucose
Diagram, of bomb calorimeter, 63
  illustrating early studies of Hopkins, 2, 3
  illustrating effects of differing bodily stores of vitamin A, 253, 260, 261
  illustrating effects on growth of different proteins and amino acids, 88, 93
  illustrating influence of food upon vitamin C content of blood, 179
  illustrating relation of temperature and time to losses of vitamin C, 184
  illustrating relation of vitamin A intake to growth, 252, 253
  of bone trabeculae as influenced by the calcium content of the food, 127
  of digestive tract, 32, 35
  of stratification of food in the stomach, 35
  showing growth on diets containing different amounts of added table salt, 111
  showing relation of milk consumption to total calcium intake, 331
  sugar consumption statistics, 17

SUBJECT INDEX 437

Diaphysis of bone, 275
Diet, planning of, in terms of food groups, 358, 360–364
Dietaries, American, distribution of cost and nutrients, 351
  effects of long term experiments
    (with calcium), 124–127
    (with riboflavin), 219–220
    (with vitamin A), 264–265
    (with vitamin C), 181–182
  planning of, 346–364
    at different levels of cost, 360, 361, 362–364
    in terms of food groups, 360, 362–364
  of about 4000 American families studied 1934–37, 319, 354–355
Diets A and B, 5, 329–330
Dietary recommendations, 10, 79, 80, 81, 98, 100–101, 133, 150, 151, 180, 206–207, 223, 233, 266, 289–290, 352, 356, 360–364, 415–419
Dietary standards, *see* Dietary recommendations
Difference between merely adequate and optimal in nutrition, 3–7, 124–133, 178–181, 219–222, 264–265, 372–373
Digestibility of fats, 21
Digestion, 19, 28–43
Digestion-products, 29, 43–45, 391
  as building blocks, 29, 31, 43
Digestive enzymes, 391
Dip in curve of increasing calcium content of growing body, 133
Disaccharide(s), 16–17
Discovery, of antineuritic factor (thiamine), 198–203
  of antirachitic factor(s), 277–280
  of antiscorbutic factor (vitamin C), 172–175
  of riboflavin by differentiation of original "vitamin B," 217–218
  of thyroxine, 162, 163, 167, 168
  of vitamins, 1–3
Disinfection of swallowed food by gastric juice, 36
Dispensability *vs.* indispensibility of individual amino acids, 89–91
Distribution, of expenditures for foods, 318, 351

  of food calories in the dietary, 23, 230, 351, 356, 357
"Distribution standards," recommended by M. S. Rose, 356, 357
Diversification advantageous to agriculture, 381–382
Division of food money, 318, 351–352
Division of foods into 10 to 12 groups, 317, 318, 319–340
DMF = Decayed, missing and/or filled (teeth), 313
Dog, use of, in studies of riboflavin, 224
  in studies of teeth, 302–303
Dried legumes-and-nuts, 10, 230, 317, 318, 321–323, 358, 360, 362–364
Drinking-waters as source of calcium, 136, 306
  of fluorine, 312
  of iodine, 163
Duration of infection as influenced by vitamin A, 262–263

Eating, effect on energy metabolism, 56, 59–60
Economics of food, 346–382
Economy, of different food groups, 318
  of increased consumption of fruits, vegetables, and milk, 346
  of preservation and distribution of food, 348–350
Ectoderm, 310
Edestin, 94, 95
Education in foods and nutrition in England during the Second World War, 370
Education in nutrition, 346–348, 350–364, 369–382
Effectiveness of nutrition policy and education, 369–382
Effects of different levels of calcium intake, 125–133
  of riboflavin intake, 219–222
  of vitamin A intake, 264–265
  of vitamin C intake, 178–182
Effects of digestion, 28
Efficiency in the use of nutritional knowledge, 317–340, 346–348, 350–364, 369–382

438 SUBJECT INDEX

Efficiency of cow and of hen in transforming grasses to human food, 267
Egg(s), 10, 94, 96, 117, 118, 135, 153, 154, 208, 209, 218, 229, 230, 231, 268, 287, 333, 334, 336, 337–339, 358, 360, 362–364, 396, 408
    as one of ten to twelve food-groups, 317, 318, 337–339, 358, 360, 362–364
    as sources of amino acids, 336
    of calcium, 135, 230, 351
    of calories, 230, 351, 357
    of iron, 153, 154, 351
    of niacin, 231
    of phosphorus, 135, 351
    of protein, 95, 102, 230, 338, 351
    of riboflavin, 229, 230, 231, 339
    of thiamine, 208, 209, 231, 339
    of vitamin A, 230, 267, 268, 339
    of vitamin C, 187, 230, 339
    of vitamin D, 281, 287, 339
    consumption of, 333
    place in the diet, 337–339, 351, 358, 360, 362–364
    prominence in diet largely influenced by economic conditions, 338
    protein, amino acid data, 336
    white, 208, 229, 268, 396, 408
    yolk, 153, 208, 229, 268, 396, 408
Eggplant, 396, 408
Electrolyte(s), 110
Elementary composition of body, 108
Elements, "acid-forming," 113, 117, 118
    "base-forming," 117, 118
    mineral ("minerals"), 3, 6, 14, 25, 107, 170, 327–333, 337, 338, 404–414; *see also* under name of each
    amounts in the body, 108
    those essential to normal nutrition, 108–109
Emulsification of food fat in the small intestine, 38
Enamel (of teeth), 301, 309–310
Enamel-forming cells, 309
Endive (escarole), 135, 396, 408
Endocrines, 161–165
Endocrinology, 161–168
Energy, 13, 20, 28–29, 44–45, 47–84
    as "ability to do work," 48, 49
    basal metabolism, 54–60
    distinction between "the caloric and the popular" senses of the word emphasized by the Council on Foods and Nutrition of the American Medical Association, 50
    expenditure per hour under different conditions of muscular activity, 70
    has different meanings, 47–49
    metabolism, effect of food, 58–60
    effect of mental activity, 67–72
    effect of muscular activity, 67–72
    influenced by habitual level of food intake, 60
    by muscular activity, 59
    by size and composition of body, 57
    by surface area of body, 67
    in myxedema, 166–167
    measurement of, 51–57, 58
    normal, at rest, higher in males than in females of like physique, 57
    needed during physical development, 79–81
    Recommended Dietary Allowances, 415–417
    requirement, 48, 51, 67–84
    for typical occupations, 72
    of infants and children, 79–81, 416–417
    of the elderly, 81–82
    values of average American dietary, 351
    of foods, 62–65, 393–403
    of individual nutrients, 62–64
Enriched bread and flour, 155, 212–214, 232, 320–321, 369, 375
Enrichment program, 209, 212–214, 320–321, 369, 375
Entrance to college at earlier age than formerly, 1
Environment, internal, 6, 8, 49–50, 126–128, 133, 207, 221, 225, 259–266, 328–330
Enzymes, 29–31, 33, 34, 36, 38, 40, 43, 85, 86, 113, 141, 219, 240, 243, 391
    containing iron, 141
    digestive, 391

SUBJECT INDEX 439

Epinephrine, 86, 423
Epiphysis in growth of bone, 275
Epithelium, 310
  as affected by level of intake of vitamin A, 259
Erepsin, 43, 391
Ergosterol, 281
Erucic acid, 390
Erythrocyte(s), 142, 144–145, 146, 147
Erythropoiesis, 147, 242
Escarole (endive), 135, 268, 396, 408
Essential amino acids, 88–93, 98–99, 336
Estimation of amount of iodine needed, 168–169, 418
Establishment of the relationship of iodine to goiter, 162–169
Excelsin, 94
Exchange of material in body tissue, 44, 87
Exercises, 9–11, 25–26, 45, 66, 82–83, 103–104, 119, 138, 157, 170, 192–193, 214, 236, 245, 269, 290, 297, 315, 340–341, 365, 382
Expediency and social justice in national food policy, 369–382
Expenditure of energy, 47–51
Expenditures for food, 318, 346–368
Experiments, covering entire life cycles and successive generations, 4–6, 124–128, 219–221, 264–265, 329–330
  leading to discovery of vitamins, 1–3
  with school boys by Corry Mann, 328–329
Extrinsic factor, 146, 147
Eye(s), as influenced by riboflavin, 218–219, 222
  as influenced by vitamin A, 256–257

Factors, in dental caries (exciting and predisposing), 304
  determining the nutritive values of proteins, 85–96, 98–103
FAO = Food and Agriculture Organization of the United Nations, 9
Farina, uncooked, 396, 408
Fat(s), 14, 20–23, 25, 28, 37, 38, 40–42, 44–45, 59, 62, 64, 75–78, 251, 275, 286–288, 314, 317–318, 332, 339, 351, 357–360, 362–364, 389–390, 391, 393–403, 418

action of, in slowing the passage of food from the stomach, 22, 23, 37
and oils, as one of ten to twelve food groups, 317, 318, 339, 360, 362–364
as nutritionally essential, 21, 418
chemical nature of, 20–21
commercial, 20–23, 339
content of foods, 394–403
digestibility of, 21
emulsified form of, in milk and eggs, 332
energy value of, 62
in cookery, 20–23
in dietetics, 20–23, 352, 357, 358, 360, 362–364
in everyday food problems, 22, 23, 322, 339
in mechanical and thermal protection of the body, 41–42
in part reconstituted in the body, 41–42
non-fuel functions in the body, 75
nutritive value and place in the diet, 21, 22–23, 339, 418
solubilities of, 20–21
storage of, in the body, 42, 44
Fate of the foodstuffs in the body, 28–45
Fat-like substances, 21
Fat-soluble substances, 21; see also Vitamins A, D, E, and K
Fatty acids, 20–21, 389–390
  nutritionally essential, 21
Feces, 39
Feeding, as influencing the composition of milk, 154, 332
  in schools ("school lunches"), 369
"Ferments," see Enzymes
Ferritin, 141
Fig(s), 396, 408
Fig bars, 397
Filberts, 402
Fish, 10, 117, 230, 234, 333–337; see also under individual names
  consumption of, 333
Fish-liver oils, 268, 286–287
"Fixed acid," 113
Flexibility of the body at birth, 128
Flounder, "sole," 402
Flour, 64, 135, 155, 208, 209, 213–214, 229, 232, 319–321, 397, 408

Flour (Continued)
  white, enriched, 397, 408
  whole wheat, 397, 408
Flours and cereals as one of ten to twelve food groups, 360, 362–364
Flower-buds as food: broccoli, 325
Fluctuations in composition of milk, 332
Fluoride, and public water supply, 313
  mode of action in reducing incidence of caries, 313
Fluorides and the teeth, 311–313
Fluorine, 311–313
Folic acid, 147, 242–243
Follicular conjunctivitis in vitamin A deficiency, 257
Food(s), acid-forming, 117, 118
  allowances for children, 80
  as commodities, 317–345, 346–368
  as fuel, 31
  base-forming, 117, 118
  calories and control of body weight, 72–77
  compared as sources of calcium, 134–136, 404–414
    of energy (calories), 64–65, 394–403
    of essential amino acids, 336, 337
    of iron, 151–156, 404–414
    of phosphorus, 134–136, 404–414
    of protein, 102, 394–403
    of riboflavin, 228–231, 404–414
    of thiamine, 207–210, 404–414
    of vitamin A value, 267–269, 404–414
    of vitamin C, 187–192, 404–414
  composition and nutritive values, 393–414
  corrective and constructive functioning of, 7
  from goitrous regions found poor in iodine, 164
  in relation to "a higher level of cultural attainment," 7
  in relation to teeth, 301–316
  nutritional characteristics, 317–345
  tested by feeding successive generations, 4
  see also under names of individual foods
Food and Nutrition Board, 8

Food budgets as guided by nutritional knowledge, 358–364
Food groups, ten, relative cost and contribution to diet, 318
Food habits, 6–8, 369–382
Food plans, low cost, 360, 361, 362, 364
  moderate cost, 360, 361, 363
Foodstuffs, different uses of the term, 13
  energy values of, 62–64
  summary of the fate of in the body, 44–45
  see also Food(s), Nutrients, Carbohydrates, Fats, Proteins
Food-supply as "nutritional environment," 317–318
Frankforters, 408
Freedom in the choice of food, 377, 378–382
Frequency and duration of infection as influenced by vitamin A, 262–263
Frequency of goiter in men drafted from regions where drinking water was poor in iodine, 163–164
Frequency of "insufficient intake" of vitamin A in New York City, 257–258
  of vitamin C, 181
Freshmen, taller yet younger than those of thirty years ago, 1
Fructose, 16
Fruit(s), 10, 16, 36, 76, 81, 102, 114, 118, 135–136, 153, 155, 156, 172, 173, 177, 183, 189–192, 208–209, 229–231, 234, 268, 311, 314, 317, 318, 326–327, 339–340, 351–358, 360, 362–364, 373, 376, 393–414
  as aid to digestion, 36
  citrus, 173–174, 318, 326
  juices, 10, 16, 36
  place in the diet, 326–327
  sugar, see Fructose
Fruits-and-vegetables, 10, 118, 134–136, 153–155, 156, 183, 189–192, 208, 209–211, 228–231, 234, 268, 311, 314, 317–318, 326–327, 340, 351–358, 360, 362–364, 373, 376, 393–414

SUBJECT INDEX 441

as food, 323–327
as sources of calcium, 134–136, 404–414
  of energy (calories), 64–65, 393–403
  of iron, 153, 155–156, 404–414
  of phosphorus, 134–136, 404–414
  of protein, 394–403
  of riboflavin, 228–231, 234, 404–414
  of thiamine, 208–211, 404–414
  of vitamin A value, 268, 404–414
  of vitamin C, 189–192, 404–414
change of status from supposed luxuries to recognition as good investments, 340, 373, 376
favorable effects on the teeth, 311
in the planning of diets, 352, 360, 362–364
Frying, 231
Fuel values of foods, 62–65, 393–403
Full-life and successive-generation experiments in nutritional research, 4–6, 124–128, 219–221, 264–265
Function(s), antiseptic, of the acid of normal gastric juice, 36
nutritive, of amino acids, 85–93
of fat, 22–23, 41–42, 75
of food, general, 13
of the mineral elements, 109–113, 116–117; *see also* under name of each
of proteins in the body, 85–96
of the stomach, 32–37
see also the discussion of each nutrient
Fundus, 34–35

Galactose, 16, 391
Gasoline-engine analogy of body, 50–51
Gastric juice, 110
Gelatin, not adequate as sole dietary protein, 87, 94
Girls, dietary recommendations for, 79, 101, 133, 151, 180, 266, 356, 357, 362–364, 416–417; *see also* Dietary recommendations

Gland(s), endocrine, 161–165
salivary, 33–34, 391
of internal secretion, 161–162
thyroid, 161–168
Gliadin, 87, 88, 94
Glossary, 420–427
Glucose, 16, 39–40, 391
Glutamic (glutaminic) acid, 86
Glutathione, 86
Glutenin, 94
Glyceride, 20, 389
Glycerol, 20, 28, 391
Glycine, 86, 89
Glycinin, 94, 336
Glycogen, 18, 19, 39–40, 44, 73
Goiter, 161–170
early history, 161–162
experimental production, 164
geographic distribution, 162–163
other causes than iodine deficiency, 165
prevention by iodide, 165–166, 169–170
prevention in school children, 165–166
Gooseberries, 408
Governmental and volunteer services for better nutrition, 369–382
Grain(s) as leading source of calories, 319
Grain products, 135, 155, 208, 209, 267, 318, 319–321, 351, 352, 357, 360, 362–364; *see also* name of each
after enrichment may logically take a larger place in the diet, 320
Granules of starches, 18
Grapefruit, 119, 190, 191, 397, 408
as source of vitamin C, 190, 191
Grape(s), 115, 397, 408
juice, commercial, 397, 408
sugar, *see* Glucose
Grasses, richness in vitamin A value, 267
Green and yellow vegetables, 230, 268
Greens, 134, 135, 136, 188–189, 241, 242–243, 267, 268, 296
of different values as sources of calcium, 135–136
Grouping of foods, 317
Groups of foods, 317–340, 360, 362–364

Growth (and development), 1, 87–96, 111, 128–133, 155, 166–167, 203–204, 218–220, 252–254, 284–285
   as indicated by height and age at college entrance, 1
   as influenced by calcium content of food, 124–133
      by individual amino acids, 87–93
      by iodine deficiency, 166–167
      by proteins of food, 87–89, 93–96
      by riboflavin, 218–220
      by thiamine, 203–204
      by vitamin A, 252–254
      by vitamin D, 284–285
      by whole wheat *vs.* white bread, 155
   of normal bone, 275–276
Guidance, nutritional, in food economics, 317–364, 346–382
Guineapigs in studies of teeth, 308
Gums, 176, 305, 308, 309–310

Haddock, 397, 408
Halibut, 397, 408
Halibut liver oil, 286
Ham, fresh, 409
   smoked, 397, 409
Handicap of being born calcium-poor, 129–133
"Hard water" as source of calcium, 136, 306
Hazelnuts, 409
Health as a positive quality of life, 4, 6, 7, 9, 128–133, 179–181, 203–205, 218–222, 259–265, 369–370
Health in the United Kingdom during the Second World War, 370
Heart, beef, 397, 409
Heart, work of, 47, 73
"Helping Families Plan Food Budgets," 358–364, 377
Hemeralopia (nightblindness) as influenced by vitamin A, 256–258
Hemicellulose(s), 19
Hemoglobin, 109, 141–148
Herring, 402, 409
Hippuric acid, 115
Histidine, 86, 91, 336

Histology of vitamin A deficiency, 256–259
   of vitamin C deficiency, 176
   of rickets, 275–277
History of beriberi, 198–203
   of rickets, 277–280
   of scurvy, 172–175
Hominy, 409
Honey, 16, 397, 409
Hormones, 32, 43–44, 85–87, 161–163, 165–169; *see also* Adrenaline, Secretin, Thyroxine
How food nourishes the body, general, 13; *see also* individual nutrients
Hundred-Calorie portions of foods, 64, 65
Hundred-gram portions, 393–403
Hydrogen, 108
Hydroxyglutamic acid, 86
Hydroxyproline, 86
Hygiene, of the gums, mouth, and teeth, 303, 304
Hypochromic anemia, 143, 147
Hypoplasia of teeth, 302–303; *see also* Teeth

Ice cream, 230, 330, 349, 358, 397, 409
Improvement of already-adequate diet, 4–8, 123–133, 178–182, 203–205, 259–264
Improvement of British health during Second World War due to nutritional guidance of food policies, 370–372
Improvement of nutrition both an economic and an educational problem, 369–373
Improvement of nutritional environment by means of the enrichment of foods, 369–375
Improvement of physique of college students, 1
Incidence of "insufficient intake" of vitamin C, 181
   of pellagra, 232
   of riboflavin deficiency, 221, 222
   of rickets, 280
   of vitamin A deficiency, 257–258
Income as affecting food consumption, 334–338, 373–374, 376

Income, relation of, to food consumption, 346, 348
Increases of calcium and phosphorus content of body during growth and development, 129
Indispensability of fat (or fatty acid), 21, 418
Indispensable amino acids, 88–93, 98–99, 336
Infection, as influenced by riboflavin deficiency, 219, 221–222
as influenced by vitamin A deficiency, 256–259, 262–263
Inferiority attributed to racial factors may be due to food supply, 7–8
Inorganic foodstuffs, 107; *see also* Mineral elements
Insulin, 87
Interchangeability of fat and carbohydrate, 21–23, 40–42, 44–45
Interglobular spaces, 302
Internal environment, 5–8, 50, 123–133, 177–181, 221–222, 256–262, 346
International unit, of vitamin A value, 254–255
of vitamin C, 182
of vitamin D, 285
Intestinal mucosa, 391
Intestine, 32, 37–39
Intrinsic factor, 146, 147
Invertase, 391
Iodine, 108, 110, 161–170, 418, 419
in foods, 164
in soils and waters, 162–164
requirement, 166–169, 418–419
"Iodized salt," 169–170, 419
Ions, 107, 110; *see also* Mineral elements
Iron, 108, 109–110, 141–157, 351, 404–414
content of average American dietary, 351
in dietary, contributions of different types of food, 149–156, 318, 351
in foods, 151–156, 404–414
in eggs, 153, 154, 408
in fruits and vegetables, 153, 155–156, 404–414
in grain products, 153, 155, 157, 404–414
in meats, 152–154, 404–414

in milk, 154–155, 410
in hemoglobin and other body compounds, 141
of foods, probably exaggerated impressions as to differences in availability, 156
relative concentration in the blood, 141
requirements in normal nutrition, 148–150, 151
of adults, 148–150
of children, 151
Irradiated (activated) ergosterol, 281
Irradiation, 278, 280
Isoleucine, 86, 91, 99, 336

Juice, gastric, 35, 36, 37, 391
intestinal, 37–38, 391
pancreatic, 37–38, 391

Kale, 135, 153, 187–189, 229, 234, 268, 269, 325–326, 397, 409
Keratinization of epithelium in vitamin A deficiency, 258–259
Keratomalacia caused by vitamin A deficiency, 257
Kidney, 153, 209, 228, 397, 409
Kilogram-calorie (kilo-calorie), definition, 48
Knowledge of nutrition, how made effective, 1–9, 369–382; *see also* Exercises
Kohlrabi, 231, 402, 409

"Labile methyl factor," 244–245
Lachrymal gland, 257
Lactalbumin, 94, 95, 336
Lactase, 391
Lactation, 44, 79–80, 92, 96, 99–100, 130, 180, 263, 266, 362–364, 416, 418, 419
Lactic acid, 115, 205, 425
Lactoflavin, *see* Riboflavin
Lactose, 16, 17, 391
Lamb, 153, 208, 333, 397, 409
Lamb-and-mutton, consumption of, 333

SUBJECT INDEX

Lambsquarters, 115, 268
Lard, 20, 21, 397
"Lard substitute," 20, 21
Lauric acid, 390
Lean meat, poultry, and fish as a "food-group," 333-337, 358-360, 362-364
Leaves, as sources of calcium, 121, 134-136
   as sources of other factors, 241, 242-243, 296
   as sources of vitamin C, 188-189
   as vegetables, 267
   outer green much richer than inner pale, in vitamin A value, 267-268
Lecithins, 21
Leeks, 135-136, 409
   calcium well utilized, 136
Legumes, 188; see also under name of each
Legumes (mature) and nuts as a "food-group," 10, 230, 317, 318, 321-323, 358, 360, 362-364
   as offering exceptional nutritive return in proportion to their cost, 318, 321, 323
   economy of, 318, 321-323
Lemons, 173, 397, 409
   juice, 397, 409
Length of life increased by addition of calcium to an already adequate diet, 125-126
   of milk, 329-330
   of vitamin A, 264-265
Lentils, 409
Lettuce, 134, 135, 188-189, 268, 397, 409
   calcium well utilized, 136
   difference between inner and outer leaves, 268
   widely variable in vitamin A value, 267-268
Leucine, 86, 91, 99, 336
Levels of health, 3-7, 123-133, 178-182, 219-222, 264-265, 346
Levulose, see Fructose
Liberality of calcium in long-term nutrition, 124-128
   of riboflavin, 219-221, 225, 227
   of vitamin A, 264-265
Life-cycle of red blood cell, 142
Linoleic acid, 21, 390, 418

Linolenic acid, 21, 390
Lipase(s), 30, 36, 40, 391
Lipids (Lipins), 21; see also Fat(s)
Lipoids, 21
Liver, 142, 153, 154, 208-209, 228, 229, 259-261, 268, 286-287, 409
   and liver-extracts in the treatment of pernicious anemia, 146, 147
Lobster, 409
Local factor in rickets, 276, 282, 283
Loganberries, 409
Longevity, see Length of life
Losses in cooking, of thiamine, riboflavin, and niacin, 231
   of vitamin A value, 269
   of vitamin C, 182-187
Low cost food plans, 360, 361, 362, 364
Lumen, 38
Lung, as influenced by vitamin A, 258-259
Lymph, 38
Lysine, 86, 88, 89, 91, 99, 336

Macaroni, 397, 409
Macaroons, 402
Mackerel, 410
Magnesium, 108, 112-113, 117
Maintenance requirement of calcium, 123
   of iron, 149
   of phosphorus, 122
   of specific amino acids, 98-99
   of total protein, 96-98
Maize, 87; see also Corn
Malic acid and malates, 114-115
Malt, 17
Maltase, 391
Maltose (malt sugar), 17, 391
Man, see Men
Manganese, 108, 113
Mangoes, 410
Margarine, 10, 22, 360, 397, 410
Matrix in growth of bone, 276
Mature legumes and nuts as a food-group, 10, 230, 317, 318, 321-323, 358, 360, 362-364
Mayonnaise, 402, 410
Means by which animals convey nutriment from one generation to the next, 218

SUBJECT INDEX 445

Meat(s), 10, 117, 118, 135, 137, 146, 152–154, 208, 209, 228–230, 233, 235, 241, 268, 287, 317, 318, 333–337, 351–352, 357, 358, 362–364, 394–414; *see also* name of each kind
  as sources of amino acids, 336
    of calcium, 135, 230, 335, 351
    of calories, 64, 230, 351, 357
    of iron, 152, 153, 337, 351
    of niacin, 231, 335
    of phosphorus, 135, 337, 351
    of protein, 95, 102, 230, 335, 351
    of riboflavin, 228, 229, 230, 231, 335
    of thiamine, 206, 208, 209, 211, 231, 335
    of vitamin A, 230, 267, 268, 337
    of vitamin C, 187, 230, 337
    of vitamin D, 287
  consumption of, 318, 333
  economic place in the food supply, 333–335
  protein, 95
Meats-and-fish, 230
Meats, fish, poultry, and eggs as a food-group, 333–339
Mechanism of digestion, 28, 31–39
Men, dietary recommendations for, 72, 96–98, 130, 133, 148–150, 168, 178–180, 207, 223, 340, 398, 407, 411, 413, 415
Menstrual iron loss, 149–150
Mental activity, as affecting energy metabolism, 67–68
Mental alertness, as affected by thyroxine, 166–169
  by vitamin A, 252–253
Metabolism, general, 28, 44–45; *see also* discussions of Energy and of individual food factors
  influence of age, 79–82
Metaplasia in vitamin A deficiency, 258
Methionine, 86, 91, 92, 99, 244, 336
Methods of nutrition policy should be both economic and educational, 373–378, 381–382
Milk, 2, 10, 17, 64, 81, 94, 95, 96, 117, 134, 135, 154, 164, 208, 209, 218, 226, 228, 229, 230–234, 235, 267–268, 287–289, 294, 314, 318, 327–333, 349–358, 360, 362–364, 377, 382, 397–398, 410
  as source of calcium, 134, 318, 327–332, 377, 410
    of essential amino acids, 336
    of iron (and copper), 154, 410
    of phosphorus, 332, 410
    of protein, 94, 95, 96, 103, 309, 310, 312, 332, 336, 397
    of riboflavin, 227–230, 330, 410
    of thiamine, 208–209, 377, 410
    of vitamin A value, 267–268, 318, 328, 330, 410
    of vitamin B_{12}, 241
    of vitamin C, 318, 410
    of vitamin D, 287–288, 410
    of vitamin E, 294
  condensed, sweetened, 398, 410
  effect of increased feeding to boys, 328–329
    to experimental animals through entire lifetime, 4–5, 329–330
  equivalents in different forms, 349
  evaporated, 349, 398, 410
  fluid whole, 349, 397, 410
  from goitrous *vs.* non-goitrous regions, 164
  in breadmaking, 319–321
  malted, dry, 410
  non-fat (skim), 398, 410
  physical properties as affecting digestibility and nutritive value, 327, 332–333
  skimmed, dried, 349, 398, 410
  whole, dried, 398, 410
Milk (with its products other than butter) as one of ten to twelve food groups, 317–318, 327–333, 360, 362–364
Milk sugar, 17, 391
Milling, effect of, on nutritive values of grain products, 198–201, 208–209, 212–214, 320
Mince pie, 402
"Minerals," *see* Mineral elements
Mineral elements, 5–8, 25, 107–190, 318–320, 324, 331, 337, 338, 404–414; *see also* under name of each
  amounts in the body, 108
  those essential to normal nutrition, 108–109

Moderate cost food plans, 360, 361, 363
Molasses, 402, 410
Monosaccharides, 15–16, 391
Mottled enamel, 311–313
Mouth, 33–34, 176, 221, 232
Muscle, 109, 112, 252–253, 256, 284
 as competing with bone for phosphorus, 284
 see also Meat
Musculature as influenced by nutrition, 252, 253
Mustard greens, 135, 268, 398, 410
Mutton, see Lamb
Myoglobin, 141
Myristic acid, 390
Myxedema, 166, 167, 169

National Nutrition Conference, 8–9
National Research Council, 8
 Recommended Daily Dietary Allowances, 415–419
"Nature and Nurture," 7, 373
Nectarines, 410
"Negative control" experimental animals, 254
Neuritis, multiple peripheral; see Beriberi
Neutrality, 114–118
New Zealand spinach, 115
Niacin, 231–233, 235–236, 404–417
 allowances of, 233, 416–417
 contents of foods, 404–414
Nicotinic acid, see Niacin
Nightblindness, 256–258
Nitrogen, 107, 108; see also Protein
Nitrogen balance experiments, 96–98
Nomenclature of enzymes, 29–31, 391
Norleucine, 86
"Nurture can assist Nature to a larger extent than Science has hitherto thought," 7, 373
Nutrient, definition of, 13
Nutrients, demonstrated in a typical food, 14
 more abundant, 13–25
 see also under name of each
Nutrition, as a matter of governmental policy in Great Britain, 346–347
 for desired body weight, 67–82
 new view of, 1–8
 notwithstanding recent advances, is still a fertile field for scientific research, 370
 now carries a larger responsibility than hitherto, 347
 three main aspects of: (1) energy, (2) building and upkeep, (3) regulation, 13
Nutrition Foundation program, 374–375
"Nutrition policy," 369–382
"Nutritionally complete" proteins, 94
"Nutritionally essential" ("indispensable") amino acids, 88–93, 98–99, 336
Nutritionally essential unsaturated fatty acids, 21, 339, 418
"Nutritionally incomplete" proteins, 94
Nutritive values of foods, 393–414
Nuts, 10, 94, 102, 234, 317, 321–323, 394–414
 as source of protein, 321–323
 of thiamine, 321–323

Oats and oatmeal, 118, 135, 153, 164, 208, 319, 336, 398, 410
 as food, 319
 from goitrous vs. non-goitrous regions, 164
 protein, amino acid data, 336
Obesity, 77–82
Objectives of nutritional recommendations, 265
Observations of effects of shortage of vitamin A, 256–259
Odontoblasts, 301
Oil, arachis (peanut), 20, 21, 390
 coconut, 20, 389
 codliver, 10, 255, 257, 278, 279, 286, 314
 corn (maize), 20, 21
 cottonseed, 20, 21, 390
 fish liver, 267, 268, 281, 286–287, 339
 halibut liver, 286
 mustardseed, 390
 of marine animals, 390

SUBJECT INDEX 447

olive, 20, 402
palm, 20, 389
palm kernel, 20
pecan, 21
percomorph, 286
rapeseed, 390
salmon, 287
sesame, 20
soybean, 20, 21
Oils, place in the diet, 20–21, 339, 360, 362–364
Okra, 269, 398, 410
Old age, energy need in, 81–82
Oleic acid, 20, 390
Oleomargarine, *see* Margarine
Olive(s), 398, 411
  oil, 20, 402
Onion, 186, 231, 269, 398, 411
Optimal as distinguished from merely adequate nutrition, 3, 7, 124–133, 178–181, 219–222, 264–265, 372
Orange(s), 64, 118, 135, 153, 173, 179, 191, 208, 229, 398, 411
  as source of vitamin C, 173, 179, 326, 411
  relation to calcium metabolism, 136
Organic acids, 14, 114–115; *see also* under name of each
Ossification, *see* Calcification
Osteoblasts, 276
Osteoid tissue, 276
Ovalbumin, 94, 336
Overweight, 77–82
Ovovitellin, 94, 336
Oxalic acid, 115, 134–136, 405, 407, 413
Oxidation-potential higher in juices of some foods than others, 183–184
Oxygen, 107, 108
Oxygen consumption of body; *see* Energy
Oysters, 118, 402, 411

Palmitic acid, 20, 390
Pancreas, 30, 32, 391
Pancreatic amylase, 30, 391
Pancreatic duct, 32
"Pangs" of hunger, 22

Pantothenic acid, 243, 249
  shortage as a possible factor in some anemias, 148
Parsnips, 398, 411
"Partially incomplete" proteins, 94
Pasteurization of milk, 349
Pathology, of vitamin A deficiency, 252–254, 256–259
  of shortage of vitamin C, 176–178
  of vitamin D deficiency (rickets), 276–280
Peaches, 191, 398, 411
  canned, 398
  dried (sulfured), 398, 411
Peanut(s), peanut butter, and peanut meal or flour, 10, 20, 102, 208, 209, 234, 322, 336, 398, 411
Pears, 118, 398, 411
Peas, 10, 18, 186, 191, 208, 209, 231, 268, 269, 318, 321–323, 399, 411
  canned, 411
  dried, 208, 209, 399, 411
  economy of, 318, 321–323
  fresh, 209, 268, 269, 399, 411
  mature, split, 399, 411
Pecans, 399, 411
Pellagra, 221–222, 224–228, 231–236
  description of, 231–232
  prevalence of, 232
  prevention by food, 233–235
  references, 236–239
  relation of food to, 233–236
Pelvis, malformations of, may result from rickets, 277
Peppers, 188, 399, 411
Pepsin, 29, 31, 36, 391
Peptides, 24
Peptones, 24, 391
Percomorph oil, 286
Peristalsis, 38
Petechiae, 176
Phaseolin, amino acid data, 336
Phenylalanine, 86, 91, 99, 336
Phosphates, 113; *see also* Phosphorus
Phosphoric acid, 113
Phosphorus, 108, 109, 113, 116, 117, 121–122, 128–133, 135, 276–277, 306, 332, 337, 404–414, 419
  absorption of, 275–276, 283–284
  competition of muscles and bones for, in growth, 284

Phosphorus (Continued)
  content of average American dietary, 351
  deficiency in certain regions, 121–122
  in foods, 351, 404–414
  in growth and development, 122–123
  occurrence and functions, 121–122
  requirements in nutrition, 122–123, 419
"Physical regulation" of body temperature, 61
Physical training rendered more effective by superior nutritional wellbeing, 347–348
"Physiological economy in nutrition," 99–100
Physique, 7
Pineapple, canned, 399, 411
  fresh, 399, 411
  juice, canned, 411
Place of fruit, vegetables and milk in the diet, 357–359
Planning of dietary, 267, 346–364
  in terms of ten to twelve food groups, 317–340, 358, 360–364
Plasticity of cooking-fats, 20–21
Plums, 115, 399, 412
Poke, 115
Policy in nutrition education, 369–378, 381–382
Policy is made effective by both economic and educational methods, 373–382
Polypeptides, 391
Polysaccharides, 17–19
Pork, 153, 208, 209, 228, 229, 233–234, 334, 379, 399, 412, 427
Potassium, 108, 112–113, 117
Potatoes, 10, 18, 118, 134, 135, 153, 164, 183, 186, 189, 191, 208, 211, 230, 231, 268, 318, 323–324, 399, 412
  from goitrous vs. non-goitrous regions, 164
Potatoes-and-sweetpotatoes as one of ten to twelve food groups, 317, 323–324, 358, 360, 362–364
Potentialities, constructive, in diet, 264–265
Precursors of vitamin A, 251, 255, 267–269

Pregnancy, 44, 79–80, 92, 96, 99–100, 130, 180, 263, 266, 362–364, 416, 418, 419
Prevalence of pellagra in the United States, 232
Prevention of goiter in school children, 165–166
Primary or direct food crops, 317
Problem of best use of food is both economic and educational, 350–358
Processing of crops through farm animals, 317
Program of The Nutrition Foundation, 374–375
Proline, 86
Prominence of different types of food in average American dietary, 318–340, 351, 360
Proteases, 30, 391
Protein(s), 14, 23–25, 30, 42–45, 59–60, 62–64, 85–103, 116–118, 317–336, 351, 391, 394–403, 416–417
  allowances recommended by National Research Council, 100–101, 416–417
  amount of, estimated from quantitative determination of nitrogen, 97–98
  amounts needed in nutrition, 96–101
  amounts recommended for growth, pregnancy, and lactation, as well as for maintenance, 99–101, 416–417
  as factors in acid-base balance, 116–118
  classification of as "complete," "partially incomplete," and "incomplete," 94
  content of average American dietary, 351
  contents of edible portions of typical foods, 102; *see also* under names of individual foods in the Appendix, 394–403
  energy value of, 62–64
  mixture of a wheat-and-milk dietary, nutritional efficiency of, 101–102
  of beans, soybeans, and peas, 318, 321–323, 336

SUBJECT INDEX 449

of peanuts and peanut butter, 322–323
recommended allowances of, 97–101, 416–417
requirement figured as a percentage of the total food-calorie need, 100
requirements of adult maintenance, 96–98
of men and women compared, 98
specific dynamic effect of, 59–60
supplementary relationships among, 87–90, 95–96, 101–102
Proteoses, 24, 391
Prothrombin, 296, 426
Protoplasm, 86
Provitamins A, 251
Provitamins D, 278–281
Prunes, 114–115, 153, 399, 412
Pteroylglutamic acid (PGA), 147, 242–243
Ptyalin, 33, 391
Pulp (of tooth), 301
Pumpkin(s), 412
Puppies as experimental animals for research on teeth, 302–303
Purslane, 115
Pyloric region of stomach, 35–37
Pylorus, 35–37
Pyorrhea, 309
Pyridoxine (vitamin B_6), 148, 240–241, 245–246
shortage as a factor in some anemias, 148
Pyruvic acid, 206

Quinic acid, 115

"Rachitic rosary," 276
Rachitis, see Rickets
"Racial factor" in basal metabolism, 57
Radishes, 399, 412
Raisins, 399, 412
Rancidity of fats in relation to vitamin E, 294
Raspberries, 403, 412
Readings (Suggested Readings), see Suggested Readings

Readjustments of family budgets in the light of nutritional knowledge, 346–364
Reasons of social justice to see that no child lacks food needed for full health, 370
Recommendations of the nutrition conference of the British Medical Association, 371–372
Recommended daily allowances for specific nutrients, 8–9, 69–72, 79–80, 96–101, 123–124, 130, 133, 148–151, 168–169, 178–181, 206–207, 223–227, 233, 265–266, 289–290, 415–419
Reducing diets, 72–79, 82
Reduction of body weight, 72–77
References, see Suggested Readings
Regions of the stomach, 34–37
Regularity of elimination of undigested food residues, 19
Regulation in the body, 13, 19, 29–31, 64, 72–79, 107–119, 205; see also Glands
Regulatory functions, processes, and substances, see Regulation in the body
Reproduction and lactation, as influenced by calcium, 123–127
by riboflavin, 220–225
by vitamin A, 263–266
by vitamin E, 294–295
Requirements, human, for calcium, 123–124, 416–417
for calories, 67–84, 416–417
for essential amino acids, 98–99
for iodine, 166–169, 418–419
for iron, 148–151, 416–417
for niacin, 233, 235, 416–417
for phosphorus, 122–123, 419
for protein, 98–101, 416–417
for riboflavin, 223-227, 416-417
for thiamine, 206–207, 416–417
for vitamin A, 265–266, 416–417
for vitamin C, 178–182, 416–417
for vitamin D, 289–290, 416–417
Reserve alkalinity, 115–119
Respiration apparatus (for measuring gaseous exchange), 51–58
Respiration calorimeter, 51–54
Respiratory exchange, 58–59
Respiratory system as influenced by vitamin A, 258–259

Restoration of growth in a girl upon receiving adequate thyroxine, 168
Rhubarb, 115, 412
Riboflavin, 5, 148, 217–231, 233–236, 318, 329, 404–414, 416–417
  allowances, benefits of liberal, 219–221
  as essential to growth, 218
  deficiency frequent in American dietaries, 221
  distribution in nature, 218–219
  effects upon health and length of life, 219, 221–222, 224–225
  foods as sources of, 228–230, 404–417
  in relation to health and disease, 221–222
  intake levels as influencing growth and health, 219–222
  measurement of, 222–223
  "necessary for the maintenance of the defense powers of the organism," 221
  references, 236–239
  requirements in nutrition, 219–227, 416–417
  shortage as a factor in some anemias, 148
Rice, 118, 153, 198–201, 208, 209, 399, 412
  as food, 319
  brown, 399, 412
  converted, 412
  white, uncooked, 399, 412
Rickets, 122, 275–290
  clinical, wide range of severity, 278–281, 284–285
  definition of, 276
  different types, 276, 281–282
  experimental, 278, 281–284
  incidence of, 276–277, 280
  "low-calcium," 282–283
  "low-phosphorus," 282, 284
  nature of, 276–280
Roasting, 231
"Rock bottom" requirements of minimal-adequate nutritional needs, 3; see also Requirements
Rocks as sources of iodine, 163
Roots (and tubers) as sources of vitamin C, 189–191

"Roughage," undigested food residue, 19
Rowing, the work of, as influencing food requirement, 70
Running, the work of, as influencing food requirement, 70
Rutabaga(s), 399, 412
Rye as food, 319

Saccharose, 16; see also Sucrose, Sugar, and Sweets
Saliva, 33, 36, 110, 391
Salmon, 399, 412
  oil, 287
Salt (table salt), 110–112, 418
Sardines, 399, 412
Saturated fatty acids, 389–390
Sauerkraut, 115, 399, 413
Sawing, the work of, as influencing food requirement, 70
Scallops, 399, 413
Scurvy, 172–182
Seafoods, 169
Seawater as source of iodine, 163
Secondarily derived foods, 317
Secretin, 32, 35, 86
Seeds, relatively rich in phosphorus, 121
Serine, 86
Sex difference in basal metabolism, 57
Shad, 403, 413
Shad roe, 403, 413
Shaft of bone, 275
Shivering in regulation of body temperature, 61
Shredded wheat, 399, 413
Shrimps, 413
  canned, 413
Sitting, energy metabolism during, 70
Sleeping, energy metabolism during, 70
Soda, destructive effect of, on thiamine, 211
  on vitamin C, 183–186
Sodium, 108, 110–113, 117
"Soft curd" milk, 333
Soils as sources of iodine, 163–164
Sorghum as source of sugar, 16
Soup, 10, 36
Sources of calcium other than ordinary, 134–138

Soybean, 94, 96, 403, 413
  flour, flakes, grits, medium fat, 403, 413
  protein, amino acid data, 336
Specific dynamic action of foodstuffs, 59–60
Spinach, 115, 134–135, 208, 228–229, 268, 399, 413
Squash, 399, 413
  pie, 403
  summer, 399, 413
  winter, 399, 413
Stair-climbing, work of, 70
Standards, dietary, see Allowances, Dietary recommendations, Recommended daily allowances for specific nutrients
Standing, energy requirement of, 70
Starches, 18–19, 33, 391
Starch sugar, see Glucose
State nutrition services, 374
Statement of United States Department of Agriculture on vitamin A values of butter and fortified margarine, 411
Stearic acid, 390
Stearin, 390
Sterols, 21, 281
Stewing, 231
Stomach, 34–37, 391
  digestion in, 28, 32, 34–38
  four main functions of, 37
Storage, of fat in the body, 44, 45, 72–77
  of vitamin A in the body, 255, 259–262
  of vitamin D in the body, 288–289
  see also the discussion of individual nutrients
Strawberries, 399, 413
Students enter college younger yet taller, 1
Substrate, 30
Successive-generation experiments, 4–6, 124–128, 219–221, 264, 265
Succus entericus, 37
Sucrase, 391
Sucrose, 16–17, 391; see also Sugar and Sweets
Suet, 20
Sugar(s), 16–17, 230, 310–311, 339–340, 360, 362–364, 391, 400, 413
  consumption, 17, 318, 340
  intake and the teeth, 305, 310–311
Suggested Readings, 11–12, 26–27, 45–46, 66, 83–84, 104–106, 119–120, 138–140, 158–160, 170–171, 193–197, 214–216, 236–239, 245–250, 270–274, 290–293, 298–300, 315–316, 341–345, 365–368, 382–387
Sulfates, 113, 116
Sulfur (sulfuric acid, sulfates), 108–119
Summary of the fate of foodstuffs, 44
Sunlight in relation to rickets, 276–281
Sunshine and soundness of the teeth, 308
Supplementation of the proteins of bread and cereals by those of meats, milk, and eggs, 95–96, 101–103, 334, 335–337, 338
"Surface-area relationship" (metabolism as proportional to body surface), 57
Surveys of food consumption, 346–350, 354–355
Sweetcorn, 16, 18
Sweetpotato, why written as a single word, 323
Sweetpotatoes, 26, 186, 231, 267, 268, 269, 323–324, 400, 413
Sweets, 16, 17, 317, 318, 339–340, 360, 362–364
Swimming, energy expenditure in, 70
Swiss chard, 115, 134, 395, 406
Synthesis of nutrients in plants and animals, 24
System of naming enzymes, 30

Tangerines, 400, 413
Tapioca, 400, 413
Tartaric acid and tartrates, 115
Teeth, 109, 301–316
  defects, classification of causes, 303
  evidence that food is a factor, 304–305, 314–315
  relation of calcium and phosphorus, 306
  of fluorine, 311–313
  of general health, 305
  of sugar intake, 310–311

Teeth, relation (Continued)
  of vitamin A, 309–310
  of vitamin C, 308–309
  of vitamin D, 306–308, 315
Tendergreen, 136
Terminology of enzymes, 29–31
Thiamine, 113, 198–219, 231, 318, 319–321, 404–414, 415–419
  and the Enrichment program, 212–214
  contents of foods, 207–210, 404–414
  designated "water-soluble B" by McCollum, 203
  discovery and chemical identification, 198–203
  functions, 201–206
  human requirements, 206–207, 416–417
  losses in cooking, 231
  measures of, 206
  nutritional functions, 203–206
  Recommended Dietary Allowances, 416–417
  relation to appetite, 203–205
  relation to carbohydrate, lactic acid, and pyruvic acid metabolism, 205–206
  relation to growth, 203–205
  requirements in nutrition, 206–207, 415–419
  stability in storage and preparation of foods, 210–213, 231
Threonine, 86, 90, 91, 99, 336
Thyroid, 60, 73, 161–169
Thyroxine, 86, 162, 165, 166–169, 242
Tissues, 109
  building of, 29, 43–44
Tocopherol(s), see Vitamin E
Tomato, 10, 118, 183–187, 190–191, 208, 210–211, 229–230, 234, 318, 326, 381, 400, 413
  as source of vitamin C, 318, 326
  catsup, 413
  juice, 414
Tomatoes-and-citrus-fruits as one of ten to twelve food groups, 317–318, 358, 360, 362–364
Tooth, see Teeth
Tooth decay, see Caries
Tooth, imperfect formation, 302, 303
  structure of, 301–302

Trabeculae as influenced by the calcium content of the food, 127–128
Triglycerides, 20, 389; see also Fats
Trypsin, 30, 43, 391
Tryptophane, 86, 87, 88, 89, 91, 99, 336
Tuna fish, 400, 414
  canned, drained solids, 400, 414
Turkey, 333, 400, 414
  consumption of, 333
Turnip(s), 190, 191, 229, 400, 414
  greens, 135, 186, 189, 231, 268, 269, 326, 400, 414
  calcium well utilized, 136
Types of food, 317, 340, 351–358, 360–364
Tyrosine, 86, 92

Ultraviolet light, 278, 280, 281, 285–286
Undernutrition, effect on energy metabolism, 60
Underweight, 75–76
United Nations, 9
United States Pharmacopeia (U.S.P.), 255, 285
Unlike values of the calcium of different greens, 135–136
Unsaturated fatty acids, 21, 240, 389–390
Upkeep of body tissue, 13, 44, 85, 87
U.S.P. Unit of vitamin A same as International Unit, 255

Valine, 86, 91, 99, 336
Values of proteins in nutrition, how determined, 93–96
Variations in composition of milk, 332
Veal, 153, 400, 414
Vegetable soup, 400, 414
Vegetables, 10, 16, 81, 155–156, 172–174, 187, 208, 209–210, 229, 230, 231, 234, 235, 267, 268, 269, 294, 317, 318, 324–326, 360, 362–364, 394–414; see also under name of each
  green and yellow, as one of ten to twelve food groups, 317, 318, 324–326

SUBJECT INDEX 453

Villi, 38
Vinegar, 115
"Viosterol," 281, 286
Vision as influenced by vitamin A, 256–258, 265–266
Vitamins, 1–3, 15, 25, 175, 332; *see also* individual vitamins
Vitamin A (value), 5, 251–269, 309–310, 311, 318, 323, 324–326, 353, 354, 404–414, 416–417
   in growth, development, and health, 252–254, 256–259
   measurement of value, 254–256
   optimal *vs.* minimal adequate levels, 264–265, 266, 416–417
   recommended daily allowances, 266, 416–417
   requirements in human nutrition, 265–266, 416–417
   storage in the body, 254, 259–262
   unit, International, 255
   U. S. Pharmacopeia, 255
   values of foods, 251, 267–269, 404–414
Vitamin B (B_1), *see* Thiamine
Vitamin B_6 (pyridoxine), 148, 240, 241, 245–246
Vitamin B_{12}, 146, 147, 241–242, 246–247
Vitamin B_{14}, 242, 247
Vitamin C (ascorbic acid), 148, 172–192, 308–309, 314, 318, 324, 325, 326, 332, 353, 354, 404–414, 415–417
   allowances, of, 180, 416–417
   complexity of conditions which influence its rate of destruction, 182–187
   conservation of, in the preparation and preservation of foods, 182–187
   content of the blood as influenced by intake and other factors, 178–182
   content of typical foods, 187–192, 404–414
   contributions of different types of foods in the typical dietary, 187, 318
   destructive effect of alkali upon, 182–186
   experimental variations of concentration in milk, 332
   experimental shortage in man, 181
   influence of acidity upon its conservation, 184–186
   in maintenance of intercellular cement substance of tissues, 175–176
   losses due to solubility, 186–187
   losses in cooking, 186
   metabolism and requirement, 178–182
   relation to healing of wounds, 177, 181
   relation to resistance to bacterial toxins, 177
   relation to teeth, 308–309
   unit, International, 182
Vitamin(s) D, 275–290, 306–308, 314–315, 416–417
   allowances, 289, 416–417
   assay, 285
   discovery of, 277, 278, 280
   may increase the rate of growth and general development, 284
   multiple nature of, 280–281
   nutritional function, 281–285
   relation to teeth, 306–308, 314–315
   requirements, 289, 416–417
   sources, 285–288
   storage in the body and transfer from mother to offspring, 288–289
   unit, International, 285
   U. S. Pharmacopeia, 285
Vitamin D_2 (calciferol), 281, 287, 288
Vitamin D_3, 281, 287, 288
"Vitamin D milk," 281, 287–288
Vitamin(s) E, 294–295, 298–300
Vitamin G, *see* Riboflavin
Vitamin(s) K, 296–297, 300, 419
Vitamin M, 242–243, 247–249; *see also* Folic acid
Vitamin P, 245, 250

Walking, the work of, as influencing food requirement, 55, 70
Walnuts, 400, 414
Water, 10, 110, 163, 418
Water balance, 73, 74, 110–111
Watercress, 135, 189, 326, 329, 400, 414

Watermelon, 118, 191, 400, 414
Weight, body, standard tables, 75
Weight changes, 72–77
Wheat, 18, 101–102, 118, 135, 155, 164, 208, 229, 319
Wheat germ, 155, 209, 229, 234, 414
White bread, enriched, 208, 209, 395, 405
White sauce, 400
Whole wheat protein, amino acid data, 336
Women, dietary recommendations for, 69, 98, 100, 133, 150, 180, 223, 266, 289, 356, 362–364, 416–419; *see also* Allowances, Dietary recommendations
Work, external, 44
  internal, 44, 47
  mental, 49, 67–68
  muscular, various forms, energy requirement of, 70, 72

Xerophthalmia, 256–257, 258, 427
Xerosis in vitamin A deficiency, 257
X-ray studies of rickets, 279, 280

"Yardstick" of good nutrition, 8–9, 415–419
Yeast, 203, 233, 321, 336, 400, 414
  of high vitamin content, 321
"Yeast foods" used in breadmaking, 135, 321

Zein, 87, 88, 89, 94, 95
Zinc, 108, 113, 120
Zones of desirable margin above the needs of minimal adequacy, 5–6, 123–133, 178–182, 204–207, 218–222, 223–227, 252, 255–265